The Origin of Life

By A. I. Oparin, *Associate Director, Biochemical Institute, U. S. S. R. Academy of Science*

Translation with Annotations
By Sergius Morgulis, *Professor of Biochemistry, University of Nebraska, College of Medicine, Omaha*

SECOND EDITION
With a New Introduction by the Translator

Dover Publications, Inc., New York

This Dover edition, first published in 1953, is an
unabridged republication of the work originally
published by The Macmillan Company in 1938,
with a new Introduction by the translator.

Library of Congress Catalog Card Number: 53-10161

Manufactured in the United States of America
Dover Publications, Inc.
180 Varick Street
New York, N.Y. 10014

Inscribed with affection

to

NICOLE.

S. M.

INTRODUCTION TO
THE SECOND EDITION

THIS REMARKABLE BOOK was translated by me about fifteen years ago because I felt keenly that Oparin's contribution had such great importance for scientists and non-scientists alike that it should be available to all English-reading people. It is a tribute to its true merits that the book should be reprinted after a lapse of so many years, and I gladly yield to the request of the publishers to write a preface for this edition.

If I were to change the name of this book, I would suggest "LIFE'S COMING INTO BEING" instead of the less cumbersome title "THE ORIGIN OF LIFE." This is not out of sheer caprice, but in order to escape some connotations of the latter title which tend to obfuscate essential basic assumptions and to that extent put the wrong slant upon the problems to be formulated. To begin with, the title conceals two significant misconceptions. One concerns the duration of the process. "Origin," especially to those brought up in the biblical tradition, implies a finite and sharply delineated event of creation, not a process extending over infinite time. Modern paleontologists tell us that evolution of living things, which has blossomed out with a profusion of plant and animal species of almost endless variety, has occupied a period of something like a billion years. The Earth has retained an unmistakable record of this for nearly half a billion years. It will aid the reader to orient himself with regard to the evolution of species, to be reminded that in this inconceivably long span of half-a-billion years, registered in the Earth's crust by some historical remains, the foot-marks left by man and his close predecessors encompass barely one million years, perhaps two-tenths of one per cent. But the origination of life, which is the subject matter of Oparin's book, precedes by about another billion years the story of the "Origin of Species" in which Darwin picks up the thread, and of this earlier period there is no existing record. While Darwin's is a well documented story and his ideas, though highly controversial, can be bolstered with substantial factual material, Oparin's story embracing probably another billion years lacks the support of ascertainable facts. By its very nature, a theory of how life had come into being must be highly specu- lative. Lacking a solid factual basis, the soundness or acceptability of such a theory can only be judged by whether or not, or to what extent, it conforms to the cri- terion of reasonable consistency with established knowl- edge in various fields of scientific inquiry. The origin of life was not an occurrence ascribable to some definite place and time; it was a gradual process operating upon the Earth over an inconceivably long span of time, a process of unfolding which consumed perhaps more millions of years than was required for the evolution of all the species of living things. It is one of Oparin's great contributions to the theory of the origin of life that he postulated a long chemical evolution as a necessary preamble to the emergence of Life. One might think of the evolutionary process passing through three distinct chemical phases, from inorganic chemistry to organic chemistry and from organic chemistry to biological chemistry. And it is true that, if the organic chemist is familiar with wonders undreamed of by the inorganic chemist, the wonders witnessed by the biochemist in his daily tasks stagger the imagination and sharpen the envy of the organic chemist. These transitions in the history of our Earth were not isolated events but a continuous flux requiring eons for their realization. In interpreting the significance of the word "origin" one must free oneself of the cultural tradition and conceive it as something entirely outside the ordinary human framework of time.

The second misconception stems from associations clustering about the word "Life." To most people Life connotes something that crawls, creeps or at least wiggles if not by means of well articulated appendages at any rate by temporary protoplasmic protrusions, or cilia, or delicate flagella. Life need not perhaps be visualized in the form of a stalking elephant but to the layman it may seem inconceivable except as some unicellular organism of microscopic dimensions. But even the most primitive unicellular organism has a complexity of structure and function that staggers the mind and is removed from the beginnings of Life by a genealogy extending for millions upon millions of years. Possibly, as Oparin so convincingly tells us, it all began some two billion years ago as a venture in colloidal systems of microscopic size separating from the "hot thin soup," to use Haldane's happy description of the primordial ocean.

The biologist, unlike the layman, knows no lines of demarcation separating plant life from animal life, nor for that matter living from non-living material, because such differentiations are purely conceptual and do not correspond to reality.

It is interesting to consider the influence which the identification of life with cellular organisms exerted on the theory of spontaneous generation. The famous and now classical experiments of Pasteur on such primitive organisms as bacteria are believed to have disposed for all time the question of the spontaneous generation of living creatures with the enunciation of the principle that every living thing must come from another living thing. The cruder and more naive experimenters, whose efforts at solving the problem of spontaneous generation were dubiously rewarded with swarms of maggots or flies, got the wrong answer because they, unlike Pasteur, lacked skill, scientific acuity, critical judgment, and above all else a knack for cleanliness, but all have formulated the question alike. Basically the question was whether non-living matter can be transformed into living matter; in other words, whether biogenesis is possible. But Pasteur's unequivocal experiments have given no answer to this basic problem. They merely furnished irrefutable proof that living organisms, no matter how simple they might be, cannot be generated from organic matter. Yet, sometimes in the course of evolution of our planet inorganic and organic matter must have become endowed with organization which after hundreds of millions of years enabled it to develop into organisms. These in turn, after many more hundreds of millions of years, have spread over the surface of the planet populating the soil, water and air with an infinite variety of plant and animal forms. It may never be possible to devise experiments to prove or disprove the possibility of biogenesis, and even Pasteur's experiments do not disprove this, but biogenesis seems to be a reasonably consistent logical necessity.

It is more pertinent to inquire, if such a transformation of lifeless into living matter occurred once upon a time, whether this is happening at all times. "There is no scientific basis," says Kavanau, "that life may not be originating continuously upon the earth. The fact that we have no evidence of such *de novo* origin is of no particular significance, for if there is such origin we must anticipate that it would be in units far too small to be treated in the manner in which we are accustomed to dealing with organisms. . . . It is likely, however, that the changes in the conditions at the earth's surface, since the most favorable period for the origin of life, have been so great that present-day *de novo* origin, if it occurs, is highly infrequent."

The conditions on the Earth during the past couple of billion years have undergone such radical alterations that biogenesis may no longer be possible. However, as Oparin points out, even if biogenesis were operating at the present time, the innumerable predatory organisms which populate the Earth would quickly destroy the products of biogenesis.

It will in no measure detract from Oparin's credit for this brilliant idea to point out that no less illustrious a biologist than Charles Darwin himself expressed a similar thought in a letter he wrote in 1871 (for the uncovering of this letter we are indebted to G. Hardin):

"It is often said that all the conditions for the first production of a living organism are now present, which could ever have been present. But if (and oh! what a big if) we could conceive in some warm little pond, with all sorts of ammonia and phosphoric salts, light, heat, electricity, etc., present, that a protein compound was chemically formed ready to undergo still more complex changes, at the present day, such matter would be instantly devoured or absorbed, which would not have been the case before living creatures were formed."

The origination of life was a transition from organic to biological chemistry, from lifeless to living matter, from the inanimate to the animate realm of Nature. But what is Life? Is it some new property of organic matter acquired in the course of evolution or is it something which resulted from the organization of organic matter? Irritability, motility, growth, reproduction may be good aids to differentiate a live from a dead organism but it is questionable whether these represent the fundamental properties of primordial life. There is good reason to think that a certain period of the Earth's history must have been marked by complete sterility, i.e. absence of organisms; therefore, the fundamental property or properties of living systems must have appeared in highly complex protein macromolecules antedating the appearance of cellular organisms. Proteins containing nucleic acid are the only constituents of organisms which are known to possess the capacity to grow and to reproduce directly by self-duplication or by replication. But as organic compounds they can neither grow nor reproduce. Neither viruses nor genes, both of which represent nucleoprotein systems, can duplicate or replicate themselves unless they are incorporated within a suitable cell or nucleus. Considered simply from the point of view of capacity to reproduce, are these nucleoproteins living or non-living systems? Being unable to furnish the free energy needed for syntheses associated with their reproduction, they lack the fundamental property characteristic for living systems of converting, transporting and storing energy. An ability to metabolize, involving some system of catalysts is another fundamental property which cannot be conceived of except in conjunction with a mechanism for converting free energy, and we are deeply indebted to H. F. Blum (*Time's Arrow and Evolution*, 1951) for his masterly analysis of this extremely important aspect of this subject.

One should add, as a fundamental property of living systems, a characteristic of their metabolism to form only one of the two optically active antipodes (i.e. either the D or the L form of an active compound but never both, as is the case in organic synthesis). It is not clear how this remarkable characteristic of living systems had arisen or whether it contributed to the transformation of non-living to living matter.

Almost a hundred years ago Engel propounded the thesis that life is a manifestation of the existence of proteins, but he did not know that in reality life is a manifestation of catalysis by means of enzymes which are proteins. Chemical reactions in plant and animal organisms proceed at very high velocities. Without catalysis there could be no life. In fact, the bulk of protoplasm is filled with enzymatically specific active proteins. Yet enzymes are not living matter. Nearly every enzyme requires some inorganic component which may itself be catalytically active but in combination with protein this activity is enormously increased. Possibly the enzymes have evolved from these inorganic catalysts and thereby the tempo of biochemical reactions has been stepped up a thousand or even a million fold. The unfolding of the tremendous diversity of living organisms within the last half-a-billion years, as compared to the relatively very slow evolution of the preceding billion years may have resulted from the association of the primitive metal catalysts with proteins. But we know that the protein catalysts (enzymes) had already been operating at the very dawn of the appearance of plant and animal life. Although enzyme systems have been highly diversified in the course of evolution, their basic pattern has persisted through the geologic ages. It might almost be asserted that the earliest organisms had acquired the basic principles of biochemical catalysis and no new principles had been invented to replace them. Thus, the very lowly Bryozoa are known to have maintained morphological uniformity for hundreds of millions of years. If we assume that the Bryozoa have also maintained physiological uniformity throughout their inconceivably long life history, it must be concluded that the enzymes of heavy metal electron transfer have been operating in cellular respiration ever since living organisms have inhabited the Earth. Evolution has flowered from the Bryozoa (and probably long before them) to the vertebrates, but the heavy metal electron transfer enzyme system has persisted through all these hundreds of millions of years as the basic design of cellular respiration.

Similarly, if we consider the lowly bread mold (Neurospora), also of very ancient and venerable geologic age, we witness the persistence over millions of years of enzyme systems which, with some modifications, are still found operating in higher organisms, including man.

The coenzyme factors (the so-called vitamin B complex) seem to be universally distributed and, what is more significant, the chains of biochemical reactions by which each factor is synthesized appear to be the same in most divergent organisms. The biochemical unity suggests that the coenzymes became part of a basic metabolic plan laid down even before evolution, acting through natural selection, had created a highly diversified flora and fauna.

The only known means for storing, transforming and mobilizing energy for the metabolism in living organisms is the system of high energy phosphate bond, namely Adenylic Acid $\rightleftharpoons$ Adenosinediphosphate $\rightleftharpoons$ Adenosinetriphosphate. This system, which is chemically related to the nucleic acids, played a paramount role in the transfer of free energy from the very beginning of life, and undoubtedly played a very critical role in the transition from the non-living to the living state. The system has thus been preserved through the long geologic ages apparently unchanged. Though this, too, is one of the most essential endowments of life and, since non-living became living matter, it persisted in the organized cellular structure, yet this all-important system for transfer of free energy, outside its biological setting, is just organic matter.

If life is a manifestation of the existence of proteins, or more correctly a manifestation of catalysis by means of protein enzymes, the origin of life must have coincided with the origin of proteins if not actually preceded by them. Did protein precede the enzymes or did the enzyme the proteins? If growth and reproduction depend upon nucleoproteins, the nucleoproteins should have antedated the emergence of protein and of living organisms. But the synthesis of proteins could not have occurred without the aid of energy transformers or appropriate enzymes. This line of reasoning of what came first in the processional of life can be continued *ad infinitum* without any tangible gain in understanding because this line of reasoning starts from a wrong premise. One becomes captive of a chain of arguments attempting to solve the paradox of how substances, absolutely indispensable to the existence of living systems, came into being *before* the living systems existed, which alone seem to possess the ability to produce these essential components. The problem is really quite insoluble since it is formulated upon a tacit assumption that the emergence of living from non-living could only have followed a hierarchical order, thus A $\longrightarrow$ B $\longrightarrow$ C $\longrightarrow$ D $\longrightarrow$ E $\longrightarrow$ L but life could have originated not as the end link of a chain of consecutive events but by simultaneous coordination of several factors

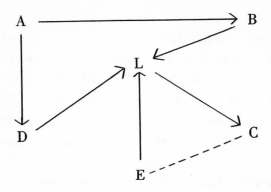

As long as the cell is considered as the unit of life, the origin of life must remain a paradox. But like the erstwhile atom in chemistry, the cell has lost its prestige as the ultimate unit in biology. Both the atomic and the cellular theories have become obsolete. The cell, like the "indivisible" atom, is now recognized as a highly organized and integrated system built up from extremely small and distinct particles. Whether the ultimate particles of life have been found and identified is very doubtful, some of the units themselves being highly organized entities, but the concept of a cell as the unit of life has been thrown out of the window together with the atom.

It has long been recognized that a cell consists of two main parts, the nucleus and cytoplasm. The nucleus is further differentiated into a nucleolus and chromosomes, the latter consisting of tiny particles, the genes, which are arranged in fibrils and are propagated by self-division. These particles are composed predominantly of nucleoproteins extremely rich in desoxyribonucleic acid (DNA). This DNA is not only the unique nuclear constituent but is most likely the genetic material. The nucleus is extremely poor in enzymes and its only demonstrable biochemical potentiality is the synthesis of nucleic acids. Removed from the cell, however, the isolated nucleus rapidly loses its viability and fails to function when it is replaced into an enucleated cell. Without the necessary mechanisms to furnish its energy requirements, it is completely dependent upon the cytoplasm, but it is not parasitic. In all probability it supplies the cytoplasm with ribonucleic acid (RNA), and their interrelationship should be described as symbiotic. Speaking figuratively, a nucleus isolated from the cytoplasm has no future, nor much of a present either.

Protoplasm is a highly complex colloidal system of such lability that it tends to break down spontaneously. During life it is in a steady dynamic state, and energy furnished by the metabolic mechanism is constantly required to maintain its structure intact. But since metabolism is a regular sequence of chemical reactions which must occur at the right time and at the right place, the protoplasm must be a highly integrated system of enzymes whose activity is strictly controlled (by alternate activation and inactivation). Any disturbance in the enzyme pattern will tend to destroy the orderly structure of the protoplasm; any alteration of the protoplasmic structure will disturb the harmonious functioning of the enzymes.

The cytoplasm consists of several types of particles possessing varying degrees of complexity of organization, such as mitochondria, microsomes, Golgi bodies, chloroplasts, etc.

The mitochondria are large liponucleoprotein organelles occupying perhaps a third of the cytoplasm. They consist of a complex of enzymes so completely interdigitated as to constitute practically a single entity structurally and a regular power house functionally. They catalyze a great variety of reactions consisting of aerobic oxidations (fatty acids, amino acids, tricarboxylic cycle) as well as oxidative phosphorylations and some syntheses.

However, separated from its nucleus, the cytoplasm has no enduring future. It still displays for a while various functions (irritability, contractility, respiration, etc.) and maintains itself with the energy delivered from its particulates, but deprived of the companionship of its nucleus beyond a certain time limit, its ability to grow, reproduce, differentiate as well as synthesize specific proteins fails to materialize.

The life of the cell can thus be regarded as the resultant of the continuous interaction between nucleus and cytoplasm. But the interaction is conditioned upon the fitness between them so that the interaction is in the nature of a symbiosis. It is significant that the nucleus with its inclusions (genes), which alone has no durable present, and the cytoplasm (with its various inclusions), which alone has no enduring future, can by proper juxtaposition synthesize proteins for growth and reproduction with the aid of nucleic acids and with aid of high energy phosphate derivatives of adenylic acid as transformers and transmitters of energy. Thus, the cell becomes a very efficient organism. Furthermore, the protein synthesis is directed toward highly specific proteins which imprint a high degree of specificity upon the manifestations of life in different organisms. And, it may be added parenthetically, provided it is not destroyed by some accident or extraneous influence, that the cell acquires a future and that future is infinity.

A few random examples of biological symbiosis may serve to emphasize the profound significance of this phenomenon as the pattern which might have been operative not only at the cellular or particulate level but even at the macromolecular level in the transformation of non-living to living matter.

Hemoglobin, the red blood pigment, has been usually regarded as a strictly animal product. In recent years it was discovered that hemoglobin is formed in the root nodules of legumes harboring nitrogen fixing bacteria. The far-reaching significance of this biological observation lies in the fact that neither the root nodules nor the microorganisms, by themselves, are capable of effecting this synthesis. Only in the infected nodule is hemoglobin being synthesized. Two entirely different living systems enter a symbiotic partnership and out of this interrelationship something new emerges, the synthesis of a complex substance, which neither system alone could fulfill. It is true that in this instance the creative situation terminates in a biochemical blind alley (and the course of evolution is full of blind alleys) but instead of bringing forth a "freak" of nature this event could conceivably have opened a new biological era.

Another pertinent story can be told about chlorophyll, a green pigment closely related chemically to hemoglobin. This pigment is found in plants in special organelles, the chloroplasts. Chlorophyll absorbs light waves in the purple and red range of the spectrum and thus traps radiant energy. This gives the plant cell containing chloroplasts a source of free energy to perform anabolic processes which cells lacking this mechanism are unable to accomplish. It is interesting to note that chlorophyll itself is unable to accomplish the photosynthetic reaction except as a component of a chloroplast. Chloroplasts are small green bodies enclosed in the cytoplasm of higher plants and of green algae. The reaction sequence of photosynthesis begins and ends within the chloroplast. Isolated from the surrounding cytoplasm the chloroplast can evolve oxygen from water when exposed to light but it cannot use carbon dioxide as oxidant in this reaction. Nor can the isolated (intact) chloroplast carry out photosynthesis, which indicates that this depends upon cooperation with the cytoplasm. In other words, photosynthesis which is one of the most important means for accumulating free energy available in nature has emerged from a symbiotic arrangement. Neither participant in the partnership is capable of accomplishing this synthesis. Existing separately and independently chlorophyll, chloroplast and cytoplasm may have remained at the level of organic matter. The concatenation of all three (by chance or accident) within the plant cell opened up new vistas of evolutionary potentialities by tapping the inexhaustible source of the sun's energy and making it available for biological progress.

A concluding word should be added about viruses. Both the virus and the gene represent the simplest substances known to be autoreproducible. Both are largely or entirely nucleoprotein macromolecules. Plant viruses contain only ribonucleic acid (RNA) and animal viruses contain both RNA and DNA, whereas genes contain desoxyribonucleic acid (DNA). Nevertheless, viruses and genes have some things in common. Thus, neither can reproduce itself except within a suitable type of cell. However, if the genes (nucleus) and cytoplasm fit each other (i.e., belong to the same or closely related species) their symbiotic relationship culminates in normal development; if the virus and host cell fit each other, the virus usually multiplies and in doing so destroys the host (parasitic relationship). The discarded virus, unless it can invade another cell, reverts to the status of non-living matter. But, as Andrewes points out in his 1951 Leeuwenhoek Lecture, a stable virus-host cell equilibrium may become established and "reach a state of closer and closer union, culminating in the blissful surrender of perfect symbiosis." Could viruses have become transformed into genes?

Thermodynamically directed chemical evolution could conceivably proceed indefinitely without changing from a non-living to a living state. Only when organic matter had achieved a high degree of organization, and had acquired diverse propensities through the concatenation of such substances (with chance as the only arbiter) did primordial life emerge as a new dimension in nature: matter perpetuating its own organization. Natural selection, operating upon chance variations, set the evolutionary direction along numerous pathways which living things have followed irresistibly.

S. MORGULIS

August 6, 1952
Omaha, Nebraska

For a long time I have been greatly intrigued by the question as to how life on Earth began and for more than fifteen years have been actively engaged in searching for a solution of the problem which has stirred me so deeply. The fruits of the meditations and researches along these lines have been presented in a series of scientific articles and popular essays. In 1923 I published a booklet devoted to this problem in which my views according to which life appeared in the gradual evolution of primary organic substances were first expounded. Subsequently I attempted to develop this idea further and to substantiate it with data derived from various investigations carried out by astronomers, geologists, biochemists and others working in related fields. The information garnered from these various sources has been incorporated in 1936 in my book, "The Origin of Life," a translation of which is now offered to the reader.

The problem of the beginning of life still intrigues my curiosity and stirs my imagination, and I am therefore greatly beholden to The Macmillan Company for undertaking the publication of a translation which will bring this book before the large English-speaking public. I hope that it will attract the attention of American and of other English-speaking investigators and will further promote the study and research of a tremendously complex and important problem presented in this book.

I am particularly indebted to Professor S. Morgulis who has taken upon himself the task of translating my book and who has accomplished this so perfectly, rendering skillfully in English the exact meaning as well as the spirit of my discussion.

PROFESSOR A. I. OPARIN.

Moscow, November 21, 1937.

CONTENTS

THE ORIGIN OF LIFE

CHAPTER I

THEORIES OF SPONTANEOUS
GENERATION OF LIFE

THE QUESTION OF THE ORIGIN OF LIFE, of its first appearance on Earth, still occupies the human mind, as it has
done since the most remote antiquity. It may be safely
said that it is one of the most important problems of natural history. No religious or philosophical system, no outstanding thinker ever failed to give this question serious
consideration. During different epochs and at different
stages of civilization the question was answered differently, but this question was always the focal point of a
sharp philosophical struggle which reflected the underlying struggle of social classes. For a very long time the
question of the origin of life was treated not as a subject
of scientific research but entirely from the point of view
of religio-scholastic concepts. The ancient religious teachings of China, Egypt, Babylon traced the origin of life to
various traditions and legends, and invariably attributed
the appearance of life to some creative act of God. But
we will not concern ourselves with these theories and shall
consider only very cursorily those philosophical systems
which, though no longer of any significance so far as our
modern approach to this problem is concerned, have a
purely historical interest. E. Lippmann [1] in a recent book
presents a fairly complete survey of all the theories of
the origin of life, from ancient times to the beginning of

the twentieth century, and we refer to this book the reader who is interested in this aspect of the problem. Here we shall sketch only the essential landmarks of the history of our problem.

In the introduction to his book Lippmann draws the interesting parallel between the ancient conceptions of the architecture of the World and the conceptions of the origin of life. "Everyday experience gave irrefutable evidence in the course of thousands of years of the movement of the Sun around the Earth with such probability that there could be no doubt on this score. Similarly evident was the 'fact' that very frequently, under favorable conditions, living things originate from lifeless matter. This 'fact' seemed so obvious that there was no necessity for a more detailed study of this phenomenon. Therefore, since the most remote times, we find among the various peoples all over the world the solid conviction, based frequently on observation, that the simplest animals, both of the lowest and highest order, can originate spontaneously." And this author notes further that these everyday, superficial observations so powerfully affect human concepts, that the belief in the possibility of spontaneous generation of various living things from all sorts of rotting material has been sustained for thousands of years and persists even to the present day. Even in our own time of crowning achievement in the exact natural sciences the layman of civilized European countries not infrequently believes that worms are generated in manure, that the enemies abounding in garden or field, the various parasites operative in our daily existence arise spontaneously from refuse and every sort of filth.

It is easy to understand the tremendous significance of such daily experience in the formulation of conceptions among the ancient peoples, who lacked the methods for an exact study of natural phenomena. Such "irrefutable evidence" formed the basis of theories of many philosophers of the Ionian school (600 B.C.) according to which living organisms originated in sea slime by the action of heat, sun and air. Thus, for instance, the oldest philosopher of this Greek school, Thales [2], taught that living things developed from the amorphous slime under the influence of heat. Anaximander (611–547 B.C.) claimed that everything living arises in sea ooze and goes through a succession of stages in its development [3]. Xenophane (560–480 B.C.) taught that all organisms originate from earth and water [4].

It is necessary to point out, however, that the conception of spontaneous generation of living things, entertained by Greek philosophers on the basis of everyday observation, was intimately interwoven with their teaching of the perpetuity of life. Although they considered the origin of life from lifeless inorganic matter, this strictly speaking did not imply a primary phenomenon, since in the view of these philosophers the entire universe was conceived to be living. Thus, according to Anaxagorus (510–428 B.C.), neither creation nor destruction of life was possible and, although in his opinion plants, animals and man all came from the earth's slime, nevertheless it was essential that this should be fructified by unchanging and infinitely small seeds (spermata), the ethereal embryos, which were carried into the earth from the air with rain water [5].

Similarly, Empedocles (490–444 B.C.) maintained that plants and animals were formed from live inorganic substance either by a process of generation from similar sources or by a process of self-promulgation from dissimilar sources. In the latter case the fructifying and life-giving principles were the warmth of the sun, earth and of the rainfall from the sky. Democritus, like Anaximander, thought that the organic world took its origin in water and that animals passed through a long developmental process before they became such as we find them today. But this philosopher already advanced the theory of the mechanical self-creation of life resulting from an inherent movement of the atoms: the atoms of lifeless, moist earth meet accidentally and unite with atoms of the live and energizing fire [6].

The views of Epicurus (341–270 B.C.) are likewise very interesting in this connection and are expressed in the materialistic poem of Lucretius "On the Nature of Things". According to this source, Epicurus taught that under the influence of the moist heat of the sun and rain worms and innumerable other animals arose from the earth or manure. This, however, is no more remarkable than the hatching of the chick from a lifeless egg, since the Earth, which is the mother of plants, animals and man is already endowed with the power of propagation. And, furthermore, like a real mother, she very nearly loses all her pristine powers of propagation with advancing age [7].

The views developed by Aristotle (384–322 B.C.) have an entirely different and particular significance for the future history of the study of the origin of life. It fell to this philosopher's lot to offer mankind the most complete synthesis of the achievements of ancient science, embracing the entire factual material which had accumulated up to that time. His teachings subsequently became the foundation of the medieval scientific culture and for two thousand years dominated the mind of mankind. Aristotle develops his conception of the origin of life principally in his books "On the Parts of Animals", "On the Movements of Animals", "On the Origin of Animals" and finally "On Plants". Apparently his views had undergone some modification in the course of time, but ultimately he laid the foundation of the theory of spontaneous generation of living things.

According to this theory animals not only originate from other similar animals but living things do arise and always have arisen from lifeless matter. Aristotle teaches that living things, as well as other concrete things, are produced by the union of some passive principle "matter" (by which Aristotle apparently refers to what we now designate as substance) with an active principle "form", this form being the "entelechy" or soul of living things. It imparts organization and movement to the body. Thus, matter by itself is devoid of life but is vivified, purposefully molded and organized by the aid of the energy of the soul, whose inner essence (entelechy) endows matter with life and keeps it alive. But the soul is already present in the primary elements of which living things are made; to a lesser degree it is a property of the earth, but to a greater degree of water, air and fire. Therefore, what form the soul will endow depends first of all on the predominance of one or the other element. Thus, the earth produces principally plants; water produces aquatic animals; air, terres-

trial organisms; while fire gives rise to the supposed deni-
zens of celestial bodies, such as the Moon. The form of
living things originating from their like depends upon the
"animal heat", but of those generated spontaneously from
inorganic matter upon the "sun's heat". Slime, manure,
and similar decaying matter do not of themselves produce
living organisms but only under the fructifying influence
of rain saturated with air and of the Sun's heat.

Aristotle suggested the possibility of spontaneous generation of a great variety of living organisms. He maintained that not only plants but also a number of animals
could be observed to originate from the earth. According
to Aristotle ordinary worms, larvae of the bee or wasp,
ticks, fireflies and many other insects develop from the
morning dew, or from decaying slime and manure, from
dry wood, hair, sweat and meat, while tapeworms are born
in the rotting portions of the body and excreta. Mosqui-
toes, flies, moths, manure beetles, cantharides, also fleas,
bed bugs and lice (either full grown or as larvae) are generated in the slime of wells, rivers or sea, in the humus of
the fields, in manure, in decaying trees or fruits, in animal
excreta and filth of every sort, in vinegar dregs as well as
in old wool.

However, not only insects and worms but even more
highly organized living creatures may originate spontaneously according to Aristotle. Crabs and various molluscs
were thought to come from the moist soil and decaying
slime, eels and many kinds of fish to come from the wet
ooze, sand, slime and rotting seaweeds; even frogs and under
certain conditions salamanders may come from slime.
Mice are generated in moist soil. Some higher animals

and even man may have a similar origin, though in the case of the latter his first appearance is in the form of a worm.

We have dwelt to such length on the views of Aristotle because the entire history of the problem of the origin of living things has been dominated by the teachings of this philosopher. By his overwhelming authority Aristotle gave credence to data derived from naive direct observation and thus predetermined for many centuries in advance the future fate of the theory of spontaneous generation. An important part in this matter was played by the acceptance of Aristotle's teachings by the Roman and more particularly by the neoplatonic (Plotinus) philosophers and through them by the fathers of the Christian Church, in particular by Basilius (315–379) and Saint Augustine (354–430)[8].

Basilius taught that just as the Earth once upon a time produced various grasses, trees and animals by the command of God so to this day this ability has been retained in full force and living creatures such as grasshoppers, mice, etc., may be produced from the earth. Saint Augustine accepted the spontaneous generation of living creatures as an irrefutable truth and in his teachings was concerned only to reconcile this phenomenon of nature with the viewpoint of the Christian Church. He argued that just as God usually makes wine from water and earth by way of the grape and grape juice but on occasion, as in Canaan of Galilee, can dispense with the grape and make wine directly from water, so also in the case of living creatures He can cause them to be born either from the seed or from inorganic matter containing invisible seeds (occulta semina). Saint Augustine thus beheld in the phenomenon of spontaneous generation of living things the will of God, which interferes with the usual orderly sequence of events, and established the theory of spontaneous generation as a dogma sustained by all the force of authority of the Christian Church.

It is, therefore, clear why further development of the problem of the origin of life remained for a long time within the framework of the teaching of spontaneous generation. The medieval scholars in their works merely corroborated the "facts" described by Aristotle of the origin of living creatures from decaying matter, or even supplemented these with still more phantastic observations and experiments of their own. As a fitting comment upon the typical methods of studying nature in the Middle Ages mention may be made of the widely accepted tales of the goose tree, of the vegetable lamb or of the homunculus.

On the authority of very prominent scholars and numerous travellers of that period geese and ducks came from sea shells, which themselves had come from the fruit of trees. Birds could also be born directly from these fruits. This legend of the goose tree was already expounded by Cardinal Pietro Damiani at the beginning of the eleventh century. The English encyclopedist Alexander Neckam (1157–1217) evolved the theory of the origin of birds from fir trees which came in contact with the salt of sea water. Subsequently this theory of the vegetable source of geese and ducks was so generally accepted that the use of their meat became common on fast days, a practice which was later prohibited by a special edict of Pope Innocent III [1].

It is interesting that this theory of the goose tree survived until the end of the seventeenth and even the beginning of the eighteenth century. A number of authors gave their own observations and produced more or less phantastic drawings which portrayed the gradual development of birds from the fruit of trees. Evidently this legend originated from a naive interpretation of superficial observations of a peculiar species of barnacle, the so called sea ducks (Lepas anatifera). The full-grown specimens of these sea animals attach themselves to rocks, stones, bottoms of boats and occasionally to a tree which has fallen into the water, and they form a calcareous membrane resembling a shell. On the shores of northern Scotland, Ireland and of the neighboring islands this occurs at the same time of year when the young polar geese arrive from the North. These two events were somehow associated with each other and phantasy filled in the rest of the imaginary picture of the relation of these birds, which came no one knew whence, with the little "sea ducks" attached to the trunks of trees.

Possibly analogous superficial observations were the basis of another legend, the vegetable lamb, which many travellers to the Orient have reported (Odorico da Pordenone (1331), Maundeville (1300–1372) and others). According to their reports these travellers had heard tales of or had even seen plants and whole trees whose melon-like fruit contained full formed lambs which the local population used for meat [9].

The story of the homunculus takes its origin in certain alchemical experiments and apparently started in the first century of our era. It is based on the idea that by mixing the passive female with the active male principle it is pos-

sible to reproduce artificially the phenomenon of generation and to obtain an embryo of the little man, homunculus.
This story prevailed throughout the Middle Ages and even
in the sixteenth century the famous physician and alche-
mist Paracelsus (1493–1541) gave an exact recipe for the
preparation of homunculus. For this purpose it is necessary to place human sperm into a special vessel and to subject this to a series of complicated manipulations for a
definite time, when finally the little man is produced. He
requires human blood for his nourishment.

Paracelsus was a confirmed protagonist of the theory
of spontaneous generation of living beings. He believed
that some special law governed the organism of animals
and man, a vital force which he called the "spirit of life"
(spiritus vitae), and which determined the formation and
further development of the organism. Paracelsus elaborated his theory of the origin of life in conformity with
these philosophical conceptions and even described a series
of observations on the spontaneous generation of mice,
frogs, eels, turtles, etc., from water, air, straw, decaying
wood, etc.[10]

Although in the last half of the sixteenth and especially
in the seventeenth century observation of natural phenomena becomes more exact and experimentation is already
achieving a place for itself, the idea of a primary spontaneous generation of living things still dominates completely the minds of the investigators and scholars. The
famous Brussels physician Van Helmont (1577–1644),
who had so mastered the technique of exact, critical experimentation that he could tackle the complex problem of the
nutrition of plants, still considered the possibility of spon-

taneous generation of living creatures as beyond the per-adventure of doubt. Furthermore, he actually supported this theory with many observations and experiments. It is to Van Helmont that we owe the well known recipe for obtaining mice from wheat kernels. Since he believed that human sweat can furnish the generating principle, it was enough to place a dirty shirt into a vessel containing wheat germ and after 21 days, when fermentation would cease, the vapors from the shirt together with the vapors of the seeds would generate live mice. Van Helmont was particularly surprised to find that these artificially produced mice were the exact replicas of natural mice originating from the semen of their parents [11].

Harvey (1578–1657), the discoverer of the circulation of the blood, did not reject spontaneous generation although he coined the famous phrase "Omne vivum ex ovo" (all living from the egg). But he interpreted the word "egg" very broadly and considered entirely possible the "generatio aequivoca" (spontaneous generation) of worms, insects, etc., through the action of special forces liberated in decay and analogous processes [12].

Thus the dogma enunciated by Saint Augustine of God's will, which arbitrarily interrupts the usual inherent order of things, continued to dominate over the minds of leading men even as late as the first half of the seventeenth century, when in all other branches of knowledge the exact and inflexible laws of nature had already been established. Even such luminaries of the human intellect as Descartes (1596–1650) and Newton (1643–1727) accepted unqualifiedly the theory of spontaneous generation of living organisms from lifeless matter. It is true that Descartes

considered spontaneous generation as a natural process, occurring under still imperfectly understood circumstances,
particularly when moist earth is exposed to sunlight or
when there is decay. He believed that various plants and
animals such as worms, flies and other insects can originate in this manner. Newton gave little attention to biological problems but he was firmly convinced in the possibility of spontaneous generation and even pointed out that
plants were produced from the attenuated emanation from
the tail of comets.

The experiments of the Tuscan physician Francesco
Redi (1626–1697), who had the honor of being the first
to demolish by experimental proofs the faith in spontaneous generation which held uninterrupted sway for many
centuries, constitute justly the turning point in the history
of the spontaneous generation theory. In the treatise "Es-
perienze intorno alla generazione degl' insetti" (1668)
he described a series of experiments demonstrating that
the little white worms in meat were nothing but fly larvae.
He placed meat or fish in a large vessel covered with Nea-
politan muslin and for greater security placed on top of
the vessel a frame over which muslin was stretched. Although flies swarmed over the muslin no worms appeared
in the meat. Redi reports that he had succeeded in observing how flies deposited their eggs in the muslin but that
worms in the meat developed only when the eggs got to
the meat. From these observations he concluded that decaying matter merely offers a place or nest for the developing insects but that the deposition of eggs is a necessary
preliminary without which the worms never appear.

However, Redi did not succeed in shaking off completely

the notions of spontaneous generation. In spite of his brilliant experiments and their correct interpretation he still admitted the possibility of spontaneous generation from decaying matter, as, for instance, the origin of intestinal worms or of wood worms. Similarly, he thought that the little worms enclosed in oak galls came from the plant juices. Only later was this view discarded, thanks to the investigations of the Paduan physician and naturalist Vallisnieri (1661–1730).

Nevertheless, the belief in spontaneous generation of animals and plants was so firmly rooted that, in spite of numerous experimental refutations, it persisted throughout the entire eighteenth and even until the beginning of the nineteenth century. Even Lamarck [13] (1744–1829) in his "Philosophie Zoologique" mentions the possibility of spontaneous generation of mushrooms and certain parasites, although this is contrary to his general outlook on nature. Only very gradually and thanks to the refinement in the technique of observation of natural phenomena and, above all, to the more detailed knowledge of the complicated structure of living organisms did it become apparent that such complex organizations could not possibly have been formed from amorphous silt or decaying matter. In this manner the belief in spontaneous generation of all highly organized living things was banished from the domain of science. But the idea of a primary origin itself had not died out and indeed received a further impetus in the eighteenth and nineteenth centuries so far as the simplest and tiniest of living things, the microorganisms, were concerned.

At about the same time when Redi performed his famous experiments, the Dutch investigator Leeuwenhoek (1632–1723) discovered, with the aid of a microscope which he constructed, a new world of living things unperceived by the unaided eye. In his letters to the London Royal Society, Leeuwenhoek described, in great detail, these tiny "live beasts" (viva animalcula) which he found in rain water exposed for a long time to the air, in various infusions, excreta, etc. With his primitive microscope Leeuwenhoek examined representatives of practically every class of microorganism known at the present time, and furnished pictures and remarkably exact descriptions of infusoria, yeast, bacteria, etc.[14]

The curious discoveries of this Dutch investigator attracted wide attention and inspired numerous followers. Wherever decay or fermentation of organic substance took place, observers found microorganisms present. They were found in all sorts of vegetable infusions and decoctions, in rotting meat, in spoiled bouillon, in sour milk, in fermenting wort, etc. It was only necessary to put easily decomposing substances for a short time into a warm place when almost immediately live microscopic creatures developed where they were absent before. With the belief in spontaneous generation still widely held, the idea that the origin of living microorganisms from lifeless matter was actually taking place before one's eyes in these infusions and decoctions, easily gained ground.

Leeuwenhoek himself did not entertain this view and maintained that the microorganisms developed from something which got into the infusions from the air, and this was also corroborated experimentally by the tests made by Louis Joblot [15]. This follower of Leeuwenhoek boiled hay infusion teeming with microorganisms for 15 minutes and poured equal portions in two different vessels. One was tightly closed with parchment before the contents cooled, while the other vessel was left open. In the latter tiny living creatures (probably infusoria) developed, but not in the former. On removing the parchment cover the infusion in the first vessel was likewise quickly swarming with microorganisms.

The experiments of Joblot, however, had not convinced his contemporaries and the theory of spontaneous generation retained its wide sway among scientists. It even received a particularly brilliant formulation in the works of the famous French biologist Buffon (1707–1788). Buffon perceived in the process of spontaneous generation a corroboration of his general hypothesis of the existence of a special vital principle. He regarded all living matter as consisting of "organic molecules" or particles which did not themselves change but united with each other into kaleidoscopic combinations. When the dead organism decomposed its individual existence came to an end, but the materials of which it was composed again recombined forming new living organisms. He believed that microorganisms were thus created [16].

The same idea was developed by Buffon's contemporary, the Scotch minister Needham (1713–1781), who thought that there was inherent in every microscopic particle of organic matter a special "vital force" which vitalized the organic material of the infusion. Needham thus elaborated the vitalistic conception of the essence and creation of life which was quite prevalent at the time. However, the significance of the contributions of this scientist for the problem we are considering lies not so much in the discoursive part as in the far-reaching experimental investigations, which Needham made in the attempt to prove the possibility of spontaneous generation of microorganisms.

Needham reports: "I took a quantity of mutton gravy hot from the fire and shut it up in a phial closed with a cork so well masticated that my precautions amounted to as much as if I had sealed my phial hermetically." As a further precaution, he then heated the vessel on hot ashes but, in spite of all this, after a few days the vessel was found to teem with microorganisms. He studied by a similar procedure various organic liquids and infusions but always with the same result. From these observations he quite naturally concluded that the spontaneous generation of microorganisms from decomposing organic substances was not only possible but even necessary [17].

The Italian scientist, the Abbé Spallanzani (1765) subjected to a devastating criticism not only the views of Buffon and Needham but also their experiments. Spallanzani, as well as Needham, performed experiments with the object of either confirming or refuting the theory of spontaneous generation, but he was led by his experiments to diametrically opposed conclusions. Spallanzani maintained that Needham succeeded in generating organisms only because the vessels with their contents were not sufficiently heated and, therefore, were incompletely sterilized. He himself made hundreds of experiments with vegetable decoctions and various organic liquids which were subjected to more or less prolonged heating and were sealed immediately to prevent air from entering, because Spallanzani believed that air carried the germs of microorganisms. In every instance when this operation was carried out with proper care, neither did the liquid contents of the vessels undergo decomposition nor did living organisms appear in them.

Needham objected, first, that on prolonged heating of the liquids the air in the vessels became vitiated and this was responsible for the failure of microorganisms to develop; second, that prolonged heating destroyed the "vital force" of the organic decoctions, which is apparently capricious and unstable and cannot withstand for long such severe treatment. Therefore, Needham did not deem that he heated his liquids too gently but rather that Spallanzani heated his liquids too vigorously and thus destroyed the creative force of the infusions.

To meet these objections Spallanzani repeated his experiments and performed with exceptional care a large series of tests planned to answer all of Needham's criticisms [18]. Nevertheless, he failed to convince his contemporaries and the theory of spontaneous generation of microorganisms counted many defenders among scientists until the middle of the nineteenth century.

Especially much work and experimental skill was consumed in the attempt to clarify the significance of the air in the generation of living things in liquids subjected to preliminary heating. The prominent French chemist L. Gay-Lussac (1778–1850) demonstrated by direct analyses that oxygen was lacking in vessels which were sealed after their contents were boiled; in other words, the component of air which sustains oxidation and respiration was lacking. This evidently gave support to the views developed by Needham. To elucidate the role of oxygen still further

Gay-Lussac filled with mercury a glass tube sealed at one end (eudiometer) and inserted it into a dish containing mercury. A single grape was introduced under the mercury and crushed with a wire inserted through the mercury. The juice from the crushed grape rose to the top of the sealed tube and for a long time remained clear and apparently thoroughly sterile. However, on admitting a bubble of oxygen into the tube the juice quickly started to ferment and became filled with microorganisms [19].

This experiment, which had been used later very extensively by the adherents of the spontaneous generation theory, is significant in that the source of the contamination, as we know now, was the germs on the surface of the mercury, which neither the experimenter nor his commentators had taken into consideration.

In 1836 the well known German naturalist T. Schwann, the founder of the cellular theory, put the problem of the significance of oxygen to a new experimental test. He passed air through a heated tube into a vessel containing sterile meat bouillon and demonstrated that under these circumstances the bouillon did not spoil and that with a constantly renewed stream of sterile air there was thus no spontaneous generation. However, entirely different results were obtained when these experiments were made with liquids containing sugar. Although both kinds of experiment were carried out practically the same way, in the latter case a mass of living microorganisms frequently appeared [20].

In the same year Fr. Schulze performed similar experiments, except that the air entering the vessel with the sterile liquid was freed from germs not by heat but by passing through concentrated sulfuric acid, and with the same results. However, when Schulze's experiment was repeated a number of times contradictory results were obtained and in some instances microorganisms developed in the liquid [21].

Somewhat later (1853) two Heidelberg professors, H. Schröder and Th. von Dusch, simplified the experiment and sterilized the air by filtering it through a layer of sterile cotton, which retained the microorganisms. In this way they were able to free the air from every infective cause without subjecting it either to chemical influence or to heat. These experimenters actually found that heated meat decoction or beer wort could remain unchanged for many weeks. But under similar conditions milk or meat without water quickly spoiled and became filled with microorganisms [22].

Thus, in spite of the fact that these experiments all tended to disprove the possibility of spontaneous generation, they did not carry sufficient conviction because, for some inexplicable reason, they did occasionally fail and microorganisms did appear in the tested fluids. We know, today, that these occasional failures were due to accidental technical slips, but at that time each failure could easily furnish and actually did furnish the pretext for the interpretation, that spontaneous generation need not necessarily occur always but only under certain favorable conditions. Dumas, Naegeli and many other prominent scientists of the middle of the nineteenth century accepted this interpretation.

The dispute over the problem of the spontaneous generation of microorganisms reached its highest pitch, when in 1859 F. Pouchet [23] published the articles in which he

tried to prove experimentally the possibility of spontaneous generation, since it seemed entirely improbable that
liquids would regularly become infected with air-borne
organisms. In his extensive work, embracing nearly 700
pages, Pouchet developed the vitalistic theory of autogeneration, which was essentially similar to those of Buffon
and of Needham. He maintained that each event of autogeneration is preceded by fermentation or decomposition
of organic substances and that only substances which are
found in living organisms can generate new life. Under the
influence of fermentation and decay organic particles of
dead bodies split up. For a brief period they wander as
free particles but are ultimately reunited by their inherent
tendency for association, thus giving rise to new living
things. Since Pouchet postulated the pre-existence of some
"vital force" necessary for the generation of organisms he
never assumed that living things arose simply *de novo* in
the solutions of inorganic substances. Pouchet repeated on
a large scale the work of his predecessors in an effort to
test his theory and always obtained positive results: in the
organic liquids, which he investigated, microorganisms invariably developed.

Pouchet's work made a big impression upon his contemporaries. The French Academy of Sciences offered a prize
for exact and convincing experiments which would throw
light upon the question of the autogeneration of living
things. This prize was awarded to Louis Pasteur [24], who in
1862 published his investigations on spontaneous generation and in a series of brilliantly executed experiments,
which left no room for scepticism, demonstrated the utter
impossibility of the formation of microorganisms in vari-

ous infusions and solutions of organic substances. Pasteur succeeded only because he did not follow blindly the path of empiricism, because he had a broad conception of the entire problem, because he found a rational explanation of all the earlier experimental attempts and pointed out the sources of error of his predecessors. Pasteur first of all clarified the problem of the presence of microorganisms in the air which, as was shown previously, was regarded as one of the chief sources of contamination. The adherents of the spontaneous generation theory, and particularly Pouchet, not infrequently expressed doubt as to the presence of germs in the air and demanded a demonstration of those "swarms of microorganisms" which were supposed to inhabit the air.

Pasteur solved this problem by the aid of a very simple method. He sucked air through a tube plugged with gun cotton. As was already shown by Schröder and Dusch, the finest suspended particles floating in the air are retained in the cotton and should, therefore, remain in the tube. After a lapse of 24 hours the suction was stopped, the cotton plug with its dust deposit removed and dissolved in a mixture of ether and alcohol whereupon the solid particles settled out and, after being washed with the solvent, were examined under the microscope. It was demonstrated that thousands of organisms were thus collected which in no wise differed from various microorganisms or their germs and, furthermore, the presence of large numbers of organisms in our surrounding atmosphere was thus finally proven.

Pasteur showed later that the germs floating in the air may furnish the source of infection. First of all, he repeated, by a somewhat modified and improved technique, Schwann's experiments, boiling organic liquids in round-bottomed flasks whose necks were drawn out and fused to a platinum tube. The latter were heated to a red glow over a gas flame. In this way air entering the flask, after the boiling had ceased, passed through the red-hot platinum tube and was freed from germs. The air was cooled by a stream of water before actually entering the flask. When the flask was thus filled with air, the drawn-out neck was sealed off in a flame and the sealed flask could be kept in this condition for any length of time. When experiments were made by this procedure, the solutions without exception remained unspoiled and no microorganisms appeared in them. But if the neck of the flask was broken off and a cotton plug, through which air had been filtered, was introduced into the solution, the neck being again quickly sealed, the contents of the flask after a brief interval became filled with molds, bacteria and even infusoria. It followed, therefore, that the boiled solution did not lose its ability to sustain microorganisms and that the germs of the air arrested by the cotton plug could actually and very easily develop in this fluid.

Later Pasteur sterilized the air, with which the flasks were filled, without the aid of heat, by passing it, as Schröder and Dusch did, through a cotton plug, or by an original method which he himself devised. Generally Pasteur half filled the round flask with the fluid to be studied, softened the neck in a torch flame and pulled it out in the form of a letter S. The contents were then boiled without further precautions. When steam was being discharged vigorously, the flame was removed and the flask allowed to cool off. Under these conditions the contents remained unchanged even though there was direct contact with the outside atmosphere through the bent tube, because dust and germs carried in with the air became imprisoned in the bend of the tube. However, as soon as the bent portion of the tubulature was cut off, the contents became quickly inhabited by microorganisms. In these experiments the air was no longer subjected to any treatment and yet no contamination of the liquid occurred so long as the entrance was blocked to germs floating in the air.

Further experiments of Pasteur have shown that the number of viable microorganisms in the air was far from constant, varying according to the season of the year or locality. The largest number of germs was found in the atmosphere of cities and thickly inhabited places. The air from fields or forests has fewer microorganisms while in mountainous regions, especially at high altitudes, the number of tiny creatures floating in the air is negligible. It is possible, therefore, to open flasks with sterile contents at such altitudes without necessarily inoculating them. In a number of instances such flasks were once more sealed off and remained sterile, although mountain air which was not purified had entered those flasks.

At the same time Pasteur demonstrated that air was not the only source of contamination of organic fluids. He showed that germs of microorganisms are found on the surfaces of all objects used in the experiments, and for this reason all these surfaces must be scrupulously disinfected. Pasteur showed that the development of microorganisms in the experiments of previous investigators had always been due to the failure, owing to methodological

shortcomings, to exclude completely every source of contamination. Thus, for instance, Pasteur demonstrated by
direct experiments that the grape juice in Gay-Lussac's
tests was contaminated with microorganisms adhering to
the surface of the mercury. In other cases the vessels were
not sufficiently sterilized. And, as Pasteur so brilliantly
proved it by numerous experiments, if every source of
error was removed, the solutions could be made sterile in
one hundred per cent of the trials. Furthermore, Pasteur
succeeded in showing that such easily decomposing fluids
as urine and blood could be preserved for an indefinite
time without heating or any other treatment, provided they
were removed from the organism with precautions against
contamination by germs from the outside. Under such conditions the body fluids do not decompose and can be kept
indefinitely.

Pasteur, therefore, not only obtained exact and uniform
results but also explained satisfactorily the contradictory
findings of other investigators. He refuted the hypothesis
that decaying infusions generate microorganisms and demonstrated that, on the contrary, decay of these fluids was
the result of the activity of microorganisms, which had
been introduced from the outside.

Obviously the adherents of the autogeneration of microbes did not capitulate at once and many experiments
were still performed after the publication of Pasteur's
work, which seemed to indicate the possibility of spontaneous generation under some special conditions. The most
serious and interesting were the experiments of Bastian [25],
who showed that microorganisms appear in boiled hay infusions even when the flasks are opened on mountain tops

or when the air with which they are filled has been heated. Pasteur's investigations corroborated Bastian's experiments so far as the factual findings were concerned, but he denied that they had really anything to do with spontaneous generation of organisms. Spores of the hay bacillus are present in infusions. These are very resistant to heating and retain the ability to multiply even after prolonged boiling. If hay infusions are autoclaved at 120° or if they are boiled twice in succession, they remain sterile just as other organic liquids, provided they are not subjected to air-borne contamination. The two successive boilings act in the following manner: the first time only the vegetative forms of bacteria are killed off, the spores remaining unaffected; upon cooling the boiled infusion these spores develop into bacteria, which are killed by the repeated boiling before they have formed new spores.

After Bastian no one offered any serious criticisms of Pasteur, and every attempt to disprove his theses or to discover instances of spontaneous generation of some microbe proved entirely futile. From our present point of view this is quite understandable, since microorganisms are not merely bits of organic matter, as was thought before Pasteur. A close study of these simplest living things has revealed that they possess a delicate and complicated organization. In this respect the structure of the unicellular microorganisms differed but little from the structure of the separate cells composing the multicellular organisms. It is totally improbable that such a complex and at the same time strictly definite organization could appear in a very short time, before our eyes, so to speak, from unorganized solutions of organic substances. Such a supposition is no less absurd than the idea of the origin of frogs from the May dew or of lions from the desert sand.

Thus, it seemed that the theory of the spontaneous generation of living beings was interred forever, yet in a comparatively short time it was once more resurrected in a somewhat refurbished and modernized form. In a number of diseases of man, animals and plants, as for instance in typhus, smallpox, hoof and mouth disease of cattle, mosaic disease of tobacco and potato no bacteria or any other pathogenic microorganisms could be discovered. However, the unquestionable infectiveness as well as the general symptoms of these diseases are so very similar to bacterial infections that the causative agents had to be recognized as living things analogous to bacteria, and have been designated as viruses. Viruses are of such infinitesimal size that they cannot be detected even under the most powerful microscopes and for the same reason pass easily through bacterial filters. Ultrafiltration experiments have established that the magnitude of these various viruses is somewhat of the order of 50-70 millimicrons [a millimicron is one millionth of a millimeter], and are thus considerably smaller than ordinary bacteria [the magnitude of cocci is usually 500-2000 millimicrons]. There is no evidence that viruses occur anywhere except in the living or in recently deceased animals. In recent years a number of investigators have made reports of the successful cultivation of filterable viruses in artificial nutritive media, but these reports must still be regarded with some doubt because, on account of the tremendous difficulty of such cultivation, the experiments are extremely unreliable. The successful propagation of filterable viruses has been possible only in the presence of suitable living cells.

To this day the problem of the nature of the filterable viruses has not been definitely solved. Some investigators regard them as unorganized solutions but the opinion prevalent now is that we are dealing with living organisms of infinitesimal dimensions and Gardner [26], therefore, designated them as ultramicrobes. This viewpoint is partly substantiated by the fact that there are a number of organisms, whose dimensions are intermediate between those of ordinary bacteria and of the ultramicrobes. Thus, for instance, Bacillus pneumosintes, isolated from grippe patients, ranges within the limits of 100 and 250 millimicrons.

Although, as we have seen, the nature of the ultramicrobes is far from having been clarified, many scientists have supposed that these infinitesimal living creatures may originate spontaneously from unorganized solutions of organic substance. Even such a careful student as Gardner notes as follows: "It is not very probable that viruses can be generated spontaneously but it may be mentioned parenthetically that perhaps Pasteur definitely disposed of the theory of spontaneous generation without having taken into consideration the ultramicroscopic forms of life. Therefore, this may be still regarded as an open question so far as viruses are concerned." However, even in this form the point of view can hardly be accepted. No matter how minute the ultramicrobes are, if they are living organisms they must be endowed with a definite and complex organization which makes it possible for them to perform a number of vital functions. The spontaneous generation of such an organization from molecules dispersed chaotically in a solution is just as impossible in principle as is the generation of structures characteristic of the bacterial organism.

We must, therefore, reject categorically the possibility of autogeneration of living things in the manner that has been postulated and described in this chapter, and we are forced to search for some other interpretation of the origin of life on Earth.

CHAPTER II

THEORIES OF THE CONTINUITY
OF LIFE

By his experiments Pasteur demonstrated beyond per-
adventure of doubt the impossibility of autogeneration of
life in the sense as it was imagined by his predecessors.
He showed that living organisms cannot be formed suddenly before our eyes from formless solutions and infusions. A careful survey of the experimental evidence reveals, however, that it tells nothing about the impossibility
of generation of life at some other epoch or under some
other conditions. Incidentally, Pasteur himself, with his
usual reserve, placed such an interpretation on his own experiments. His contemporaries, however, put a broader
interpretation on his data, considering them as absolute
proof of the impossibility of a transition from dead matter to living organisms. For instance, the famous English
physicist Lord Kelvin (1871) expressed himself very
clearly that, on the basis of Pasteur's experiments, the impossibility of autogeneration of life at any time or anywhere must be regarded established as firmly as the law of
universal gravitation. The same viewpoint has been shared
by a number of investigators, for whom life is radically
different from the rest of inanimate nature. Therefore, in
their opinion, it is wrong even to pose the question of the
origin of life, since life is as much an eternal category as
matter itself. Life is eternal, it only changes its form but
is never created from dead substance.

At first sight the impression is gained that Pasteur's experiments caused a complete reversal in the conceptions of naturalists with regard to the origin of life. Previously it was believed that living organisms were easily generated from dead matter, before our very eyes, so to speak; then the attitude was taken that life can never originate but must exist eternally. This contradiction in viewpoints is only apparent and a careful examination of the question shows that both the theory of spontaneous generation and the theory of the continuity of life are based on the same dualistic outlook on nature. Both theories start essentially with the same assumption that life is endowed with absolute autonomy determined by special principles and forces, applicable only to organisms, the nature of which is radically different from the principles and forces operative in the inanimate kingdom.

But from the opposite point of view, from the point of view of the unity of forces operative in living and non-living nature, the spontaneous generation of organisms, as described in the preceding chapter, is altogether impossible and unthinkable. As already emphasized before, even the simplest of living organisms possesses a very complex structure or organization. We are not familiar with physical or chemical forces which could cause under the described experimental conditions the appearance of organisms from structureless solutions of organic substances. Therefore, the sudden generation of organisms can be explained either with St. Augustine as an act of divine will (miracle) or as the result of some special vital force. Actually, throughout the history of this problem, the conception of a spontaneous generation is intimately associated with the idea of a "vital force". It is the Aristotelian "entelechy" embracing all matter and forming it purposefully into living organisms. It is the spirit of life, "spiritus vitae" of Paracelsus, the "archai" of Van Helmont which, according to his views, reside in seeds and direct the processes of creation and of autogeneration. Finally, it is Leibniz' "monads" which represent the immutable centers of force of a spiritual character. Similarly, the later adherents of the spontaneous generation of life, Buffon, Needham, Pouchet, are all among the most convinced vitalists who believe that a vital force, capable of vivifying the organic substance of solutions and infusions, is dormant in every microscopic particle of organic matter. The action of this force is not bound by any general physical laws, it is entirely "sui generis" and, therefore, can transform non-living into living matter in the wink of an eye.

It is hardly necessary to prove that the same vitalistic conception, the same dualism is at the bottom of the theory of the continuity or eternity of life. No matter what form the theories of continuity of life may assume, they always leave an unabridgeable gap between the kingdom of organisms and of inorganic nature. But to say that life never had an origin and existed eternally, is to imply that there is an absolute autonomy of living organisms.

F. Engels [1] in his "Dialectics of Nature" subjected both the theory of spontaneous generation and the theory of eternity of life to a withering criticism. Discussing the views according to which new living organisms can arise from the destruction of other organisms, he points out that such an assumption is contrary to all our modern knowledge. "Chemistry by its analysis of the process of decomposition of dead organic bodies shows that, with every advancing step in this process, products are formed which are nearer to the inorganic world, products which are progressively less utilizable in the organic world. But the process may be given a different direction and the decomposition products may be made utilizable, if they enter the properly adapted existing organism." Furthermore, with regard to experiments attempting to prove the primary generation, he remarks ironically: "It would be foolish to try and force nature to accomplish in twenty four hours, with the aid of a bit of stinky water, that which it took her many thousands of years to do."

But Engels likewise rejects the conception of the eternity of life. He quotes a very characteristic statement by Liebig: "It is sufficient to admit that life is as old and as eternal as matter itself, and the entire argument about the origin of life loses apparently all sense by this simple admission. And, really, why can we not imagine that organic life is just as much without beginning as is carbon and its combinations, or as is all uncreated and indestructible matter and the forces which are eternally bound up with the movement of matter in universal space." Engels shows that such a view can only be based upon the recognition of some special life force as the form-giving principle, which is entirely incompatible with the materialistic world conception. Engels notes further that Liebig's assertion about carbon compounds being as eternal as carbon itself, is inexact if not actually erroneous. Engels points out that carbon compounds are eternal in the sense that under constant conditions of mixing, temperature, pressure, electrical potential, etc., they repeat themselves always. But to this day no one has ever asserted that, for instance, even such simple carbon compounds as CO_2 or CH_4 are eternal in the sense of having existed at all times, instead of being constantly formed from certain elements and decomposed again into the same elements. If living protein is eternal in the same sense as other carbon compounds, it must not only break up constantly into its elements, as actually happens, but it must also be constantly formed anew from these elements without the cooperation of preexisting protein. This is diametrically opposed to Liebig's results.

The same holds true, even in a larger measure, with regard to living organisms. The idea that living things always arise under definite conditions has nothing to do with the conception of the eternity of life. On the contrary, it emphasizes the necessity of generation of organisms from non-living matter. But the adherents of the theory of the eternity of life assume that at all times some principle existed eternally, which passed on from organism to organism, and without which the origin of living things would be impossible. Following this path of reasoning we invariably fall into the pit of vitalistic conceptions.

Engels shows that a consistent materialistic philosophy can follow only a single path in the attempt to solve the problem of the origin of life. Life has neither arisen spontaneously nor has it existed eternally. It must have, therefore, resulted from a long evolution of matter, its origin being merely one step in the course of its historical development.

We shall consider only two fundamental theories based on the conception of the continuity of life: the theory of cosmozoa and the closely related theory of panspermia, and Preyer's [2] theory of the eternity of life. Although the Preyer theory is of later date, it will be discussed first because it stands quite apart from the other philosophical outlooks and, besides, it has now chiefly a historical interest only. On the other hand, the panspermia theory passed through many phases and is still to be found in many works of contemporary scientists.

Starting from the empirically verifiable proposition that all organisms are derived from similar organisms, Preyer poses this question: "Is not the problem of the origin of life based on a wrong assumption that the living must have come sometime from the non-living? All organisms invariably originate from other living organisms. On the other hand, inorganic non-living substance has always and still does now originate not only from other lifeless matter but also from living organisms which either discard it as a dead mass or leave it behind after death."

But if the living has never originated from non-living substance and has always come from the living, then it must have existed even at the time when the Earth was still a molten mass. Preyer actually accepts this conclusion and regards as living not only the present-day organisms but also the molten liquid mass which existed in the remote antiquity. "If we rid ourselves of the idea wholly arbitrary and unsupported by facts that protoplasm can exist only in its present composition, and of the old convenient prejudice that at first there was only inorganic substance, we can without fear take the next bold step, discard altogether all belief in a primary origin, and recognize the timelessness of the current of life."

On such foundations Preyer sketches approximately the following picture of the continuous life. Originally the entire fiery liquid mass of the Earth was a single mighty organism whose life was manifested in the motion of its substance. But as the Earth began to cool the substances which could no longer remain in the liquid state separated as a hard mass and formed the dead inorganic substance. This process continued further, but at first the molten liquid masses alone represented life on Earth in contradistinction to the inorganic bodies. "Only when these combinations had in the course of time petrified on the Earth's surface, i.e. died out, combinations of elements appeared which till then had remained in gaseous and liquid state, and which have gradually taken on the semblance of protoplasm, the foundation of everything living to-day. . . . We, therefore, assert that motion is the beginning of life in the world, and that protoplasm is the residuum which must have been left over after the substances now regarded as inorganic had separated out on the cooled surface of the planet."

Thus Preyer develops his deeply idealistic but very ancient conception of a universal life essence, and places an extraordinarily broad and indefinite interpretation on the idea of "life." If we leave out the interpretation and concern ourselves only with the question of the origin of present protoplasmic organisms, the theory has absolutely nothing concrete to offer us. Nevertheless, it lasted for some time and enlisted a large number of followers, which only characterizes the type of ideas about the origin of life which was dominant at the end of the last century.

The other theory, which later was designated as the cosmozoa theory, attempted to reconcile the principle of eternity of life with the conception of the origin of our planet. All adherents of this theory assumed that life existed eternally, that it was never created, never separated from dead material. But how then did life originate on the Earth? The Earth itself is not eternal, since it must have had a beginning sometime, having separated from the Sun, and certainly during the early period of its existence could not have been populated with organisms, simply because of unfavorable temperature conditions. To overcome this difficulty, the idea was promoted that germs of life dropped to the Earth from the interstellar and interplanetary spaces just as they get into Pasteur's flasks from the outside air. This conception was first elaborated in 1865 by Richter[3], who proceeded from the assumption that, owing to the very fast movement of cosmic bodies, small fragments or hard particles could have become detached, and that viable spores of microorganisms could also have been carried away from the cosmic bodies together with these detached particles. The particles, floating in the interstellar space, could be carried accidentally to other cosmic bodies and, landing on a planet where conditions for life were already favorable (moderate humidity and temperature), commence to develop and later become the ancestors of the entire organic kingdom of that planetary body. Richter assumed that somewhere in the universe there were always cosmic bodies present on which life exists in cellular form. Later this idea was also developed by Liebig[4] who believed that "the atmosphere of celestial bodies as well as of whirling cosmic nebulae can be regarded as the timeless sanctuary of animate forms, the eternal plantations of organic germs." Therefore, the existence of living organisms in the universe is eternal, organic life is never really created but only transmitted from one planet to the next. The problem, according to Richter, is not how life originates but how the germs of life can be carried from one celestial body to the other.

Richter paid special attention to the possibility of transfer of viable germs through the universal spaces separating celestial bodies. He pointed out that organic germs in a dormant state can exist a long time without water or nourishment but become revivified as soon as the conditions favor this, and therefore germs can endure very long journeys. The only danger to the existence of these germs comes from the rise in temperature resulting from the tremendous friction as the body falls through the Earth's atmosphere. However, some meteorites contain traces of carbon and other easily inflammable substances. If those substances could reach the Earth without burning up, it is quite possible for germs also to traverse the atmosphere without losing their viability.

H. von Helmholtz[5] developed a similar idea a number of years after Richter. This well known German physiologist stated that organic life either had to begin sometimes or else it must have existed eternally, but he inclined to the second alternative and thought that live germs were brought to the Earth by meteorites. He based this possibility upon the fact that meteorites, on passing through the Earth's atmosphere, are heated only on the surface while the interior remains cool. He comments as follows: "Who would deny that such bodies floating everywhere in the universal space do not leave behind them the germs of life, wherever the planetary conditions are already suitable to promote organic creation!"

However, in his introduction to Thomson's "Treatise on Theoretical Physics" Helmholtz [6] has this to say about the theory of cosmozoa: "If anyone is inclined to regard this hypothesis as not very probable or indeed highly questionable, I have nothing to say against this. But it seems to me that if every attempt to create organisms from inanimate matter has failed us, it is entirely within the domain of scientific discussion to inquire whether life had ever been created, whether it is not just as old as matter itself and, finally, whether germs are not carried from one celestial body to another, taking root and developing wherever they find favorable soil."

Thus, even Helmholtz did not feel entirely convinced in the correctness of his reasoning. The theory itself, too, soon disappeared from the scientific horizon, since the most painstaking search of meteorites failed to reveal in them not only organisms or their remnants, but even traces of sedimentary or biochemical formations. Only in the very last few years Ch. Lipman [7] attempted once more to resuscitate these ideas. He examined a number of rocky meteorites for possible traces of living organisms. Using a very intricate technique to preclude the possibility of contaminating the meteorites with earth bacteria, he came to the conclusion that live bacteria and their spores are found in the interior of the meteorites. The organisms which he succeeded in isolating were identical with the bacterial forms existing on the Earth. This makes it very probable that, in spite of all his precautions, Lipman did not succeed in preventing earth bacteria from contaminating the meteorites while they were ground to a powder. Even in different regions of our planet there are different forms of microorganisms, and it would be extremely strange if exactly the same bacterial forms found on the Earth were present also on some remote planets.

At the beginning of the twentieth century the idea of the transfer of germs from one celestial body to another was again revived in the form of the so-called theory of panspermia, originated by the great Swedish physical chemist S. Arrhenius. Being a strong adherent of the conception that life is scattered throughout universal space, he showed very convincingly, by means of direct calculations, the possibility of transfer of particles from one celestial body to another. The principal activating force is the pressure exerted by light rays, discovered by Clerk Maxwell and brilliantly verified experimentally by P. Lebedev.

Arrhenius [8] draws the following picture of the transfer of small particles, including microorganismal spores, through the interstellar and interplanetary space. The upward air currents, which are especially powerful during large volcanic eruptions, may carry the tiniest particles of matter to a tremendous height of sixty miles or more above the Earth's surface. In the upper layers of the atmosphere, due to a number of causes, there are always electrical discharges which are strong enough to shoot these material particles from the Earth's atmosphere into the interplanetary space, where they are driven farther and farther by the one-sided pressure of the Sun's light rays. Under certain conditions, this results in the formation by our planet of something like a comet's tail but, of course, of incomparably smaller dimensions. This tail is formed by the finest particles of matter always leaving the Earth and repelled by the action of the Sun's rays. According to Arrhenius, similar phenomena occur on the other planets also.

In this way tiny particles of substance must be cast off all the time from the Earth's surface as well as from the surface of other celestial bodies. If a planet is inhabited by live organisms, particularly microorganisms, their spores would be thus carried off into the interstellar space. Arrhenius calculated that bacterial spores with a diameter of 0.0002-0.00015 mm. move with very great speed in the empty space under the influence of pressure of the Sun's rays. Separated from the Earth, such spores will pass beyond the limits of our planetary system in 14 months, and in 9000 years will reach the nearest star, a-Centauri.

The movement of spores of microorganisms may be not only away from but also back towards the Sun. Living germs carried off into the interstellar space may meet with particles of cosmic dust of relatively large size. If a spore attaches itself to a particle with a diameter of over 0.0015 mm. its movement is reversed and it then moves towards the Sun, because the light pressure will no longer be able to overcome the gravitation of the heavy particles to the Sun. Arrhenius thinks that in this way the Earth could be covered with microorganismal spores arriving into our solar system from other stellar worlds. Of course, this could only happen if the spores were still in a viable condition after completing this very long journey through space.

This aspect of the problem naturally received special attention from Arrhenius and other adherents of this theory. Arrhenius discusses in detail all the dangers to living germs lurking along their path from planet to planet. According to Arrhenius the absence of moisture or oxygen and the extreme cold of the interplanetary space present no terrors for the microorganismal spores, nor does the heating of the particles, as they fall rapidly through the Earth's atmosphere, endanger their existence. From his calculations Arrhenius concludes that the heat does not exceed 100° and lasts only a short time. Since bacterial spores are known to remain viable after such treatment, he thinks it is reasonable to regard the transport of viable germs from one planetary system to another as the cause of the origin of life on Earth. This theory has many supporters, being especially energetically upheld by Kostychev [9].

However, the farther research is carried in this direction, and the better we become acquainted with the world around us, the more new facts come to light, which contradict radically this theory and make it seem less and less probable that such a transfer of viable germs from one celestial body to another really occurs.

As is well known, modern astronomy recognizes our solar system, consisting of a central body with planets whirling around it, as a rather unusual phenomenon in the universe of stars. In order that such a system could have been formed it was necessary for some celestial body, some star of approximately the same mass as our Sun, to come relatively close to it at a remote period of its existence. As a result of attraction between the Sun and that passing star,

a colossal cloud of superheated gases was thrown out from
the surface of the Sun, out of which our planetary system,
including the Earth, was subsequently formed.

But this sort of meeting or approach between two stars
in the universal space could be only an extremely rare
event. The following simple model may serve to illustrate
this point. Assume that in the model the Sun's dimensions
are reduced to those of an ordinary apple. If we desire to
picture, on the same scale, the distance between the Sun
and the star nearest to it we would have to place one apple
in Moscow and the other in New York. It is easy to see
how little probability there is that the apples (celestial
bodies) would ever meet. The famous contemporary English astronomer Jeans[10] says that, according to calculations, the probability of any star becoming a Sun surrounded by planets is about one to one hundred thousand.
He also observes that it is extremely difficult to imagine
life of a higher order capable of developing on celestial
bodies radically differing from our own planet warmed
by the Sun. He concludes, therefore, that, from the point
of view of space, time and physical conditions, life is cir-
cumscribed by its existence in an insignificantly little nook
of the universe.

Thus modern astronomical conceptions offer no support
to the ideas of a ubiquitous distribution of life germs
throughout the universe. Of course, this does not mean that
life exists only on our Earth. We still have too little information to deny completely the possibility of existence of
organisms on some other planets, whirling around stars
similar to our Sun. But there can be no doubt that these
worlds inhabited by living organisms are much farther re-

moved from our solar system than are the nearest stars. Therefore, the transport of living germs from one plane- tary system to another would require not thousands of years, as Arrhenius thought, but at least many hundreds of thousands or even millions of years.

These long periods alone would make transport of viable germs extremely improbable. But the investigations of the last years on short wave interstellar radiations remove such a possibility completely. The lethal action of light rays of short wave length, particularly the ultraviolet rays, on microorganisms and their spores has long been known. Fre- quently, even a brief radiation is sufficient to sterilize com- pletely a given medium and to destroy all the microorgan- isms and spores. The light of the stars is rich in ultraviolet rays but the atmosphere around our Earth protects us from their destructive effect. Life germs carried beyond the limits of this atmosphere would be inevitably killed off by the ultraviolet radiation penetrating the interstellar spaces.

The believers in the theory of panspermia attempted to ward off this objection by pointing out that since the photo- chemical reactions provoked by ultraviolet rays kill the microorganisms only in the presence of oxygen and water, their lethal effect would not be exerted in the vacuum exist- ing in the interstellar spaces. These objections are not very convincing since photochemical reactions may proceed with the aid of the elements of water contained in organic com- pounds. But these can be entirely neglected nowadays since the discovery of the very short rays of cosmic radiation. These rays have much shorter wave lengths than the ultra- violet or even the Roentgen rays (X-rays), and the changes brought about under their action are no longer purely chemical, but much more far-reaching intra-atomic changes. Their effects in the interstellar space have now been the subject of numerous investigations, which have been reviewed recently by J. Lewis [11] in a very interesting article on "The Origin of Elements". In this article many facts are presented showing that substances unprotected by an atmosphere (for instance, meteorites) suffer far-reaching transformations under the influence of the interstellar radiation. At the same time a number of extremely profound changes take place within the atoms leading to the formation of new elements. For instance, iron and nickel are transformed to aluminum and silicon, which in turn may be further transformed to magnesium, sodium, and helium.

Life germs wayfaring in the interstellar space unprotected against cosmic radiation would not only be absolutely doomed to perish, but even their inner chemical structure would in a comparatively brief time suffer radical changes under the influence of radiant energy. We must, therefore, once and for all give up the idea that life germs floated towards our Earth from the outside cosmic spaces. We must, instead, search for the sources of life within the boundaries of our own planet.

CHAPTER III

THEORIES OF THE ORIGIN OF LIFE
AT SOME DISTANT PERIOD OF THE
EARTH'S EXISTENCE

FROM THE PRECEDING TWO CHAPTERS we learned that
neither the theory of the spontaneous generation nor the
theory of the continuity of life solves rationally the problem of the origin of life on Earth. These theories invariably
come in conflict with the objectively established facts derived from a careful and detailed study of the world
around us. This is not hard to understand since these
theories are based on the tacit assumption of an absolutely
impassable hiatus between animate and inanimate nature.

Already in the second half of the last century attempts
were made to solve the problem of the origin of life on the
basis of materialistic conceptions and we find such tendencies in the work of Bastian [1]. Although he, like the vitalists, set out to prove the possibility of autogeneration of
microbes, he did so along principally different lines. Thus,
unlike Pouchet, Bastian considered it entirely possible that
living things originated from inorganic substances without
the intervention of any specific vital force (archebiosis).
Ch. Darwin [2] in one of his letters to Wallace criticized Bastian's experiments and considered them altogether improbable. While he admits the correctness of the idea of archebiosis, he pointed out that spontaneous generation had not
been proven. According to Darwin life must have originated

sometime, somehow, but how this happened was still unknown.

A. Weisman[3] somewhat later developed the same idea. Rejecting decisively any vitalistic tendencies, he believed that life must have arisen sometime or other from inanimate matter. He thought that, at the very beginning and under conditions unknown to us now, the simplest, tiniest organismal forms, the "biophores" were created. The more highly organized beings developed from these at a later period.

Haeckel's theory of archegony[4] is based on similar ideas. He refused to believe that the hypothesis of cosmozoa can explain the origin of life on Earth. Since at one time the Earth must have been in a condition which precluded any possibility of organic life, animate substance must have arisen from inanimate substance at some moment in the development of the Earth. The fact that autogeneration of microorganisms is not observed at the present time does not contradict this assumption. It would still have been possible for organisms to originate from non-living matter at some remote period of the existence of our planet, because the external conditions at that time were entirely different from those prevailing at the present day. In Haeckel's opinion the organisms, which originated by spontaneous generation, must have been the lowest, simplest things imaginable—"homogeneous, structureless, amorphous lumps of protein." They were supposed to have resulted from the interaction of dissolved substances in the primeval sea but Haeckel does not explain just how these organisms actually originated. Indeed, he regards any detailed presentation of the primary origin as necessarily unsatisfactory, because of the lack of reliable data concerning the extremely peculiar conditions existing on the Earth's surface at the time organisms made their first appearance.

Thus, Haeckel placed the center of gravity of the whole problem of the origin of life in the peculiar physical conditions prevailing at one time on the Earth. He could see no difference between the formation of a crystal and of a living cell. The simplest living thing, the "non-nucleated monera", crystallized out mechanically from inanimate substance [5]. But herein lies Haeckel's fundamental error, because it implies that simplest organisms can actually arise all at once from inorganic matter, the whole thing depending merely on the presence of some peculiarly favorable external physical forces which determine the transformation of inanimate substance into an animate being. Furthermore, according to his theory, such forces existed only during the dim past of the Earth's history and have been so completely lost, that spontaneous generation is no longer possible at the present time.

Another German biologist E. Pflüger [6] approached this problem from a somewhat different angle. He searched for the causation of life not only in the peculiarity of external conditions but also in the properties of the substances themselves, from which organisms must have been formed. He built up his theory on the basis of the chemical properties of proteins, with which he identified indissociably the essence of the vital process. Pflüger supposed that in the organism there are two principally different categories of protein: *dead*, or storage protein, and *live* protoplasmic protein. In the first category belong such proteins as egg white, proteins stored in seeds, etc., which are chemically

very stable, inert substances. In the absence of microorganisms these proteins can be preserved an indefinitely long
time without undergoing any substantial chemical alterations. On the contrary, the *live* protein of protoplasm is
an extremely unstable substance. This instability or lability
is, according to Pflüger, the basis of all chemical transformations of metabolism within the living cell. Every living
thing undergoes more or less degradation, which depends
upon the presence of special chemical groupings in the *live*
protein. The live protein must possess the ability to become autoxidized by the oxygen of air, because carbon
dioxide is always formed in the degradation of living substance. But carbon dioxide can not be formed by the direct
oxidation of carbon atoms and the splitting off of molecules of CO_2. The products of degradation obtained from
decomposing *dead* protein or the dead protein itself are entirely incapable of such oxidation. Therefore, *live* protein
must contain some atomic groups or special radicles which
are capable of autolysis and of autoxidation. A number of
considerations led Pflüger to the hypothesis that the molecule of *live* protein is characterized by the presence of a
cyanogen (CN) radicle. Pflüger derived the fundamental
proof of this from his comparative study of nitrogenous
products of protein decomposition obtained in the metabolism of the living organism and of the corresponding
decomposition products of *dead* protein resulting from
artificial cleavage. These products differ radically from
each other, the characteristic products resulting from the
metabolism of *live* protein in the organism, such as urea,
uric acid, etc., never being duplicated in the artificial splitting of dead protein. These characteristic substances, how-

ever, can be easily reproduced from compounds containing cyanogen (CN) by an atomic rearrangement, as for instance the formation of urea from ammonium cyanide in the Whöler synthesis.

But the formation of cyanogen is associated with the absorption of much heat, and the calorimetric study of cyanogen shows that this radicle contains a large amount of energy. Pflüger supposed that in the formation of cellular substance, i.e. of *live* protein, from the food protein, the latter underwent a change, probably associated with considerable heat absorption, resulting from the chemical union between the carbon and nitrogen atoms to form cyanogen (CN). Thus, the introduction of cyanogen into living matter imparts to it lability, which explains the tendency of the protein to undergo decomposition and autoxidation. The atoms in cyanogen, according to Pflüger, have a strong oscillatory movement. The carbon atom of CN on the accidental approach of two oxygen atoms leaves the sphere of action of the nitrogen and passes into the sphere of action of the oxygens, uniting with them to form carbon dioxide.

Pflüger attempted to schematize the entire process of metabolism of matter, attributing all the properties of live protoplasm to the presence in its protein component of a definite chemical grouping of the cyanogen radicle, and on this basis developed his whole theory of the origin of life. "If one considers the beginning of organic life, it is not necessary to pay attention first of all to carbon dioxide and ammonia, because both represent the end and not the beginning of life. The beginning is to be found to a very much larger degree in cyanogen (CN)."

To solve, therefore, the problem of the origin of living

substance, one must find a solution to the problem of the origin of cyanogen. "In this respect organic chemistry gives us the very important fact, namely, that cyanogen and its compounds are formed at a red glow when nitrogenous compounds come in contact with red hot coal, or when a mixture of the two is heated to a white glow. . . . It is, therefore, obvious that cyanogen combinations were formed at a time when the Earth was either entirely or partly in an incandescent state. . . . From this it follows that life comes from fire and, in the last analysis, was formed at a time when the Earth was a red hot mass. . . . If one thinks of the immeasurably long period of time during which the Earth's surface was cooling at an exceedingly slow rate, cyanogen and its compounds had plenty of time and opportunity to follow their great tendency to transformation and polymerization, and by the addition of oxygen and, later, also of water and salts to change to a labile protein, which constitutes living matter."

Modern biochemistry has completely discarded the fundamental conceptions of a labile autoxidizable live protein, such as Pflüger postulated. Not only protein but other organic substances as well, for instance the hydrocarbons, which are very stable, chemically inert compounds, undergo quite rapid changes and transformations within the living cells of the organism. This depends upon the presence in living cells of a whole system of catalyzers, the enzymes, which increase to an extraordinary degree the speed of definite chemical reactions, thus making the metabolism of matter possible. Of course, the nitrogenous metabolism also depends upon enzymatic action, but it proceeds along lines altogether different from those which Pflüger imagined. Neither storage protein nor protoplasmic protein can be oxidized directly by oxygen of the air. The protein degradation in the living cell generally commences as a hydrolytic cleavage resulting in peptones and amino acids. These cleavage products undergo oxidation through a fairly complex enzymatic system, and not directly by oxygen of the air but by the bound oxygen of water. The nitrogen is always split off at first as ammonia. Urea, uric acid, etc., are formed by secondary syntheses and certainly have nothing to do with a cyanogen radicle in the protein molecule. It becomes, therefore, more and more doubtful whether the presence of a cyanogen radicle in protoplasmic protein is really essential. In any event, it can be said with certainty that no radicles or separate molecular groups of any of the known compounds can account for the totality of the vital properties of the organism. Pflüger undoubtedly committed a grievous error in oversimplifying the complex phenomena which constitute the cellular metabolism of matter [7].

Nevertheless, Pflüger's theory deserves an exceptional place in the development of our ideas on the origin of life. Pflüger was the first to realize the possibility of a primary origin of organic substances which, because of their enormous content of chemical energy are also extensively endowed with capacity for further change and transformation. He was the first to point out that *"carbon dioxide is not the beginning but the end of life."*

Later this statement was completely forgotten and a number of subsequent authors, discussing the conditions under which life originated on Earth, considered it indubitable that all the carbon in the atmosphere of our planet was in the form of carbon dioxide gas. A certain interest attaches to Allen's [8] theory from this point of view. Like Pflüger, he also focused attention chiefly on the nitrogen, which he regarded as different from all other elements because its compounds are characterized by considerable chemical instability (in other words, by chemical activity). This accounts for the ability of this element to form mobile atomic complexes, which are characteristic of living substance. Allen did not refer to cyanogen or some other radicle but assumed, nevertheless, that some active nitrogenous molecules were responsible for metabolism. "Every vital phenomenon represents the combination of oxygen with or the separation of oxygen from nitrogen." Allen accordingly developed a view which, though similar to that of Pflüger, was less definite and indeed rather nebulous. But when these views regarding the origin of life are compared, they are found to differ radically, since Allen assumed that carbon dioxide was the primary carbon compound. The carbon dioxide reacts with nitrogen compounds liberating oxygen. Thus primary living substance from the very start manifests all the properties found in living organisms. To furnish a source of energy for these reactions, Allen resorted to powerful electrical discharges and to solar light absorbed either by dissolved or by suspended iron compounds in water. In general he produced a highly complicated picture of the formation of living substance from non-living inorganic compounds, a picture neither definite nor convincing.

Much later, indeed in the twentieth century, H. Osborn [9] developed somewhat similar ideas in his book "The Origin and Evolution of Life". In the beginning he pictures the

Earth still uninhabited by living creatures, thickly blanketed with an atmosphere containing much water vapor and carbon dioxide. This carbon dioxide served as the source of carbon for the formation of organic substances from which organisms developed by a long process of evolution. "We may accept the hypothesis that in the earliest periods of organization of living matter there was a combination of the ten elements essential for life. Of these the four most important elements were derived from their primary combinations of water, bound nitrogen (volcanic eruptions) and carbon dioxide of the atmosphere." But Osborn fails to explain how such a transformation could occur, limiting himself entirely to the rather ambiguous statement about the "attractive force" between oxygen and hydrogen.

As will be shown later, these assertions of a primary origin of carbon dioxide in the atmosphere of our planet are entirely arbitrary and do not correspond to reality. In the history of our ideas on the origin of life they played an important though entirely negative role, because of the very significant deductions to which they led and which only helped to confuse the whole problem. Because, if at the time living things first appeared on the Earth's surface there were no organic substances, only carbon dioxide, water, oxygen, nitrogen and a number of mineral salts being present, then obviously the primary organisms must have been endowed with an ability to assimilate such substances and to be nourished by them just as contemporary plants are nourished. V. Omeljanski in his "Principles of Microbiology" [10] says: "The pioneers of life undoubtedly were some very primitive organisms which did not require preformed organic substances but were able to synthesize organic substance from inorganic compounds, from carbon dioxide, oxygen and nitrogen of the air as well as the different mineral salts. In this group of microbes with a primitive metabolism belong the nitrifying organisms, the nitrogen assimilating bacteria and perhaps also the blue-green algae."

But all these living organisms possess a complex structure, and to accomplish the synthesis of organic compounds from dead matter they must also be endowed with a specialized physico-chemical structure or apparatus. How could such combinations arise directly from carbon dioxide, water and mineral salts? V. Omeljanski, reflecting the viewpoint of his time, offers this very simple answer: "When the Earth cooled off and the existence of organic life became possible, it appeared as the result of an unknown combination of matter and energy."

By the end of the nineteenth and the beginning of the twentieth century, parallel to these attempts to picture the origin of life at some remote geological epoch, a different movement was started to solve the problem of the origin of life experimentally. The movement was an outgrowth of investigations on the so-called models of living cells, like the artificial cell of Traube. Traube[11] placed a small crystal of copper sulfate in an aqueous solution of potassium ferrocyanide. At the surface of contact a membrane of copper ferrocyanide is formed, which is insoluble in water. This membrane forms a semipermeable * bag around the

---

* A semipermeable membrane is one which permits only molecules of water to pass through it and blocks the passage of any other kind of molecule.

copper sulfate. As the crystal gradually goes into solution the osmotic pressure * within the little bag increases all the time and finally the very thin and inelastic membrane tears. The copper sulfate solution escapes through the crack and, as it comes in contact with the potassium ferrocyanide solution, new copper ferrocyanide is immediately formed which repairs the break, but now the bag has somewhat increased. As this repeats itself, the little bag continually grows, assuming a definite shape and size. Traube thought that his artificial cell imitated the growth of real living cells and that the study of this model would lead to an understanding of the physico-chemical causes of growth.

Subsequently O. Bütschli [12] prepared a model which reproduced the movements of live amebae. On rubbing a drop of olive oil with a potash solution the droplet commenced to send out pseudopodia, to move about and even to engulf hard particles very much as amebae take up algae, etc. Rhumbler [13] and many other investigators constructed analogous models, reproducing the movements, also the feeding and division of cells.

Such artificial models have scientific value only to the extent to which the phenomena they manifest are based on the same physico-chemical causes which determine these in living cells. Such models permit one to study certain phe-

* Osmotic pressure is the force with which a solution draws water molecules from a more dilute solution or from pure water, from which it is separated by a membrane. The osmotic pressure varies with the amount of substance dissolved. For instance, a solution containing 342 grams of ordinary sugar in one liter (molar concentration), if it is separated by a semipermeable membrane from pure water, draws the water to itself with a force equal to 22.4 atmospheres. An atmosphere is equal to the pressure of a column of mercury 76 cm. long or 15 pounds per square inch. The concentration of dissolved substances in blood serum is such that its osmotic pressure is about 7 atmospheres.

nomena in great detail and under less complicated conditions than those which prevail in the living protoplasm. Unfortunately, however, investigators have often been deluded
by external superficial resemblances between models and
living things, and have been led to extremely simplified
mechanistic conclusions. As an illustration of such an ex-
cessive delusion by external appearances S. Leduc's [14] experimental production of so-called osmotic cells may
be mentioned. Principally, Leduc reproduced the same
phenomena as Traube only under much more complicated
conditions. Leduc placed a piece of fused calcium chloride
in a saturated solution of potash and potassium phosphate.
An impermeable calcium phosphate membrane was formed
which acted as an osmotic bag. By changing the concentration of the solutions, by adding different substances and by
various other means Leduc succeeded in producing very
complex formations surprisingly like algae, mushrooms,
etc., in appearance, chiefly as a result of the action of osmotic pressure and surface tension forces *.

Of course, osmotic pressure undoubtedly plays a substantial role in the life of plant or animal cells. But mere
external resemblances are not enough to conclude that there
is complete identity of physico-chemical processes in living
cells and in these "osmotic" cells, as Leduc attempted to do.
Allured by the wraith of external resemblance between his

---

* Whenever two substances are in contact with each other the molecules
constituting the layer of contact, or surface, are subjected to mechanical
and electrical influences which put them under a definite tension. This imparts to the surface layer peculiar properties. Surface tension forces play an
important role in giving stability to colloidal systems. In such complex colloidal systems like protoplasm the lowering of surface tension causes an
outflow, like the pseudopodium of an ameba, while increasing the surface
tension would cause its retraction.

artificial forms and living organisms, Leduc was led to believe that his experiments actually blazed a trail for a new movement in biology, which he designated as "synthetic biology", the science of the production in the laboratory of living forms from non-living substance.

It is hardly necessary to dwell upon the complete hopelessness of this oversimplified approach to the solution of the problem of the origin of life. Just as it is impossible to explain vital phenomena on the basis of the existence of some special chemical radicle so it is impossible to construct a living organism with the aid of osmotic forces alone. The resemblance between Leduc's forms and living organisms is not greater than the external resemblance between a live person and his marble image, but no one seriously believes in Galatea's coming to life or in the visit of Pushkin's "Stone Guest".

While Leduc merely indicated the paths for synthesizing organisms, a number of authors at the beginning of this century carried these experiments farther and claimed that they had succeeded in making living things by artificial means. Of course, all these claims were founded on more or less crude mistakes and have no real value so far as the solution of the problem of the origin of life is concerned. Their interest lies chiefly in a simplified mechanical approach to this problem.

As an example of such abortive attempts at "synthesis of life" mention may be given to Kuckuck's [15] work published under the high-sounding title: "Solution of the Problem of Autogeneration". According to Kuckuck, when radium acts on a mixture of gelatine, glycerol and common salt, a peculiar culture appears on the gelatine after 24 hours, consisting of living cells which grow, divide and manifest other signs of life. This was obviously the work of a dilettante who was not sufficiently familiar with colloidal systems *, and is, of course, devoid of any real significance. Still it can not be dismissed as something casual or merely as a curiosity. To a certain extent it reflects the crude mechanistic views developed by Haeckel and his followers, though perhaps in a highly exaggerated form, and could only have originated from such conceptions and theories. Even Haeckel himself believed that simple living things could at one time have originated from inorganic matter very much in the manner of a crystal which crystallizes from a solution. All that was necessary was some specific but unknown force to bring about this change from inanimate matter to an animate thing. Kuckuck searched for this force in the phenomena of radioactivity which at that time were still very poorly understood.

Actually Haeckel had not advanced beyond the naive conceptions of primary autogeneration, except that he relegated the event to the dim past, and for the "vital force" of the vitalists he substituted specific, unusual and unknown external conditions. But just how these conditions and

* Colloidal systems or solutions are unlike true or homogeneous solutions, which are formed when such substances as sugars, salts, etc., are dissolved. Substances in the colloidal state form heterogeneous solutions being represented by relatively large masses, which can not go through (dialyze) various live or dead membranes (fish bladder, capillary wall, parchment, collodion, cellophane, etc.). They can be, therefore, separated from true solutions by the use of such membranes. Starches, proteins, and many other substances form colloidal sols. Substances in the colloidal state manifest rather striking and peculiar behavior, which constitutes the subject of a special field-Colloidal Chemistry. Besides their impermeability, they exert very slight osmotic pressure and display remarkable surface phenomena (adsorption).

forces have formed such extremely complex systems as are represented even by the simplest living organisms remained a dark mystery as much for Haeckel as for all subsequent biologists.

The numerous objections which the adherents of the theory of the continuity of life raised against theories which assumed that living organisms have been generated at some remote period in the existence of our planet, become thus quite understandable, and can all be reduced to two points. The first was expressed by Preyer [16] who referred with biting sarcasm to those mysterious conditions which were necessary for the appearance of life in geological epochs of long ago and pointed out that no one seems to understand what those conditions really were. If the conditions were the same as prevail now, the origin of life would be plainly impossible because, as Pasteur's investigations have shown, this does not occur at the present time. On the other hand, if those conditions were different, the generated organisms must have perished at once, because the viability is confined to a very narrow range of variation in external conditions.

The other objection has been formulated by S. Kostychev [17] in his popular book: "The Appearance of Life on Earth" (Russian, 1921). He argues that even the most simply organized living things possess a very complex, delicate and perfect protoplasmic structure. The various vital processes are made possible by this protoplasmic structure and perfect functional differentiation. The metabolism of matter and energy characteristic for living things would be entirely impossible without a specially adapted apparatus, and it is highly improbable that such a complex apparatus could have arisen fortuitously. If the reader were asked to consider the probability that in the midst of inorganic matter a large factory with smoke stacks, pipes, boilers, machines, ventilators, etc. suddenly sprang into existence by some natural process, let us say a volcanic eruption, this would be taken at best for a silly joke. Yet, even the simplest microorganism has a more complex structure than any factory, and therefore its fortuitous creation is very much less probable.

These arguments are of substantial significance only if we accept Haeckel's standpoint and assume that at some definite period in the Earth's existence, under the influence of some physical forces and of some unknown conditions, the living organism has originated all at once from non-living matter, just as a crystal is formed in the mother liquor. Even if this organism is the simplest monera, nevertheless it must have been endowed with every attribute of living matter, i.e., its inner structure must have been adapted to carry on definite vital functions. But it is in the highest degree improbable that this adaptation, this purposefulness of inner structure could result from the action of some blind external physical force.

All these difficulties, however, disappear if we discard once and for all the above mechanistic conception and take the standpoint that the simplest living organisms originated gradually by a long evolutionary process of organic substance and that they represent merely definite mileposts along the general historic road of evolution of matter. Then the arguments of both Preyer and Kostychev lose their force. Kostychev commits the same error in his argumentation as the anti-Darwinists did, when they tried to prove the impossibility of natural development of higher organisms possessing many organs beautifully adapted to perform definite functions. Unquestionably, a factory could never originate through some natural phenomenon and independently of man, simply because every factory is constructed in accordance with some set, previously worked out plan. Everything in the factory, beginning with the erection of the building and machinery down to the arrangement of different sections, has been calculated by the engineer with a view to fulfill definite and foreseen aims. The natural elements could not accomplish such human objectives or fulfill a previously laid-down plan.

It is inconceivable that such a preconceived plan of protoplasmic structure could exist unless one assumes a creative divine will and a plan of creation. But a definite protoplasmic organization and fitness of its inner structure to carry out definite functions could easily be formed in the course of evolution of organic matter just as highly organized animals and plants have come from the simplest living things by a process of evolution. Later we shall attempt to trace this evolution and to picture the gradual formation of living things from non-living matter. In this evolution more and more complex phenomena of a higher order became superimposed upon the simplest physical and chemical processes; new properties developed ultimately resulting in the emergence of systems which are already subject to biological laws.

From this standpoint it is easy to answer Preyer's question: under what conditions could life have appeared in the past, and why does not this happen now? We do not need to invent some special, unknown forces for this. The conditions for the origin of living things are the same as the conditions under which organic substance has been gradually evolving. The first prerequisite condition was the primary mass formation of such organic substances. It is absolutely unthinkable that such complex structures like organisms could have been ever generated spontaneously, directly from carbon dioxide, water, oxygen, nitrogen and mineral salts. The generation of living things must have been inevitably preceded by a primary development on the Earth's surface of those organic substances of which the organisms are constructed. Now, under natural conditions, we do not observe the formation of those substances which are formed only secondarily by organisms as a result of their vital activity. At one time the primary formation of such organic substances was deemed entirely impossible but this view has long since been discarded under the impact of the brilliant successes of organic chemistry. The chemist succeeded in synthesizing *in vitro*, in his flasks and test tubes under artificial conditions, practically all the known organic substances and, therefore, no one is any longer justified in questioning the possibility of a primary origin of these substances. We know well the nature of the conditions under which these syntheses can be carried out and we need, therefore, only to prove or to disprove the possibility of such primary syntheses during remote periods of our planet's existence.

Another condition essential for the origin of life is the possibility of prolonged transformations, of prolonged evolution of the primary organic substances. Organic substance is the building material out of which the complex structure of living organisms could be formed. As will be shown subsequently, to accomplish this transformation from substance to organism requires a very long time. At the present time such a transformation is entirely out of the question because, if organic substance originated anywhere on the Earth's surface, it would be extremely rapidly devoured and destroyed by the countless microorganisms inhabiting the soil, air and water. But before life had yet appeared, the Earth, of course, was entirely sterile and the organic substances which were formed could evolve in many different directions for a very long period of time. However strange this may seem at first sight, a sterile, life-less period in the existence of our planet was a necessary condition for the primary origin of life. This condition prevailed only in the remote past but does not exist now, since the surface of the Earth is already thickly populated by innumerable highly organized living things.

To establish the possibility for generation of life in the dim past of the Earth's history, it is necessary first of all to prove the possibility of a primary formation of organic substance on our planet and, secondly, to trace the further evolution of this substance. Contemporary science enables us to furnish a more or less definite answer to both of these problems.

CHAPTER IV

PRIMARY FORMS OF CARBON AND NITROGEN COMPOUNDS

In the preceding chapter it was shown that the first essential condition for the appearance of life was the mass formation of organic substances on the Earth's surface. Only in the presence of such matter rich in internal chemical energy and, therefore, capable of various transformations and changes could complex substances arise, out of which the bodies of living organisms are made. Nevertheless, most of the students of the problem of the origin of life based their theories upon the assumption that carbon dioxide was the primary carbon compound. They thought that carbon made its first appearance on the surface of the Earth in its most completely oxidized form, incapable of further chemical transformation. This proposition was tacitly accepted as axiomatic but actually it was entirely unfounded. Many astronomical and geological facts throw serious doubt on the correctness of this assumption.

To form some conception of the primary forms of carbon compounds, which originated on our planet, it is necessary first of all to learn something of those carbon compounds which are found on other sidereal bodies. This will allow us to approach the question of the transformations of carbon at the time the Earth was formed and during the first stages of the evolution of our planet.

Owing to successful spectroscopic analysis of the stars

(astrospectroscopy) we have to-day a definite conception not only of their physical state but also of the chemical composition of the stellar atmospheres. The work of the famous Pickering and his school has established that according to their spectra the stars can be grouped into a number of types. The Harvard classification [1] of stars, which is now generally accepted, may be expressed by the following scheme:

$$O—B—A—F—G \begin{cases} K—M \\ \\ R—N \end{cases}$$
$$| $$
$$S$$

The letters of this scheme indicate spectral types of stars. O-stars are distinguished among the spectral types by their exceptional brightness and enormous mass. These are the hottest stars, whose temperature even on the surface reaches 20,000 to 28,000° C. Their spectrum, which was studied by Plaskett [2], is extremely complex and by no means yet fully understood. Plaskett discovered a large number of elements, including hydrogen, helium, carbon, nitrogen, oxygen, magnesium and silicon, partly in the neutral but, principally, in the ionized state.

The next type, B, includes the bluish-white stars, in whose spectra appear first of all the helium, then the hydrogen lines. The lines of metals appear only in the subclasses of this type, which have cooled off most. The presence of un-ionized carbon has also been established. To this interesting group belong principally the bright stars of our Milky Way, especially the three bright stars which make up the girdle in the constellation Orion.

The white or hydrogen stars belong to the type A. The

spectra of these stars are rich in the so-called Balmer hydrogen lines. Helium here disappears but the metal lines, in particular the lines of sodium, calcium, magnesium, iron, chromium, strontium, etc., gradually become more and more prominent.

The stars of type F, or the yellowish-white stars, are characterized by very intense lines of calcium, both in the neutral and in the ionized state; the hydrogen lines fade out, while the G-bands come into prominence. The first traces of these bands appeared already in the previous A type, but now they become especially strong. These bands are given by hydrocarbons (organic compounds of C + H. Motor-fuels and lubricants, paraffin and natural gas are hydrocarbons).

Our own Sun belongs in the next type G (yellow stars). These stars have a much lower temperature of the surface layer (6,000-8,000° C.) than those of the preceding spectral types. Their spectra are marked by numerous lines of metals and are very complex. The spectrum of the Sun, as can be easily understood, has been studied in greatest detail, and we shall return to this subsequently.

The stars on the right side of the scheme have even lower temperatures. The types K and M, which belong here, have a surface temperature in the neighborhood of 4,000° C. The former is characterized by a very complex spectrum of many metals. The hydrocarbon band G is very clearly marked but the violet portion of the spectrum is somewhat faded out. The spectrum of type M abounds in bands indicating the appearance of a series of chemical compounds.

The red stars of type S, characterized by complex absorption and emission spectra, with a great preponderance of bands, occupy a somewhat distinct position.

Finally, the last two types R and N are the dull red stars with the lowest surface temperature, which may apparently drop as low as 1,800° C. This makes the study of these sidereal bodies rather difficult. Their spectra also abound in absorption bands, which indicate the presence of a number of chemical compounds, especially interesting among which are the carbon compounds, to which we shall refer later.

This scheme of the spectra, which at first was established empirically, has a very profound physical significance, as our investigations have shown, because it corresponds approximately to the natural sequence of thermal ionization, which is the physical cause determining the presence of different spectral phenomena. The stellar spectra are determined not only by the presence of this or that element in the surface layer of these astral bodies but also by the state of these elements and, especially, by the degree of their ionization. Thus, the difference in chemical composition of stars which previously seemed so abrupt, is now explained by the thermodynamic environment of their surface layers. For us the thing of real importance is the fact that the spectral scheme reflects the gradual decrease in the temperature of these astral bodies. On the left side of the scheme we find stars with the highest surface temperatures, and these decrease gradually as we pass from the left to the right side of the scheme. At the same time, this sequence also reflects to a certain extent the gradual evolution of the star during the second period of its existence, when according to Herzsprung's expression it becomes "dwarfed" [3].

For our purpose it is of interest to survey the appearance of carbon in the different spectral types of stars. It is important to note first of all that this element has been noted in almost all the enumerated spectral types, save only the S-stars. In the O-stars, having the highest temperatures, Plaskett discovered that the carbon was chiefly in the mono- and di-ionized condition. The surface temperatures here are so high that any chemical combinations of carbon are out of the question, and even the atom suffers material alteration by losing its surface electrons (ionization).

In the next and much cooler type B (20,000-15,000° C.) Henroteau and Henderson [4] have already found carbon in the neutral state also, but even in this case no chemical combinations can yet exist. The first signs of such combination appear in the type A spectrum. In the latest (also the coldest) subclasses of this type were first discovered traces of the G band (λ 4314 Frauenhoffer's spectrum), indicating the possibility of the appearance in such stars of the primitive carbon compounds, the hydrocarbons [5]. In the subsequent, still colder subclasses of stars the hydrocarbon bands appear more and more distinctly, as the temperature of the star's surface falls, and reach the maximum distinctness in the M and R classes. At the same time the spectra of the F, G, K, M, R and N stars reveal the cyanogen bands. Of great interest also is the appearance in the same type of spectra of the so-called Swan bands. They can be seen in the spectrum of the Sun and especially of the stars of the N and R types [6]. In former times these bands were erroneously attributed to carbon monoxide (CO) but more recently Patti, on the basis of a spectroscopic investigation of these bands, succeeded in establishing with a fair degree of certainty that the Swan spectrum is determined by the C_2 molecule. Von Klueber [7] comes to the same conclusion on the basis of the quantum theory, and thinks that the molecule of the type C_2 is responsible for the Swan spectrum since "the lines of these bands reveal such an alternating sequence of intensity as can be postulated for the symmetry of molecules consisting of two similar atoms."

It is, therefore, evident that, even at comparatively high temperatures of the star's surface, atoms of carbon commence to unite, but these unions are of only three types: carbon atoms unite with carbon atoms forming dicarbon molecules of the type C_2; or they unite with nitrogen forming cyanogen (CN) and, finally, with hydrogen giving methene (CH).

TABLE I

TYPES OF CARBON COMPOUNDS AT DIFFERENT STELLAR TEMPERATURES

Type of Star	Absolute Temperature	Carbon Combinations
O	25,000°	C^{++}; C^+; C
B	20,000—15,000°	C
A	12,000°	C; CH (traces)
G	8,000°	C_2; CH; CN
M	4,000°	C_2; CN; CH (very intense bands)
N	2,000°	C^{12}—C^{12}; C^{12}—C^{13}; C^{12}—C^{14}; CN; CH

Von Klueber [7], who in his book "Das Vorkommen der chemischen Elemente im Kosmos" made a detailed analysis of all that is known of chemical composition of stellar atmospheres, lays special emphasis on the absence from the surface of the Sun, as well as of other stars, of any combinations of carbon and oxygen, and of CO in particular, despite the fact that other oxides of metals (BO, AlO, TiO, ZrO) and even HO are already easily distinguishable. He says "CO though often quoted in the literature, has not yet been demonstrated and its presence does not seem probable even in the later types of stars. The supposition that it does exist really resulted from the erroneous interpretation of the Swan spectrum, which actually results from the molecule C_2."

We may now survey the different forms of carbon combinations which are found on our own solar system. On the Sun, which belongs to the G spectral type, carbon is present either as the molecule C_2 or as the hydrocarbons (C + H) [8], or finally as cyanogen (CN) [9]. We shall discuss the analysis of the solar spectrum in greater detail later.

We must consider the comets as sidereal bodies which emit light. A series of investigations has been devoted to the study of their spectra, but their nature and chemical composition has been clarified only in recent years. It is becoming more clearly established that comets belong to our solar system and that they apparently have something to do with the streams of "falling stars" and meteorites. Comets seem to consist of cosmic dust, of hard particles partly surrounded by a gaseous layer. Their luminosity is caused, principally, by electrical discharges in a very attenuated medium, but also, at least in part, by the heat generated upon the approach of the Comet to the Sun. The gas and dust particles, which are thereby emitted, are thrown back by the pressure exerted by the Sun's light, and form the tail of the comet. Spectroscopic studies of the nucleus and tail of comets reveal the sharp distinction in the chemical composition of both. This is easy to understand, since the nuclear spectrum to a certain extent gives us a conception of those compounds which first originated in the material composing the comet. On the contrary, the compounds found in the tail of the comet result secondarily from changes and chemical transformations induced by the approach of the comet to the Sun. These changes, of course, must be fundamentally different from those which the substances of the comet must have undergone at the time of its formation. In the nucleus of the comet, as in the other sidereal bodies, are found dicarbon C_2, cyanogen and hydrocarbons [10], but in the tail, beside the dicarbon, it is possible to demonstrate definitely the presence of ionized carbon monoxide (CO^+) also (Baldet) [11]. Here we find, for the first time, the combination of carbon with oxygen, but the secondary character of this formation in the tail of the comet is quite evident.

The study of the chemical composition of the planets of our solar system is much more difficult. As is well known, these celestial bodies only reflect the Sun's light and this alone complicates considerably their spectroscopic analysis. Besides, it is necessary to bear in mind that many substances, whose presence in the planetary atmosphere may be assumed, show no selective absorption in those regions of the spectrum which are accessible to our analysis as, for instance, hydrogen, nitrogen, helium, neon and argon. Furthermore, the gases of the Earth's atmosphere absorb a considerable part of the spectrum. Thus, for instance, ozone, although present only in very small quantities in the higher layers of the atmosphere, nevertheless cuts off the spectrum at 2900 Å and deprives us completely of the opportunity of investigating this most interesting portion of the planetary spectrum. And, finally, the most important thing in the analysis of the spectra is the fact that it is necessary at all times to account for the absorption by the gases of our Earth's atmosphere. This difficulty is now being overcome by comparing the spectrum of the planet under investigation with the spectrum of the Moon, which has no atmosphere. However, this method also has its shortcomings, because the observations can be regarded as sufficiently accurate only when the Moon and the planet can be seen at the same height, and when the observations are made simultaneously and with the same instrument. Another method depends on the application of the principle of Doppler, and consists in the study of a shift in the lines at the time when the planets rapidly approach toward or recede from the Earth. This very delicate method has made it possible in recent years to obtain some very interesting results.

In spite of all these difficulties of investigation we have now considerable data for the study of the chemical composition of the planetary atmosphere, which Russell recently summed up in his presidential address [12] before the meeting of the American Association for the Advancement of Science (December, 1934). The planet nearest to the Sun, Mercury, can be compared in many respects to our satellite, the Moon. The surface of Mercury consists of dark igneous rocks. If an atmosphere exists there, it must be extremely attenuated and reveals no evidence of condensation. Venus, on the contrary, undoubtedly has an atmosphere with heavy clouds, which hide from us the actual surface of this planet.

Every effort to discover either oxygen or water in the atmosphere of Venus has been fruitless. But Adams and Dunham succeeded in 1932 in establishing beyond a doubt the presence there of rather large quantities of carbon dioxide.

In the comparatively thin atmosphere of Mars, on the other hand, it is possible to prove the presence of water and some, though very little, oxygen. Wildt thinks that this is chiefly in the form of ozone formed under the influence of ultraviolet rays. No carbon dioxide has been found there. Von Klueber points out that some investigators believe there is vegetation on the surface of Mars, this belief being based on a number of observations. Therefore, the carbon on Mars is supposed to be in the form of organic combination, but the evidence for this is still too meagre for us to draw any definite conclusions.

Especially interesting from this point of view are the latest results of the investigation of the atmosphere of the large planets. It has been established long ago even by simple telescopic observation that Jupiter is surrounded by an atmosphere. The rapid changes in the spots on the surface of Jupiter could only be explained by the presence of clouds, which are easily formed and easily evaporated in the atmosphere of this planet. The same was found true for Saturn and somewhat later for the other larger planets. However, spectroscopic investigations of these planets for a long time failed to bring any definite results. The bands, which were seen in the spectra of these planets, remained a puzzle and until very recently could not be identified with the spectra of any known gases. Only in 1932 a young German physicist R. Wildt hit upon the right track in solving this problem and showed that some bands in the spectrum of Jupiter correspond to the bands of ammonia, while others to those of methane. This was soon corroborated by Dunham, who also discovered the complete correspondence of the carefully measured individual lines in these bands. The correspondence for ammonia was found in more than 60, and for methane in 18 lines in a part of one band. Finally, in 1934, Adel and Slipher [13] were successful in identifying all the bands characteristic for methane. It must, therefore, be regarded as settled that the atmosphere of Jupiter contains ammonia and methane, but the attempts to discover the presence of other hydrocarbons there such as ethane, ethylene, and acetylene gave negative results. However, this can be explained by the low temperature ($-135°$ C.) which prevails on Jupiter's surface, since, as is shown in the accompanying table, all these hydrocarbons boil, at the usual atmospheric pressure of 760 mm., at a considerably higher temperature, and methane alone can exist in gaseous condition.

TABLE II

Compound	Boiling Point at 760 mm.
Methane (CH_4)	$-165°$ C.
Ethane (C_2H_6)	$- 95$
Ethylene (C_2H_4)	-103
Acetylene (C_2H_2)	$- 85$

Adel and Slipher have this to say on this point: "We are thus forced to the conclusion that other hydrocarbons, if they exist at all in the atmosphere of the large planets, must exist only in very small quantities in relation to the methane present. Probably these hydrocarbons, like many others, are found in the lower strata of the atmosphere of the large planets. The free movement of a large red spot on

Jupiter leads us to believe that it is an island c
drocarbons and ammonia floating on an enori
carbon ocean, so enormous as to be coextent
planet's surface."

Saturn, like Jupiter, is also swathed in a massive atmosphere of methane and ammonia vapors but, since it is farther from the Sun, its surface temperature must be even
lower than that of Jupiter. Therefore, a considerable part
of the ammonia must already be in the solid state there, and
this is reflected in the Saturn spectrum, in which the methane bands appear very clearly. Uranus and Neptune, being
still farther removed from the Sun, have a still lower temperature, and the ammonia must have completely separated
from their atmosphere in the frozen state. This explains the
extraordinarily strong methane bands in the spectra of these
planets. The methane itself must be almost ready to liquefy
on Neptune in spite of the very low boiling temperature of
this compound. Thus, on all the large planets we find carbon in the form of compounds with hydrogen.

The study of meteorites presents very special interest in
attempting a solution of our problem, primarily because
meteorites falling upon our Earth can be subjected to direct
chemical analysis and even to a mineralogical investigation. These are the only non-terrestrial bodies whose composition can be determined with exceptional reliability and
completeness. Besides, the study of the origin of meteorites
convinces us more and more that they represent pieces or
fragments from celestial bodies closely related by their origin to our planet, the Earth. Zaslavski[14], in his article devoted to the chemical composition of meteorites, sums up
as follows our knowledge of their genesis: "Parallel with

ιe growth of our knowledge of the composition of meteorites, our conception of their origin has also become more refined. First of all, there has been established with a high degree of certainty the common origin of the two principal groups of meteorites, the rocky and ferrous (Wahl, Prior). Besides, by far the largest number of scientists regard it as an established fact that meteorites belong to our solar system, even to the interior of this system, i.e., to the small planets (Berwerth, Tschermak, Suess, Fersman, Clarke, Washington, Farrington, Tammann, Goldschmidt, I. and W. Noddack, etc.). I shall refer here to some of the most important arguments of Paneth (1931) for regarding the Earth and the meteorites as belonging to one and the same system. 1. The close resemblance in the composition of the Earth and meteorites has been well established. 2. The surprising correspondence of atomic weights of the elements which are found both in the Earth and in the meteorites can only be explained on the assumption that both isotopes of iron, nickel, chromium and that all three isotopes of silicon, etc., at one time were all fused together and were ideally mixed in the gigantic crucible, our Sun. 3. The time which has elapsed since the meteorites hardened, estimated according to the helium (radioactivity) method, does not exceed the length of time since the hardening of the Earth (about 3×10^9 years). 4. Theoretical calculations indicate the possibility of the formation of meteorites at the expense of semi-solidified planetary masses, just as in the case of the Moon. 5. Numerous astronomical observations confirm the regular periodicity in the fall of meteorites upon the Earth in relation to the season of the year and even in the course of a single day.

6. In recent years the calculations showing the distinctness of the orbits of meteorites from that of our solar system have been subject to serious doubt."

The genetic relationship between meteorites and our planet has been considered by scientists for a long time and a number of outstanding modern geochemists have been studying the structure and composition of meteorites from this point of view. Fersman [15] in his book "Geochemistry" gives an extensive review of these investigations. He shows the enormous significance of the study of meteorites for the solution of geochemical problems. To quote: "It is possible that we are just beginning to comprehend the large part which the fully thought out analysis of meteorites plays not only in determining the composition of the Earth but also for the elucidation of those laws, which govern the changes in composition between the crust and the Earth as a whole, which is necessary for the clear understanding of the total quantity of elements in the accessible crust of the Earth. We are now becoming convinced that this type of analysis of the average composition of meteorites furnishes the necessary data for a determination of the exact value of clarkes * and that with regard to a number of elements they, more than any other cosmic body, obey more closely those laws, which express the correlations of heliochemical clarkes."

He also gives a number of comparative analyses of meteorites and of different rocks. His data actually reveal a remarkable resemblance between the average weight com-

* In Fersman's terminology, a clarke represents the relative (percent) content of an element. This concept defines the relative amount of atoms of a certain element in a given cosmic body or a portion of it.

position of the Earth and of meteorites, which could not be accidental and which led Fersman to the definite conclusion, namely, that "meteorites, by the character of their elements and the structure of their atoms, are generally similar to the elements of the deepest zones of the Earth's crust and, in all probability, correspond even more closely to the composition of the central core of our planet." The stony meteorites correspond to the deep rocks, while the metal meteorites to the central core. It is easy to see from the above that the study of the composition and structure of meteorites has an exceptional significance for the solution of the problem of the nature of the primary compounds which arose in the formation of our planet.

As already mentioned, two principal groups of meteorites are distinguished, the iron (metallic) and the stone, the first consisting essentially of so-called nickel-iron, with more than 90 percent iron, up to 8 percent nickel, and 0.5 percent cobalt, and some phosphorus, sulfur, copper and chromium. They also always contain about 0.1 percent carbon, though in some instances the content of this element seems to be much greater. In the stone meteorites there is very much less iron, only about 25 percent, but there is much oxides of various metals, such as magnesium, aluminum, calcium, sodium, manganese, etc. The oxide of silicon, SiO_2, is an important component, and the carbon content is, on the average, 0.15 percent [16].

In former times these two groups of meteorites were sharply differentiated according to their origin, but Prior has proved the common magmatic origin of both. Meteorites undoubtedly represent fragments of igneous rocks, since no evidence of sedimentary rocks has been found in them. The mineralogical investigation of the meteorites proves that they were formed under conditions of more or less pronounced oxygen deficiency, which is especially true for the iron meteorites, in which even the phosphorus is in the free, unoxidized state.

Carbon, the element which interests us particularly, is found in practically all meteorites. It can be demonstrated in its natural condition in the amorphous form as well as in the form of graphite or diamond. The elementary carbon of the meteorites is unquestionably associated genetically with the iron carbides found there. The so called carbon meteorites frequently contain up to 2-4.5 percent amorphous carbon. Graphite in noteworthy amounts was discovered only in the iron meteorites in the form of clusters, plates or grains, sometimes reaching considerable sizes up to 12 grams. Yerofejev and Latchinov succeeded in obtaining 1 percent carbon in the form of diamonds from a meteorite which fell in 1886 near the village of Novo-Urei. Later, Foote and Koenig obtained diamond dust from a meteorite which fell into the Diablo canyon in Arizona, and this was corroborated by subsequent analyses of Kuntz, Huntington and others. Weinschenk also found diamonds [9] in the Magura meteorites, and in 1889 discovered cohenite, a mineral which is very common and characteristic for meteorites. This mineral represents a carbide of iron, nickel and cobalt with a general formula $(FeNiCo)_3C$. The formation of these carbides of iron and of other metals in meteorites is easy to understand since such compounds are readily formed at high temperatures and at those conditions are very stable.

Hydrocarbons must also be mentioned among the compounds containing carbon, which are found in meteorites. Whöler, way back in 1857, obtained a small amount of an organic substance resembling Ozocerite from a stone meteorite found near Kaba in Hungary. Analysis of this substance has proved that it actually was a hydrocarbon of high molecular weight. A similar substance isolated from meteorites, which fell in Coldbockfeld contained as much as 0.25 percent hydrocarbons. Melikov and Krzhizhanowski [17] later found a small amount of hydrocarbons in a silicate meteorite which fell in 1889 in the south of Russia. Von Klueber points out the several occasions when hydrocarbons were found in meteorites. Smith isolated a compound with the composition $C_4H_{12}S_5$, while in other localities compounds were found of the composition $(C_8H_9O_2)n$.

At the time, when the presence of hydrocarbons in meteorites was demonstrated, the view was still firmly held that organic substance, therefore also hydrocarbons, can originate under natural conditions only in the living cell. For this reason many scientists have frequently expressed the supposition that the hydrocarbons of meteorites are formed secondarily by the decomposition of organisms, which at some time inhabited these celestial bodies. However, every attempt to discover some signs of organic life ended in failure and at present we must regard it as a well established fact that "meteorites completely lack sedimentary, hydatogenic deposits as well as formations of biochemical character" [15]. Therefore, the hydrocarbons of meteorites, just as the hydrocarbons of previously described celestial bodies, must have had a primary origin, i.e., without any relation to organic life.

Summing up what had been said so far, it must be

pointed out that in practically all the sidereal bodies, in the atmosphere of stars including our own Sun, in the nuclei of comets, in the atmosphere of the large planets, and finally in meteorites also *carbon is found either in its elementary form, or in the form of compounds with nitrogen (CN) but more often with hydrogen.* In this respect only our Earth and Venus, the planet closest to it, offer an exception in that their atmospheres contain carbon in an oxidized state, as carbon dioxide (CO_2).

The carbon dioxide in the atmosphere of our Earth is obviously of secondary origin. A considerable part of it is directly associated with the vital activity of living organisms (respiration, fermentation), but even the carbon dioxide thrown out in enormous quantities during volcanic eruptions or from extinguished volcanoes is not primary in origin but results from the decomposition of previously formed carbonates owing to the high temperature of the deep layers of the Earth's crust and the molten state of the metamorphic rocks. V. Vernadski[18] in his "Outlines of Geochemistry" points out that not carbon dioxide but pure carbon must be regarded as the primary juvenile mineral. The metal carbides like cohenites, minerals similar to those which have been found in the basaltic islands of Disco and other islands of western Greenland, must also be regarded as primary carbon compounds[19].

Our knowledge concerning Venus is still too limited to allow us to draw any definite conclusion about the origin of the carbon dioxide contained in its atmosphere. But by analogy with the condition prevailing on our Earth we would be more justified in assuming that even there the compound is of secondary origin. Thus, all the facts presented seem more or less to support the assumption that *carbon, at least in part, first appeared on the Earth's surface in the reduced form, particularly in the form of hydrocarbons.* Let us examine the present theories of the Earth's origin and evolution in relation to this conception.

We shall take as the starting point in this discussion the generally accepted theory of Jeans on the origin of our planetary system. Jeans [20], like Chamberlin, assumes that a star in the normal course of development, i.e., without the intervention of some extraneous forces, could not form around itself seven planets. It is, therefore, necessary to search for the cause of the formation of the solar system in the influence of some outside force. Jeans further assumes that the normal course of development of the Sun was interrupted by a catastrophe some two or three billion years ago. At that time a sidereal body, a star equaling or even exceeding our Sun in mass, must have begun to approach it. Just as the attractive force of the Moon causes the rising tides in the oceans of our Earth, so the approaching star caused a grandiose tidal wave in the flaming solar atmosphere. Along the line of centers between this star and the Sun the solar atmosphere was pulled out in the form of a tremendous wave many thousands of miles in height, and this tidal wave continued to rise as the star came nearer to the Sun. Finally there was a moment, when the force of attraction exerted by this star exceeded the force of attraction by the Sun, the crest of the wave was pulled away and shot forth in the direction of the passing star. Obviously, such a break in the surface of our Sun could happen only if the approaching stellar body came too close to it. Exact calculations show that, assuming the stellar mass as equal to the solar mass, the critical distance between the star and the Sun must have been not more than 2.5 times the radius of the Sun. Of course, if the stellar mass was greater than the solar mass, this distance could have been somewhat greater. In any event, according to Jeans, the star had to come so close as to collide with the Sun, and he pictures the consequences of such a "near collision" in the following manner: as the crest of the wave, formed on the surface of the Sun, pulled away, the pressure on its lower portions diminished and this caused the entire mass of matter to fly off from the Sun in the direction of the star. Had the two sidereal bodies continued to approach one another they would have finally fused together. But the star was not moving directly toward the Sun and, having approached it as far as the critical distance, it did not collide with but passed by the Sun and, as it receded into space, its tidal effect also decreased. No more material was pulled away from the Sun's surface but the stream, which at first became separated from it, formed a long hot thread-like nebula which hung in space and was attracted by the Sun. The shape of the thread resembled a cigar pointed at both ends, the extreme thin end of the nebula farthest away from the Sun being the original crest of the tidal wave. The thick middle portion was formed at the time, when the star passing in the vicinity of the Sun was at the "critical zone" and, finally, the thin end close to the Sun was formed, when the force of the tidal pull had already decreased considerably.

The mass of this nebula and the force of mutual attraction of its component particles were sufficiently large so that this gaseous stream was relatively quickly torn into a number of separate condensations. Even at the comparatively high temperature within these gaseous masses drop-lets of molten metal and lava must have been formed, which fell toward the center of the condensations and formed the primary molten core of the planets[21]. Where the gaseous mass was most immense, the most enormous accumulations of matter in the center of the gaseous nebula occurred, which explains the fact that the largest planets of our system, Jupiter and Saturn, occupy the middle positions in the planetary chain. Farther away from the Sun are situated planets of smaller size, Uranus and Neptune and, similarly, closer toward the Sun are the relatively little planets, Mars, Earth, and Venus. Finally, the smallest of the planets, Mercury, and the recently discovered Pluto are the planets nearest to and the farthest from the Sun, both having originated from the tapering ends of the cigar-shaped nebula.

Thus, according to this theory, our Earth and all the other planets were formed from substances which go to make up the solar atmosphere. The chemical composition of this atmosphere is fairly well known to-day as a result of the numerous spectroscopic investigations of the Sun, especially the classical studies of Rowland[22] and of the famous Mount Wilson Observatory in California. We give below a table of the comparative composition of the solar atmosphere, of the Earth's crust and stone meteorites, calculated by von Klueber in comparable values (log. Q).

On the basis of an analysis of these data, von Klueber arrived at the conclusion that there is "good correspondence in the composition of the Sun, of the Earth's crust and of stone meteorites." It would be difficult not to concur with this statement, although so far as the metalloids are con-

TABLE III

COMPARATIVE ANALYSIS OF COMPOSITION OF THE SUN (LOG. Q)

Serial No.	Element	Sun's Atmosphere	Earth's Crust	Stone Meteorites
11	Sodium	8.6	8.7	7.8
12	Magnesium	9.2	8.6	9.1
13	Aluminum	7.8	9.2	8.2
14	Silicon	8.8	9.7	9.3
19	Potassium	8.4	8.7	7.2
20	Calcium	8.3	8.8	8.1
21	Scandium	5.3	3.0	
22	Titanium	6.9	8.1	7.0
23	Vanadium	6.7	6.9	
24	Chromium	7.4	7.1	7.5
25	Manganese	7.6	7.3	7.3
26	Iron	9.0	9.0	9.4
27	Cobalt	7.4	5.8	7.1
28	Nickel	7.8	6.8	8.2
29	Copper	6.8	6.3	6.2
30	Zinc	6.7	5.9	
	Metalloids			
1	Hydrogen	11.5	8.3	6.9
6	Carbon	8.5	7.4	7.2
7	Nitrogen	8.7	6.8	
8	Oxygen	10.2	9.7	9.6
9	Fluorine		6.8	
15	Phosphorus		7.4	7.0
16	Sulphur	7.2	7.3	8.3
17	Chlorine		7.7	6.9

cerned, especially hydrogen and nitrogen, there are considerable discrepancies, the Earth's crust being poorer in these elements than the Sun's atmosphere. This discrepancy would probably have been even greater, if the comparison were made between the Sun's atmosphere and the mean composition of our planet. We shall discuss later the causes of these discrepancies.

Of course, the elementary composition tells very little of the possible chemical combinations. At the temperature of 5,000-6,000° C., which prevails on the Sun's surface, chemical combinations practically do not occur, and the solar atmosphere consists principally of free atoms, and partly even of ionized atoms. Only in the Sun's spots, where the temperature is down to 3,000-4,000° C., does the spectroscope reveal considerable quantities of chemical compounds such as TiO, BO, MgH, CaH, OH, as well as hydrocarbon CH (methene).

The incandescent mass, which is the Sun's atmosphere, is in constant turbulent motion. Immense storms, colossal eruptions from the Sun's surface, energetically stir this incandescent mass and constantly alter the relative concentration of the elements in the separate horizontal layers, the heliospheres of the Sun. This has been demonstrated by a number of investigators, especially by St. John[23]. According to St. John's results in the upper zones of the external gaseous envelope of the Sun, the chromosphere, at a height of 14,000 kilometers (about 8500 miles) from the visible surface of the Sun, the gaseous mass consists principally of hydrogen and strongly ionized calcium. Next helium is found and in the deeper portions of the chromosphere appear lines of titanium, nickel, magnesium, sodium and of a small amount of chromium. Deeper yet there is a thin layer of vaporized heavy metals and, finally, beneath these is the photosphere, which constitutes the visible surface of the Sun. Observation can not penetrate beyond this level. We give here St. John's schematic representation of the distribution of elements in the different layers of the gaseous atmosphere, from which it is obvious

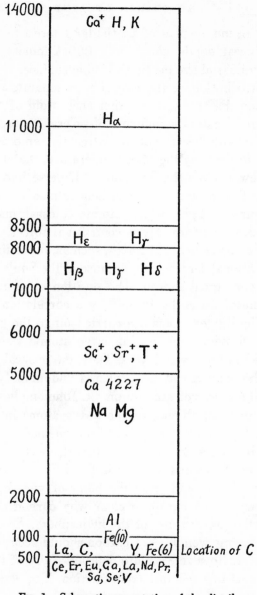

Fɪɢ. 1. Schematic presentation of the distribution of different elements in the Sun's atmosphere (after St. John).

that carbon, the element of particular interest to us, is located at great depth, about 500-1000 kilometers (about 300-600 miles) above the Sun's visible surface.

This distribution of the elements in separate zones depends upon the circumstance that each atom of the solar atmosphere is under the influence of several opposed forces. On the one hand, because of the extremely rapid movement imparted to them by the high temperature, the atoms tend to move away from the Sun and to disperse into the void of space. This centrifugal movement is also promoted by the pressure of light, which attains colossal magnitudes near the Sun's surface. These centrifugal forces, however, are opposed by centripetal forces, such as, in the first place, the gravitational force which, because of the Sun's immense mass, is very great indeed. The position of atoms in the Sun's atmosphere is determined by a correlation of these forces. The lighter atoms are carried off to the periphery while the heavier ones, having large atomic weights, are distributed in the lower layers. Thus, the general distribution of the elements of heliospheres undoubtedly follows first of all the laws of gravitation. St. John emphasizes particularly that the absence of the heavy atoms in the most remote heliospheres is not due to our method of observation but, beyond a doubt, to an actual decrease in the relative content of this or that atom in the different zones.

At first glance, and from the point of view elaborated here, it may not seem quite clear why carbon should be found in the lowest zones of the heliosphere. According to its small atomic weight (12) carbon should occupy a much higher level. However, a more detailed study of this problem explains this seeming contradiction. The element carbon is one of the substances most difficult to melt and even at 3,000° C. it does not yet liquefy. Clearly, even much higher temperatures are required to convert it to vapor. Direct spectroscopic investigation shows that even at the temperature of the Sun's surface the carbon is not in the form of free atoms but of the dicarbon compound of the type C_2, which is responsible for the Swan spectrum. In the atmosphere of the Sun, therefore, carbon atoms form combinations with each other, associate into comparatively large and heavy complexes, which give very dense and easily compressible vapors. For this reason carbon must get into the deeper layers of the Sun's atmosphere, just as water vapor in our Earth's atmosphere is found principally at the lower levels although the molecular weight of water (18) is less than that of oxygen (32) or nitrogen (28), which chiefly make up the bulk of this atmosphere.

The formation of planets from the overheated gaseous mass, erupted from the Sun's surface, commenced at temperatures still close to the temperature of that surface. The vapors of the most easily compressible elements, even under these circumstances, must have condensed into droplets which fell in the direction of the center of the future planet, thus forming its molten nucleus. Heavy metals, such as iron, nickel, etc., which do not melt easily, must have contributed the first components of this nucleus. In accordance with the conception previously developed, carbon likewise must have rapidly entered into the composition of the original molten core of the planet. The heavy carbon vapors must have condensed into drops and precipitated in the form of carbon rain or snow even at temperatures at which the formation of carbon dioxide was clearly out of the question, since carbon dioxide undergoes considerable dissociation even at much lower temperatures (about 2,800° C.). The carbon monoxide (CO) has greater thermal stability but this, too, begins to decompose with the liberation of elementary carbon at temperatures of 2,500 to 3,000° C. These considerations explain to a certain degree the absence of oxides of carbon in the atmosphere of the Sun and of other permanent stars and lead us to the conclusion that the principal mass of carbon must have entered into the composition of the metallic core of our planet as the free element. In this core, mixed with the heavy metals, including iron, the carbon must have reacted chemically first of all with these elements as the core gradually cooled off. As a result of these reactions carbides, compounds most stable at high temperature, must have been formed.

The picture we have drawn of the formation of the primary molten core of the planets is confirmed by the study of the present structure of the Earth. Geophysicists and geochemists, from numerous data pertaining to specific gravity, gravitation, seismological phenomena, etc., accept it as an established fact that the center of our planet is occupied by a metallic core of a radius of 3400 kilometers (about 2000 miles). Furthermore, the chemical composition of this core is definitely established as being quite similar to that of the ferrous meteorites and includes iron, nickel, cobalt, phosphorus and carbon. The iron sample first discovered by Nordenfeld on the beach of the island of Disco may perhaps be representative of this deep formation. This extremely rare deep rock contains carbon in the form of the familiar mineral cohenite, which is a carbide of iron[24]. A similar carbide has been found in other localities, where native iron is present, and Vernadski is of the opinion that "it is very probable that more careful investigation of these minerals will shed light on their universal occurrence in the deep basalts".

The central metal core of our planet is surrounded by geospheres, the structure and composition of which are shown in Table IV, which has been taken from Fersman's "Geochemistry".

An examination of this table shows that the elementary composition of separate geospheres is not uniform. De Launay [25], who studied the composition of the Earth's crust, concluded that there must be some connection between the partitioning of the elements in the geospheres and their specific gravity, which obeys the law of universal gravitation. He states that: "In the molten Earth, previous to the formation of a crust, the chemical elements moved away from the center for a distance inversely proportional to their atomic weight (specific gravity) as the dissociated atoms, which are not bound to each other would behave at very high temperatures, when subjected only to the influence of universal gravitational and centrifugal forces".[15] Subsequently, under the influence of the theory of atomic transformation, this view has been elaborated but even at the present time De Launay's theory is still accepted by many scientists, at least as regards the first twenty eight elements of the Mendelejev system, i.e., for those elements which constitute about 99.9 percent of the Earth's crust.

Roughly speaking, it may be imagined that each gaseous particle of the planetary atmosphere covering the central metallic core, when it first originated, must have been under the influence of several opposing forces in the same sense as was shown with regard to the Sun's atmosphere. But at this stage these forces had lost much of their effect, the centripetal force having decreased, because the mass of the planets was incommensurably small by comparison with the mass of the Sun, while the centrifugal force likewise decreased, because the gases forming the atmosphere had cooled off. The results of the interaction of these opposing forces were different so far as the different planets of our solar system were concerned. Mercury, located nearest to the Sun, had the highest temperature and at the same time was the smallest member of the planetary family, and as a result of this lost a considerable portion of its lighter elements before they could form chemical combinations during the earliest stages of its existence. At the present time Mercury is nothing but a bare rock with no gaseous envelope.

The situation as regards Jupiter and the other large planets was quite the reverse since here gravitational forces far exceeded the forces which tended to disperse the atmosphere into the void of interstellar space, and as a result of this these planets retained whole and unchanged the elements with which they were endowed by the Sun.

Our Earth occupies in this respect an intermediate position. It neither lost all of its original atmosphere nor has it retained this completely, but there was a selection of elements. The more massive gas particles with a high atomic weight or compounds with a high molecular weight were held close to the surface of the central core and gave rise to the deep igneous rocks, while the lighter particles arranged themselves in the higher zones. Finally, some gaseous elements having the least atomic or molecular weight could not be held by the attraction of the Earth and were dispersed into the void of interstellar space. This partly explains the higher specific gravity of the Earth as compared to the specific gravity of the large planets, and accounts for the difference in the composition of the solar atmosphere and of the Earth's crust. This difference, as was shown previously, consists chiefly in the smaller content of the lighter elements.

The attraction of the Earth is quite sufficient to hold, at the present time, even the lightest of the gases, hydrogen, but a simple calculation will show that at the temperatures which prevailed at the time of the formation of our planet, the Earth must have lost considerable quantities of hydrogen, helium, nitrogen, neon or even of free oxygen. Helium and neon, of course, belong to what is known as the inert gases which do not react chemically with other substances and are always in the state of free elements, and since they have small atomic weights must have been lost from the Earth. As a matter of fact, our atmosphere contains these elements only in negligible quantities, very much smaller than those in the atmosphere of the Sun and stars. Munsel and Russel point out that neon, which is very abundant in stars and nebulae, is found in our atmosphere in a concentration of only 2:1000. The other enumerated elements must have been retained to a considerable extent by the Earth's surface in so far as they formed chemical compounds with other substances or formed gas particles with a higher molecular weight. In this manner water vapor and a number of other compounds of hydrogen were retained,

TABLE IV (A. E. Fersman, 1928)

THE STRUCTURE OF THE EARTH AND OF ITS SEPARATE GEOSPHERES

Seismic limits	Depth in km.		Name of Geosphere	Thickness in km.	Pressure in Atmosphere	Temperature	State of Matter	Specific Gravity	Radiation	Relation of Mass to total Earth	Chemical characteristics	Minerals	Comments
			Inter-Stellar space				Rarefied gases Electrones	Insignificant	Cosmic Rays		H_2, He, residual O_2 and N_2 up to 300–500 km.		Meteorites from 200 up to 600 km.
	200	Atmosphere	1. Stratosphere	200–300	0.00001	−50° to −70°	Rarefied gases		Cosmic Rays	0.000002	Up to 100 km. N_2 and O_2 decrease H_2, He, O_3	Belt of periodic ozone. Limit of water vapor	Aurora borealis 85–750 km. Luminous clouds up to 80 km.
	10–15	Atmosphere	2. Troposphere	10–13	0.3–0.5	−55°	Gas Solid dust		Cosmic, Radium Rays	0.0001–0.00001	N_2, O_2, A, Ne, Kr, Xe, O_3, water vapor, CO_2		Balloons up to 377 km. Man up to 19 km. Increased thickness at poles.
	0	Hydrosphere and Biosphere	3. Biosphere	8	About 1 (up to 500)	−67.8° to +85°	Principally Colloids		Solar Rays Radium Emanation			Living matter	
	4	Hydrosphere and Biosphere	4. Hydrosphere	3.7 (mean) up to 10.8	About 1 (up to 500)	0 to +7°	Solutions	1.03	Low Radioactivity	0.02	H_2, O_2, Cl, Na, Mg, S	Water, ice	

Group	Zone	Depth boundaries (km)	Earthquake / boundary depth (km)	(<0.8, up to 8)	Not over 250	Mean temp (16° to 80°)	Principally / Colloids	Density	Increased Radioactivity in Sediments	%	Elements	Minerals	Lowest limit of oxygen, etc.
Lithosphere	Sharp Boundary — 5. Zone of weathering	15–20	20–40 km depth of earthquakes	<0.8 (up to 8)	Not over 250	16° to 80°		2.2			O₂, H₂, Si, Al, C, Cl, CO₂	Clay, quartz, limonite, gypsum, bauxite, etc.	Lowest limit of oxygen (0.5–1.0, very rarely 1.5 km.).
Lithosphere	6. Zone of Rocks			<4	<1000	Up to +100°	Colloids + Crystalloids	2.5	Medium Radioactivity	0.5		Same, also calcite, dolomite, coal	Usually absent under the ocean.
Lithosphere	7. Metamorphic zone			5–10	<2500	Up to +350°	Crystals	2.7	Increased Radioactivity	0.5		Quartz, feldspar	Usually absent under the ocean.
Lithosphere	8. Granite zone			10–15	Up to 6000	600°	Crystals	2.6–2.8	Highest Radioactivity	0.5	O, Si, Al, K, Na, Fe, Mg, Ca, etc.	Quartz, mica, feldspar, apetite, magnetite	Under the ocean usually absent or very thin.
Lithosphere	9. Basalt zone	70	60	70–85	Up to 20000	1000°	Crystals + melts	2.7–3.3	Medium Radioactivity	1.0	O, Si, Al, Na, Fe, Ca, Ti, P, S, Cl.	Plagioclases, pyroxenes, magnetite, apetite	Boundary between crystalline and glass basalt is placed at a depth of 60 km.
Lithosphere	10. Zone of Peridotite	1200	1200	1000–1200	Up to 500000	1200–1500°	Melts + glass	3.6–4.0	Low Radioactivity	36.0	O, Si, Fe, Mg, Ca, Cr, Ni, V	Olivine, pyroxenes, anortite (pyrope, diamond)	
Intermediate Geosphere	11. Zone of ferrosporic magma		1700 / 2450	750	1000000	(1000°)	Glass	5.0–5.5	Very Low Radioactivity	20.0		Olivine, pyroxelenes, pyrrites, chromite, magnetite, hematite, rutile, ilmenite	Molten zone (70–120 km.).
Intermediate Geosphere	12. Lithosporic zone — Sharp Boundary	2900	2300	750	1500000	(1000°)	Glass	6.0	"	10.0	S, Se and Te		Sharp boundary
Core	13. Central core	6370		3400	2000000–3000000	2000°–8000° probably about 5000°	Glass	9–11		31.5		Native Fe, Ni, troilite, cohenite, schreibersite, etc.	

as well as compounds of oxygen with silicon and metals, or of nitrogen with oxygen, carbon or metals (for instance, Al_2N_2, aluminum nitride).

The idea has long ago been expressed that the primary atmosphere of the Earth must have been devoid of free oxygen. Arrhenius[26] in his well known book "Life Course of a Planet" has discussed this problem in detail, and at present it is regarded as highly improbable that free oxygen was contained in the original Earth atmosphere. The amount of elementary oxygen which at the high temperatures escaped being dispersed into interstellar space or failed to enter the composition of the primary igneous rocks inevitably had to combine with other elements during later periods of the Earth's existence, since most of the components of the Earth are substances with strongly marked reducing power and avidly unite with oxygen. This view is completely substantiated by modern geochemical investigations. As can be seen from the structure of the Earth given in Table IV, the lower geospheres are entirely lacking in oxygen, but even the higher zones are far from being saturated with this chemically very active element, which even at the temperature now prevailing can easily enter into chemical combination with substances composing the Earth.

Beyond a doubt the molecular oxygen found in our present-day atmosphere was formed secondarily and at a much later epoch, as a result of the activity of living organisms. At the present temperature of the Earth the oxygen is held by the Earth's attraction and cannot become dispersed into the interstellar space. But, if all organic life on Earth would now perish, the entire free oxygen of the air, as the studies of Goldschmidt show, would disappear after a definite lapse of time, because it would be absorbed by the incompletely oxidized igneous rocks.

In his recently published "Problems of Biogeochemistry" V. Vernadski [27] considers in detail the problem of the origin of our present atmosphere and points out that the biological origin of the free oxygen cannot be questioned. However, he thinks that "the biological origin must also be assumed for the still more important gas, as far as weight and volume are concerned, namely, the nitrogen of the air." The primary atmosphere of the Earth could not contain nitrogen in the form of the gaseous element. The Earth has lost a considerable part of the nitrogen, as is borne out by the fact that the nitrogen lines are prominent in the spectra of stars and that nitrogen which is so abundant in the cosmos forms but a small part of the Earth's crust (Russell [12]). Only the nitrogen, which has reacted and formed certain chemical compounds, was retained by the Earth, but as the free, gaseous component of the Earth's atmosphere it appeared only at a much later epoch.

Thus, after the earliest period of cooling and formation of our planet, the Earth must have had the following appearance: a central molten core, abounding in native metals, covered by a membrane of primary igneous rocks and, finally, all enveloped by an atmosphere consisting principally of superheated aqueous vapor, some nitrogen and other heavier gases. The carbon, which is of special interest to us, was in the central molten core in the form of carbides of iron and of other metals, and was separated from the atmosphere by the layer of primary igneous rocks.

Contact between the substances forming the central core

with the substances composing the Earth's surface nowadays occurs very rarely and only under exceptional circumstances, because of the thickness of the present layer of igneous rocks. But, as Vernadski[26] says: "There are facts which show unmistakably that metallic carbides, the cohenites, and perhaps others, are actually present in some erupted rocks under conditions which do not exclude the possibility of formation of hydrocarbons under the influence of hot water." Furthermore, he refers to the escape of cohenites to the Earth's surface as in the basaltic island of Disco or in other localities on the Earth, where native iron ores are found.

However, at the earliest period of the existence of the Earth, which we have been discussing, the escape of carbides to the Earth's surface undoubtedly must have occurred, because at that time there was tremendous translocation and shifting of masses of the still poorly formed earth crust. It is enough to think of the catastrophe, which as some believe, resulted in the formation of the Moon and of the immense depression in the Pacific Ocean, when colossal masses of primary igneous rock were torn away and deep internal magmas must have poured out on the surface of our planet. And subsequently, too, owing to the tremendous tides within the molten core of the Earth, the deep rocks must have been thrown outside where they came into direct contact with the superheated water vapor of the atmosphere existing at that period.

As far back as 1877 D. I. Mendelejev[29] showed that hydrocarbons must be formed when carbides are acted on by water, in accordance with the reaction:

$$3 \, Fe_mC_n + 4 \, m \, H_2O = m \, Fe_3O_4 + C_{3n}H_{8m}$$

Cloez[30] investigated the hydrocarbons originating when cast iron is dissolved in hydrochloric acid, and found C_nH_{2n} compounds and others. Mendelejev treated crystalline manganese iron (containing 8 percent carbon) with the same acid and obtained a liquid mixture of hydrocarbons which by smell, appearance and reactions exactly resembled natural naphtha. On the basis of this reaction Mendelejev built his well known theory of the mineral origin of naphtha. He says further: "As the igneous rocks were folded, cracks must have been formed which at the crests opened outwards while at the depression they opened inwards. Both these types of cracks became in time filled in, but the more recent the origin of the mountain the more open must these cracks be, and water must have entered through them into the Earth's interior to such depths as would be impossible normally from a plane surface." Thus, according to Mendelejev, sea water found its way to the glowing central core, containing large quantities of carbon-iron, and by their interaction the hydrocarbons of naphtha were produced.

At present this theory has been given up, because it does not tally with many geological observations. And, indeed, it would be difficult to imagine how drops of liquid water could possibly reach the glowing mass of carbides, from which they were separated by more than a thousand kilometers' (about 600 miles) thickness of igneous rocks. However, Mendelejev's fundamental proposition of the formation of hydrocarbons through the action of water on carbides of iron has been fully corroborated by the older as well as by the newer investigations.

Away back in 1841 Schretter obtained a liquid resembling naphtha, when he allowed dilute acid to act on cast iron. Later Hahn[31] studied this reaction and found a very considerable quantity of naphtha-like liquid when he allowed a large amount of white cast iron to be acted upon for several weeks by dilute acid. Furthermore, Cloez, whose work has been referred to by Mendelejev, performed experiments wherein he obtained hydrocarbons by means of superheated water vapor acting on a ferromanganese containing 5 percent carbon. Haritchkov[32] studied the formation of gaseous and liquid hydrocarbons when solutions of magnesium chloride, magnesium sulfate and sodium chloride were heated with filings of ordinary grey cast iron containing 3 percent carbon for a long time at 100° in sealed tubes or closed bottles. Ipatjev[33], who repeated the experiments on the production of hydrocarbons from cast iron containing carbon by the reaction with dilute hydrochloric acid, salt solutions as well as steam, found that his chemical studies completely corroborated the idea of the formation of naphtha through decomposition of iron carbides by sea water.

It would be a simple matter to enumerate more investigations of similar character, but the facts already presented demonstrate with sufficient certainty that hydrocarbons are formed when carbides of iron are treated with dilute acids, salt solutions or simply with superheated steam. Similarly, carbides of other metals, especially of the alkalies and of alkaline earths, readily give rise to hydrocarbons when acted on by water.

Hydrocarbons must have originated on the Earth by a similar process during the remote past of its existence, when carbides were erupted onto its surface and were acted upon by the superheated aqueous vapor of the atmosphere of that epoch. Such primary origin of hydrocarbons apparently takes place even to-day, though under rare and exceptional conditions, but at the beginning of our planet's existence this must have occurred on a large scale. Unquestionably, the results of this grandiose process have left their mark to this time both in the atmosphere of the large planets * and in the hydrocarbons of the small planetary formations, the fragments of which fall to the Earth as meteorites. These primary hydrocarbons have not been preserved on the surface of the Earth because they were subjected to further, far-reaching chemical transformations which, as will be shown in the next chapter, formed the basis for the origin of complex organic compounds.

Summarizing the arguments presented in this chapter, it is obvious that the most essential condition for the origin of life, namely, the first mass formation of the simplest organic substances, occurred in the very dim past of our planet's existence. This is confirmed by all available data in the possession of modern science. *Carbon made its first appearance on the Earth's surface not in the oxidized form*

* Russell, in the address previously mentioned, supposed that the hydrocarbons of the large planets resulted from the reduction of carbon dioxide by elementary hydrogen, contained in large quantities in the atmosphere of those planets. According to his conception, the reaction proceeded according to the following equation:

$$CO_2 + 4\,H_2 \rightleftarrows CH_4 + 2\,H_2O$$

Russell, therefore, assumes that carbon dioxide is the original substance, but we have shown that the idea of a primary formation of carbon dioxide is very doubtful and is founded upon an erroneous interpretation of the Swan spectra as indicative of the presence of such an oxide of carbon in the stellar atmospheres. According to this view, furthermore, the presence of hydrocarbons in meteorites would be entirely inexplicable.

of carbon dioxide but, on the contrary, in the reduced state, in the form of hydrocarbons.

We must now consider briefly the history of another element extremely important biologically, namely, nitrogen. It was already pointed out earlier that, on the basis of Vernadski's data [27], nearly all the nitrogen of our atmosphere has originated secondarily and is associated, in one way or another, with the activities of living organisms. During the process of the Earth's formation neither elementary nitrogen nor oxygen could be held in appreciable quantities by the attraction of the Earth. The portion of nitrogen which was actually retained by our planet was held only because it entered into combination with other elements, forming more or less massive particles of high molecular weight. This seems the more probable since nitrogen, which is such an extremely passive substance under our present conditions, reacts readily and energetically with a number of other elements at temperatures of 1000° C. or higher.

Of the different possible compounds of nitrogen, the oxides may be considered first. The reaction between nitrogen and oxygen follows the equation: $N_2 + O_2 = 2 NO$, but this oxide, on slow cooling, easily dissociates again into a molecule of nitrogen and oxygen (at temperatures near 1000° C.). It is not likely, therefore, that nitric oxide (NO) could be the initial substance from which primary nitrogenous substances could have been produced. The compounds of nitrogen with metals, the so-called metal nitrides, seem a much more likely source. Lithium, magnesium, calcium, aluminum, iron, etc., when heated to high temperatures, absorb nitrogen avidly and form the corresponding nitrides, according to the equations:

$$3 \ Mg + N_2 = Mg_3N_2; 2 \ Al + N_2 = Al_2N_2$$

Such compounds could originate, when the igneous rocks were being formed, from the primary gaseous envelope of the central metallic core, and the probability of such formation is corroborated by the fact that metal nitrides, especially the iron nitrides, are found in the deep layers of the Earth's crust (A. Gautier[34]) and in lava from volcanic eruptions (A. Brun). Treated with water vapor the nitrides give ammonia, in accordance with the equation:

$$FeN + 3 \ H_2O = Fe(OH)_3 + NH_3$$

This compound could also have had a primary origin in the upper layers of the hot gaseous envelope through contact between hydrogen and nitrogen, in the manner in which ammonia is now prepared technologically by the Haber process ($N_2 + 3 \ H_2 \rightarrow 2 \ NH_3$).

Finally, the carbides erupted upon the surface of the Earth at temperatures close to 1000° C. could react with nitrogen to form the corresponding cyanamides, $CaC_2 + N_2 = CaCN_2 + C$, which on reacting with superheated steam give ammonia:

$$CaCN_2 + 3 \ H_2O = CaCO_3 + 2 \ NH_3 \ ^{[35]}$$

It is clear, therefore, that all possible reactions, under the stated conditions, lead to the formation of ammonia. This is also substantiated by the constant finding of large amounts of ammonia in the atmosphere of the big planets. The primary formation of ammonia is also corroborated by a number of geochemical investigations. On this topic Vernadski[18] informs us as follows: "The elimination of ammonium chloride and fluoride by volcanoes is beyond question. Its formation by decomposition of living matter, caught by the lava, can account for this only in part. Besides, the discharge of ammonia together with superheated steam (up to 190° C.) near geysers from a depth of not less than 200 meters (666 feet) as, for instance, in Tuscany or in California, certainly cannot be associated with the presence of any living things. These gases are magmatic in origin and come off together with the steam. The ammonium aluminosilicates of kaolin are present apparently in isomorphous admixtures of minerals from volcanic and massive rocks and it seems very probable that the occurrence of nitrogen in these rocks is of primary nature."

Thus, it can be assumed with a high degree of probability that *nitrogen, like carbon, first appeared on the Earth's surface in its reduced state, in the form of ammonia.*

CHAPTER V

ORIGIN OF ORGANIC SUBSTANCES
PRIMARY PROTEINS

IT WAS POINTED OUT previously that many authors
(Haeckel [1], Osborn [2], Omeljanski [3], etc.) assumed the possibility of a spontaneous generation of life on Earth at
some remote epoch in the existence of our planet. They
generally attributed this to the influence of external conditions prevailing on the Earth's surface at that time, which
were totally different from the physical conditions of the
present time. The peculiar environmental, physical conditions were held responsible for the spontaneous generation
of life, and were thus regarded as its immediate cause.
But, as Haeckel said: "To this day we have no satisfactory
conception of the extremely peculiar state of our Earth's
surface at the time of the first appearance of organisms.
. . . Therefore, any account of the primary generation
must be considered premature."

It is hardly possible to agree with this point of view
to-day. It is beyond doubt that during the epoch under
consideration (especially during the early period of the
existence of hydrocarbons) the physical conditions on the
Earth's surface were different than now: the temperature
was much higher, the atmosphere had a different composition, light conditions were different, etc., but in this there
is nothing unusual or mysterious. Quite the contrary, these
conditions are more or less well known to us and we can

not only easily picture them to ourselves but we can even reproduce them, to a large extent, in our own laboratories. Nevertheless, they do not furnish an explanation of how life had arisen on our Earth. And it is not difficult to understand this because knowledge of the external physical conditions is not sufficient for the solution of the problem of the origin of life. It is also necessary to take into consideration the inherent chemical properties of the substances from which, in the last analysis, living creatures were formed. The study of the behavior of those substances under given external influences will indicate the path which the evolution of organic substance has followed. This approach to the problem is justified especially by the fact that only at the beginning of this evolutionary process were the environmental conditions of existence different from those of our own natural environment. From the time when the primary ocean came into being, the environment in which organic substances existed resembled our own so closely that we may safely draw conclusions about the progress of chemical transformations on the basis of our knowledge of what is happening to-day.

The main difficulty in effecting this sort of reconstruction arises from the overwhelming variety of chemical transformations and reactions of which hydrocarbons and their derivatives are capable. However, for the solution of our problem it is not necessary to reproduce the process in all its details. It is important only to form a definite conception of the fundamental tendencies, of the basic trends of the behavior of organic matter in its continual evolution on the Earth's surface. In this respect modern organic and biological chemistry furnish us with sufficient factual material for arriving at thoroughly well founded conclusions.

The interaction between carbides and superheated water vapors, referred to in the preceding chapter, must have taken place at temperatures several hundred degrees high. We have a sufficiently clear idea of the changes which hydrocarbons undergo under such conditions, because the process involved in the heat treatment of hydrocarbons has been the subject of numerous investigations in connection with oil cracking and similar technological processes. Recently Paneth has shown that at temperatures close to 1000° C. we are dealing with the formation not of hydrocarbons but of their free radicles, such as methene (CH), methylene (CH_2), etc. These radicles cannot exist for long in the free state but combine with each other, forming a very large number of unsaturated * hydrocarbons of the ethylene and acetylene series. Such compounds may also be formed simply by heating saturated hydrocarbons to high temperatures. For instance, Holliday and Nuttingham [4] have demonstrated in 1931 that methane, heated to 1000° C. without any contact catalyst, changes to acetylene according to the equation:

$$2 \ CH_4 \rightleftarrows CH \equiv CH + 3 \ H_2 - 91 \ Cal.$$
Methane   Acetylene

However, in the presence of a sufficient amount of water vapor, we have not merely the formation of unsaturated hydrocarbons but also of the oxidized hydroxy derivatives. Such derivatives may be formed later also, when the un-

---

* Carbon which is tetravalent combines with four other atoms. Such hydrocarbons are spoken of as saturated. If, however, there are some free valences, the carbons combine with each other by these available valences so that two, three or four bonds hold the carbons together. Such compounds are called unsaturated, and they readily bind some other atoms, such as hydrogen, etc.

saturated hydrocarbons have been changed to saturated compounds by the action of superheated steam of the Earth's atmosphere, under which circumstances molecules of water become attached to unsaturated hydrocarbons. As an illustration of this process of hydration we may mention the reaction described by A. Tchitchibabin [5] for the conversion of acetylene to acetaldehyde, according to the equation:

$$CH \equiv CH + H_2O \rightarrow CH_3COH$$

In the presence of the oxide of iron this reaction takes place even at a temperature of 300° C.

Considerable quantities of various oxidation products of hydrocarbons, such as alcohols, aldehydes, ketones, and organic acids must have originated as a result of such transformations on the Earth's surface. In the above described reaction, as Tchitchibabin points out, if the heated moist acetylene gas contains ammonia, it is possible to observe with the naked eye the formation of a crystalline precipitate of an aldehyde-ammonia; i.e., under these conditions ammonia very rapidly combines with the acetaldehyde formed by hydration. Similarly, other oxidized derivatives of hydrocarbons (the above mentioned alcohols, aldehydes, and acids) can enter into a variety of reactions with ammonia giving rise to ammonium salts, amides, amines, etc.

As the temperature of the Earth had cooled off sufficiently to permit the formation of droplets of liquid water, torrents of boiling water must have poured down upon the Earth's surface and flooded it, thus forming the primitive ebullient oceans. The oxygen and nitrogen derivatives of the hydrocarbons already present in the atmosphere were carried down by these torrential rains and the oceans and sea, at the moment of their first formation, contained, therefore, the simplest organic compounds in solution. The interactions between the hydrocarbon derivatives and their further transformations did not, however, cease in this new aqueous medium. On the contrary, alcohols, aldehydes, acids, amines, amides, etc., continued to react with each other as well as with the elements of the aqueous environment, giving rise to a prodigious number of all sorts, and even much more complex, organic compounds. We cannot follow the extremely varied and numerous processes of evolution of organic matter in detail, and for our purpose this would be superfluous. We can certainly establish the general trend of these transformations and changes on the basis of our knowledge of the properties of these compounds.

The hydrocarbons and their derivatives are pregnant with tremendous chemical possibilities. Using them as raw material, the modern organic chemist can reproduce in his laboratory all the multiplicity of organic substances found at present in nature. He can, furthermore, synthesize artificially most of the compounds which go to make up the bodies of animals and plants and serve as the building material for living cells.

It must be noted, however, that the chemist employs in his syntheses altogether different means than the living cell. The chemist frequently utilizes halogens [i.e., derivatives of chlorine, bromine, etc.], mineral acids, strong alkalies, high temperatures and pressures, and various other powerful agents to cause organic substances to react with each other quickly and in the desired direction. The chemist has at his disposal an immense arsenal of all sorts of means, which enables him to realize the most varied reactions and to obtain the product he needs.

Under natural conditions, on the other hand, the synthesis of various organic compounds in living organisms proceeds on an entirely different basis. Here we neither find powerfully acting agents or high temperatures, nor are the molecules of organic matter subjected to chlorination, bromination or to the action of other halogens, while the medium itself remains more or less neutral, and yet the organic substances undergo a series of most fundamental alterations and transformations. It may be regarded as firmly established that all these transformations of organic matter may also proceed outside the living cell, the difference being only in the velocity with which the reactions are accomplished. In the living cell special catalysts (the enzymes) are present which increase by several hundred thousand times the speed of chemical reactions between the organic substances. The ability to react does not depend upon the presence of enzymes but upon the organic substances themselves which undergo transformation. These transformations can take place independently of the living cell, except that, without the enzymes, they proceed at an extremely slow speed. In the laboratory or in the chemical factory no progress would be possible because of this slow rate of transformation of substances, and for this reason the chemist always searches for some powerful agent by means of which to whip up the speed of a chemical reaction. However, time was not a matter of great consequence in the origin of organic substances on our planet, because the evolutionary process lasted an incalculably long period, thus permitting even slowly progressing chemical reactions to play a very significant part. For the problem under consideration here it is extremely important to study the transformations of organic substances in the living cell. This offers an opportunity to clarify the fundamental chemical reactions which organic substance may undergo in aqueous solution and which are essential for the synthesis of those highly complex compounds of which living organisms are built.

It is generally believed that reactions taking place within the living cell are many and varied, because a very large number of different substances can be isolated from plants and animals. A close examination of the subject, however, reveals the fallaciousness of this view. In spite of the truly astounding and overwhelming quantity of various substances comprising the organism of living things, all these have arisen and have been formed as a result of comparatively few simple and more or less similar reactions. All the transformations of organic matter which can be demonstrated within the living cell are based on three principal reaction types. First, *condensation,* i.e., the lengthening of the carbon chain, and the reverse process of splitting the chain between two adjacent carbon atoms; second, *polymerization,* i.e., the union between two organic molecules through an atom of oxygen or nitrogen, and *hydrolysis,* the reverse process of splitting up such unions; and, third, the process of *oxidation* with its invariable accompaniment of *reduction* (oxidation-reduction reactions). The so-called aldol condensation of aldehydes discovered in 1872 by Würtz [6] can serve as an example of the first reaction. In the case of acetaldehyde the reaction proceeds according to the equation:

$$CH_3 \cdot COH + CH_3 \cdot COH = CH_3 \cdot CHOH \cdot CH_2 \cdot COH$$

Acetaldehyde   Acetaldehyde   Acetaldol

In this reaction two molecules of acetaldehyde become welded together, so to speak, to form a single molecule of aldol, a compound consisting of a four carbon atom chain. Although in the equation, as it is written, no molecules of water appear either on the left or on the right side, it is necessary to point out that the condensation reaction is actually intimately associated with a shifting of the elements of water.

We described the welding together of two molecules of aldehyde, but a succession of condensations involving many parts may take place, leading to the formation of organic compounds with long carbon chains. Furthermore, as a result of this reaction closed rings of hydroaromatic or of aromatic compounds may be formed, such as:

Glucose
(* Aldehyde group)

Inosite

Such condensation reactions play a very important role in a large number of biochemical processes and are the basis of numerous syntheses occurring in living cells. For instance, the above described aldol condensation reaction of acetaldehyde is the basis for the synthesis of fatty acids. By the condensation of two molecules of glyceraldehyde and of the corresponding ketones simple sugars, the hexoses, are produced. The formation of tannins is associated with the closing of a hydrocarbon chain into a hydroaromatic ring, etc.[7]

Condensation reactions also proceed easily outside the living cell and their velocity can be considerably increased by means of different inorganic catalysts, such as zinc chloride in the Würtz synthesis or milk of lime in the famous Butlerov [8] synthesis of sugar by an aldol condensation of formaldehyde: $6\,CH_2O \rightarrow C_6H_{12}O_6$, etc.

As an example of the reverse process, the rupture of the union between carbon atoms, mention may be made of the splitting of pyruvic acid into acetaldehyde and carbonic acid:

$$CH_3C \!-\!\!\!\!\overset{O}{\underset{}{\overset{\|}{C}}}\!\!-\!C\!-\!OH + H_2O \longrightarrow CH_3\overset{O}{\overset{\|}{C}}\!-\!H + \overset{OH}{\underset{}{C}}\!\!\overset{O}{\diagdown}\!\!-\!OH$$

Pyruvic Acid   **Acetaldehyde + Carbonic Acid**

This reaction is of very great biological importance. All the carbon dioxide given off by organisms in fermentation and respiration originates in this or some similar manner [9].

The second type of reaction mentioned before, namely, polymerization, is also a union of two or more molecules with each other, but in this case the welding is no longer by a direct bond between two carbon atoms, the carbons becoming united to each other by an oxygen or nitrogen bridge. The synthesis of mixed esters may serve to illustrate this reaction and proceeds according to the equation:

$$\underset{\text{Acetic Acid}}{CH_3—\overset{\overset{\textstyle O}{\|}}{C}—O\boxed{H + HO}—CH_2CH_3} \underset{\text{Ethyl Alcohol}}{\rightleftarrows}$$

$$\rightleftarrows \underset{\text{Ethyl Ester}}{CH_3—\overset{\overset{\textstyle O}{\|}}{C}—O—CH_2CH_3} + H_2O$$

As can be seen from this, a bond is established between the molecule of acid (acetic acid) and alcohol (ethyl alcohol) through an oxygen atom, whereby at the place of juncture hydroxyl and hydrogen are given off and combine to form water. Fats in the living cell arise by this reaction, the fats likewise being mixed esters in which the alcohol is represented by glycerol and the acid by the various fatty acids, such as stearic, palmitic, oleic, etc.

Other kinds of organic molecules may also be combined in the process of polymerization. The formation of the simple ethers is likewise of considerable biological significance, and in this case two alcohol molecules become united through an oxygen bond, with the loss of a molecule of water, according to the equation:

$$\underset{\text{Alcohol}}{R_1—CH_2OH} + \underset{\text{Alcohol}}{R_2—CH_2OH} \longrightarrow \underset{\text{Ether}}{R_1CH_2—O—CH_2R_2} + H_2O,$$

where R_1 and R_2 designate different carbon residues.

This reaction is the basis for the formation of substances such as cane sugar, starch, cellulose and other complex carbohydrates, which play a leading role in the chemistry of the animal and especially of the plant organism.

Finally, polymerization may take place by the union of molecules through a nitrogen atom. E. Fischer[10], as is well known, has shown that two amino acids may combine with each other according to the equation:

$$HOOC \cdot CH_2 \cdot NH \boxed{H + HO} OC \cdot CH_2 \cdot NH_2 \rightleftarrows$$

Glycine   Glycine

$$\rightleftarrows HOOC \cdot CH_2 \cdot NH \cdot OC \cdot CH_2 \cdot NH_2 + H_2O$$

Glycyl-glycine

This reaction underlies the synthesis of protein substances, and this fact alone is sufficient to indicate the exceptional biological significance of this reaction.

In every instance of polymerization discussed here it will be noted that the reaction proceeds with the elimination of a molecule of water. The opposite process, namely, hydrolysis, consists in the rupture of bonds of complex organic compounds, whereby the components of the water molecule, hydrogen and hydroxyl, are added on at the point of rupture, thus:

Maltose

2 Glucose Molecule

The hydrolysis of complex organic compounds has been especially well studied in biological chemistry, because this type of reaction is very common in all vital phenomena associated with the breaking up of nutrient deposits and of foodstuffs in general, as in the development of plant seeds, in the digestive process of animals, etc. It may also take place easily outside the living cell, for instance in a simple aqueous solution, but the speed of the reaction can be greatly increased by the action of enzymes or of inorganic catalysts.

The essential feature of the third type of reaction, the oxidation-reductions, may be grasped from an example which was the first to be carefully studied, namely the so-called Cannizzaro reaction [11]. Two molecules of aldehyde can react with a molecule of water according to the following equation:

$$
\left.
\begin{array}{l}
\quad\ \ \overset{\displaystyle O}{\overset{\|}{CH_3-C-H}} \\[2mm]
\quad\ \ \overset{\displaystyle O}{\overset{\|}{CH_3-C-H}}
\end{array}
\right\}
+
\quad
\begin{array}{l}
H_2 \\[6mm]
O
\end{array}
\quad \rightarrow \quad
\begin{array}{ll}
CH_3 \cdot CH_2 \cdot OH & (Alcohol) \\[6mm]
CH_3 \cdot COOH & (Acid)
\end{array}
$$

As can be seen, one molecule of aldehyde adds on the oxygen of the water becoming oxidized to a corresponding acid, while the other molecule adds on the hydrogen becoming reduced to a corresponding alcohol. Thus a simultaneous oxidation-reduction reaction takes place at the expense of the elements of water. Whereas in the hydrolysis reaction the hydrogen and hydroxyl are added simultaneously at the point where the complex molecule ruptures, in this reaction the components of water become attached to different organic molecules.

The mechanism of the oxidation-reduction reactions in aqueous solutions was first elucidated by M. Traube [12] in a number of experiments with inorganic substances. Later A. Bach [13] showed that similar transformations form the basis of the process of respiration and of other oxidation phenomena occurring in the living cell. H. Wieland [14] describes the mechanism of this reaction somewhat differently, assuming that the substance which is to be oxidized (one molecule of aldehyde, in the above example) first of all combines with a whole molecule of water and becomes hydrated. Hydrogen is then split off from the hydrate and is taken up (accepted) by the other aldehyde molecule, or some other substance, which becomes reduced in this process. No matter which of these hypotheses we choose to adopt, the important thing to note here is that, in either event, the oxidation-reduction reaction takes place at the expense of the components of water.

It would seem strange at first glance that the great variety of chemical processes, which may properly be assumed to occur within the living cell, can all be reduced to three fundamental types, but a careful examination of biochemical phenomena sustains this view. Let us consider, by way of illustration, the chemistry of such a complex process as the fermentation of alcohol. It has long since been realized that the simple formula for fermentation: $C_6H_{12}O_6 = 2\ CH_3CH_2OH + 2\ CO_2$, is merely a summary of the entire process, showing its beginning and conclusion. But in reality the chemical process of fermentation is made up of a large chain of intermediate reactions. From the investigations of Kostychev, Lebedev, Neuberg, Harden, Embden, Meyerhof [15], and others we now have a fairly clear conception of the separate links in this chain of events and of their sequence. First of all, the sugar combines with two molecules of phosphoric acid to form a complex ester. This ester splits up into two molecules of triose-phosphate by a rupture of the bond between adjacent carbon atoms. An oxidation-reduction reaction then takes place between these resulting molecular fragments, whereby one molecule becomes reduced to glycero-phosphate while the other is at the same time oxidized to phospho-glyceric acid. Phosphoric acid is now split off, and this is followed by the so-called internal Cannizzaro oxidation-reduction reaction, which is associated with a shifting of hydrogen and hydroxyl, resulting in the formation of pyruvic acid. The latter is split between two carbon atoms with the formation of carbon dioxide and acetaldehyde. The acetaldehyde and

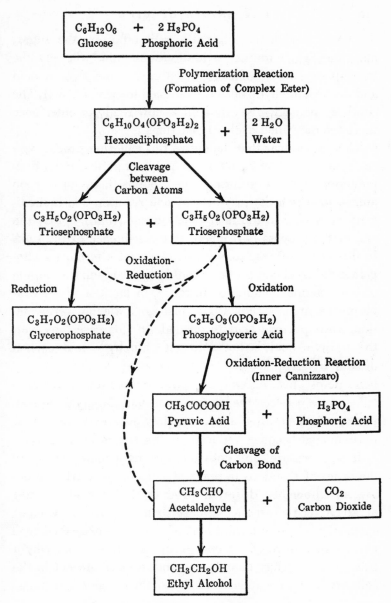

FIG. 2. Scheme of alcoholic fermentation.

the triose-phosphate, originally split off from the sugar, now undergo a mutual oxidation-reduction, whereby the triose-phosphate becomes oxidized to phospho-glyceric acid and the acetaldehyde becomes reduced to ethyl alcohol. The resulting phospho-glyceric acid is now ready to enter once more the described cycle of reactions.

Thus, it is clear that the entire fermentation process is a chain of successive reactions of polymerization, oxidation-reduction and of splitting open bonds between carbon atoms, in which the products of one reaction are immediately subjected to the next reaction, etc., until finally the end of the process is reached. If the sequence of the links in this chain of reactions were somewhat altered, an altogether different end product would represent the summation of the reactions. Thus, for instance, in lactic acid fermentation the process runs along, just as in alcohol fermentation, until pyruvic acid is formed. In this case, however, the pyruvic acid is not split into aldehyde and carbon dioxide by a rupture of the bond between two adjacent carbon atoms, but instead an oxidation-reduction reaction takes place between the pyruvic acid and the glycero-phosphate, which resulted from the previous reactions. Thus, pyruvic acid becomes reduced, giving rise to lactic acid.

It is, therefore, quite obvious that by a mere change in the order of reactions in place of alcohol and carbon dioxide an altogether different product, lactic acid, is now obtained. The effect such a mere change in the sequence of comparatively simple reactions of the above described type has on the nature of the end products is the reason why a tremendous variety of organic substances is present in the cells of living organisms. If the chain of chemical trans-

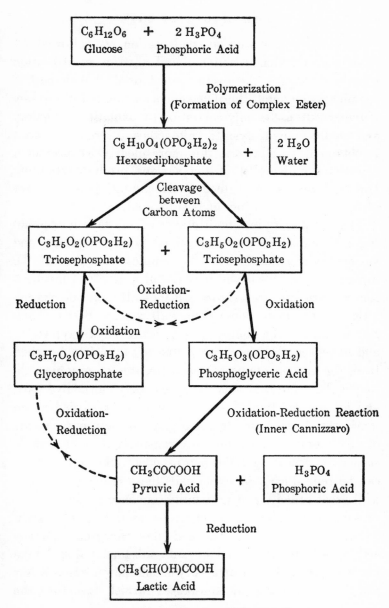

Fig. 3. Scheme of lactic acid fermentation.

formations begins with a condensation, is followed by oxidation-reduction reactions, and then a condensation takes place again, the resulting end product may be one chemical compound. But if the condensation is followed by polymerization, the polymerization by oxidation-reduction, and finally by hydrolysis, an altogether different substance is obtained. To illustrate this more clearly we present a rather incomplete list of the various products resulting from a simple sugar (glucose) depending upon the order of the reactions to which it is submitted.

The complexity and multiplicity of substances originating in living cells is thus determined by the complexity and variety of combinations of the simplest reactions of the three types described previously. But a careful consideration of these reactions shows that they all have one characteristic in common; namely, they all require the participation of water. The components of water (hydroxyl (OH) and hydrogen (H)) are either attached to or are detached from the carbon atoms of the molecules of organic substance. The water, it must be noted, plays an active part, and all the reactions described might be regarded as an interaction between water and organic substance. By virtue of this interaction the numerous transformations of organic substances occurring under natural conditions in organisms can be reproduced. In living cells these reactions proceed with great velocity and in definite sequence because of the presence of catalyzers, the enzymes, as well as of certain special conditions to be discussed later. However, the interaction between water and organic substances would take place anyway, though at a very much slower rate. Water and the simplest organic substances furnish, therefore, the

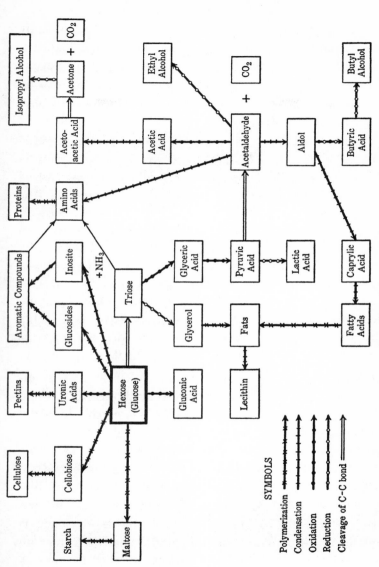

FIG. 4. Schematic representation of the transformations of glucose.

initial stuff necessary for building up the most complicated and varied organic compounds which form the material basis of "living substance." As a matter of fact, chemists have long known a number of syntheses which occur
simply when aqueous solutions of organic substances have
been kept for a time.

We shall mention only a few of the more striking examples of such syntheses. In 1861 A. Butlerov[8] obtained by
the action of milk of lime on formaldehyde a sweet-tasting
syrup which gave the usual tests of the simple sugars. The
chemical nature of the compound was only elucidated 30
years later by E. Fischer[16] who showed that the reaction
follows the empirical equation: $6 CH_2O \rightleftharpoons C_6H_{12}O_6$ with
the formation of a hexose sugar. Löw[17] changed the
conditions of Butlerov's experiments somewhat and thus
obtained a sugar solution which could be fermented by
yeast, i.e., it could serve as nutriment for heterotrophic
microorganisms. H. and A. Euler[18] have accomplished this
synthesis simply by allowing a formaldehyde solution to
which chalk has been added to stand, whereby a considerable amount of sugar was formed. They showed that at first
there is a condensation of formaldehyde to glycol aldehyde:
$2 CH_2O \rightarrow CH_2OH \cdot COH$, the sugar being formed from
the latter.

This reaction forms the basis for the entire carbohydrate
chemistry. The carbohydrates play a foremost part bio-
chemically both as a source of energy and as building
material for the living cell. The synthesis of sugar is
achieved with such ease that the question has even come up
repeatedly of its utilization in the manufacture of sugar on
a commercial scale.

As another example we may mention the synthesis accomplished in 1904 by Curtius [19]. This investigator started with an aqueous solution of a comparatively simple organic substance, the ethyl ester of glycocoll. He left the solution by a window and after some time observed the formation of slimy strands. On testing these slimy threads he found that they possessed several properties characteristic for the simplest proteins, such as the biuret reaction. As later studies have shown, Curtius actually had a fairly complex product, a polypeptide, formed in his beakers. E. Fischer [10], who studied polypeptide structures in great detail, synthesized these from halogen derivatives of amino acids, but his was an artificial procedure which does not operate under natural conditions. Curtius, on the other hand, brought about the same synthesis in his experiments through the simple interaction of water and an organic substance under the influence of light.

A. Bach [20] likewise set aside a mixture of formaldehyde and potassium cyanide in solution and, after a lapse of time, was able to isolate from this a peptone-like substance, which has the properties of the simplest proteins. In these experiments also, simply through the interaction of water, formaldehyde and CN-ions, a substance similar to compounds present in living cells was produced. When it was freed from impurities by dialysis, the substance thus obtained could be used as substrate in a nutritive medium for the cultivation of putrefactive bacteria. It is, therefore, obvious that substances can be produced by very simple procedures, as was the case also in Löw's synthesis, which are suitable as foods for microorganisms requiring organic matter for their development.

In each of these examples cited, reactions took place in aqueous solutions of organic substances simply on standing, which resulted in the formation of more highly complex molecular compounds. The well known French chemist P. Sabatier [21] has shown, on the basis of a large body of factual material, that the simplest oxygen derivatives of hydrocarbons and particularly aldehydes have an exceptionally strong tendency to polymerize. It suffices to add to them traces of various substances to induce the formation of large molecules through the binding of carbon atoms to each other either directly or through an oxygen atom. On the contrary, the opposite reaction, the de-polymerization occurs very seldom, since polymeres possess a stable molecular structure.

Summarizing briefly what has been said, we can draw the following conclusions: Hydrocarbon derivatives, such as alcohols, aldehydes, organic acids, amines, amides, etc., undergo important transformations when their aqueous solutions are allowed to stand. In these solutions the dissolved substances undergo reactions of condensation and polymerization, as well as oxidation-reduction reactions; in other words, every type of chemical change occurring in the living cell. As a result, numerous high molecular compounds, similar to those present in living cells, may appear in aqueous solutions of hydrocarbon derivatives on long standing.

Such reactions must have occurred in the warm waters of the primary hydrosphere of the Earth, in which the simplest hydrocarbon derivatives were dissolved. There is absolutely no reason to doubt that these reactions were essentially like those chemical interactions which can be reproduced at the present time in our laboratories. We may, therefore, assume that complex, high-molecular organic substances were being formed in any part of the primitive ocean and in every water reservoir, pool or drying-up basin, by a series of syntheses similar to those in Butlerov's flasks, in Curtius' beakers, or in Bach's mixtures. In this way the great variety of organic substances must have originated which are necessary for the building up of living cells. In other words, in these primitive waters materials were created out of which living organisms were to be built up subsequently.

We must allude very briefly to the very important problem of asymmetric synthesis. As is well known, many organic compounds can exist in two very similar forms. Their molecules are made up of the same atoms, and indeed of the same atomic groupings, but these groups are differently arranged in space. If some radicle, or atomic grouping, is situated on the right in one compound, the same radicle will be placed on the left in the other representative of this compound, and vice versa, as is shown below.

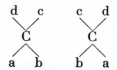

Our two hands furnish the simplest illustration or model of such an asymmetry. Placing our hands in front of us with palms turned downwards, it is obvious that in spite of their general similarity the right and left hands differ very markedly from each other in the arrangement of their separate parts. Thus, the thumb on one hand is turned to the left while on the other to the right, etc., so that each hand is a mirror image of the other. In the artificial synthesis of organic substances we always obtain an equal mixture of both asymmetric forms of the molecule (racemic mixture). This, of course, is quite understandable since the formation of one or the other form, i.e., of the right or left antipode or isomere, in a chemical reaction depends upon which of two atoms, situated to the right or to the left of the plane of symmetry, will be replaced by another atom. But since both must be under the influence of absolutely identical forces, the probability that one or the other antipode will be formed must be absolutely the same. Since incalculable numbers of atoms partake in chemical reactions, the law pertaining to large numbers operates fully so that the formation of an excess of only one antipode is entirely improbable.

In living organisms, however, we witness regularly the formation and accumulation of only one particular antipode. When an organism elaborates some substance possessing an asymmetric molecule, it always produces the same antipode. The other asymmetric form either does not occur at all in nature, or else it is produced by a different organism. Chemical asymmetry is an essential phenomenon in the structure of living organisms as it is a most characteristic property of all living substance.

L. Pasteur [22], who was among the very first to study the chemical phenomenon of asymmetry, pointed out its full significance for an understanding of the living process. He believed that "this property may be the only sharp differentiation between the chemistry of dead and living matter which can be made at present." At the same time, Pasteur posed before science the problem of the causation of asymmetry and of the methods by which asymmetric molecules in living organisms have arisen. Marcwald[23], and later McKenzie[24], succeeded to a certain extent in furnishing a solution to this problem. These investigators demonstrated experimentally the possibility of asymmetric synthesis under the influence of an optically active, i.e., asymmetric molecule. Especially interesting from this point of view is the recent work from Bredig's school[25] on the asymmetric synthesis by means of a catalyst with an asymmetric structure. Thus, Bredig and Minajev[26] have shown that when the synthesis of hydrocyanic acid with aldehyde is carried out, using quinine or quinidine as a catalyst, either the right or the left isomere of cyanhydrine is obtained. Since the catalyzers of living cells, the enzymes, are themselves asymmetric molecules, synthesis by their aid leads to the formation of asymmetric substances.

This, however, immediately raises another question as to how asymmetric molecules could have arisen in the first place. Japp[27], at the commencement of the twentieth century, enunciated the belief that such a primary synthesis of asymmetric molecules is impossible and that, like the living organism, asymmetric molecules can be derived only from other asymmetric molecules. However, this hypothesis was found to be fallacious, because asymmetric synthesis can proceed under the influence of asymmetric physical forces. Pasteur[28] had already foreseen very clearly such a possibility and thought that the Earth's magnetic field might be such an asymmetric factor. Acting upon this idea, he attempted to produce asymmetric synthesis in the field of a powerful magnet but, of course, without success, because both the magnetic field and the rotation of the Earth are symmetrical forces. Van't Hoff [29] later looked to polarized light as the possible cause for the formation of asymmetric molecules in nature. Following many failures in the hands of various investigators, W. Kuhn and Braun [30], and subsequently also Mitchell [31], applied this principle to asymmetric syntheses with complete success. These experimenters furnished indubitable proof that asymmetric molecules can be produced without the aid of the living cell.

This demonstration, nevertheless, was not enough for the understanding of how the asymmetric synthesis was realized. It was still necessary to show that on the Earth there is actually an asymmetric factor which is responsible for the appearance of asymmetric molecules. This interpretation was recently furnished by Bick. Sementzov [32], in a recent review dealing with the question of asymmetric synthesis, thus summarizes Bick's hypothesis: "It was shown a long time ago that sky light is partially plane polarized and, on being reflected from the surface of the water, is transformed into elliptically polarized light. The direction of polarization of the ray depends entirely upon astronomical causes, embracing the entire surface of the Earth, and upon the superadded magnetic field of the Earth.

"The fact that the Earth's magnetic field is asymmetric as regards the plane which passes through the point of reflection from the Earth's surface, through the Sun and through the zenith, makes it impossible to have an equal quantity of right and left light. Without the magnetic field such equality would prevail for any pair of rays symmetrically arranged with regard to this plane.

"It must, therefore, be assumed as highly probable that

the excess of one of the isomeres was produced by a photo-chemical reaction under the influence of elliptically polar-ized light. The further fixation and formation of an asym-metric flora and fauna was then assured by the asymmetric synthesis under the influence of an excess of one of the antipodes."

Vernadski [33] assumes that the asymmetric factor is to be looked for in the phenomenon which occurred at the time when the Moon had become separated from our planet. In his opinion—"the separation of the Moon imparted a spiral-like whirl motion to the substance of the Earth (prob-ably a right-hand motion) which has never again been repeated." According to this view, molecular asymmetry could have originated just at that particular moment in the Earth's history, the primary asymmetric synthesis having never repeated itself again.

Be this as it may, there is every reason to believe that in the primary hydrosphere of the Earth conditions existed which were not only favorable to the production of complex and varied organic substances but also for endowing them with optical activity (asymmetry).

While considering the problem of the primary origin of different organic compounds in the Earth's hydrosphere, it is necessary to give special attention to the possibility of protein formation under those conditions. The proteins play an exclusively prominent role in the structure of living protoplasm. F. Engels [34] observed that "wherever there is life, it is found in association with proteins, and wherever there is protein, which is not in the process of decomposi-tion, one also finds without an exception the phenomena of life." It is true that many organic as well as inorganic sub-

stances together with the proteins go to make up the protoplasm. Nevertheless, the proteins constitute the fundamental substance out of which "living matter" is built up, i.e.,
the matter present in the cells of all plants, animals and
microorganisms.

For this reason the problem of the primary origin of
proteins has always attracted the attention of investigators
who concerned themselves with the question of the origin
of life. Unfortunately many irrelevant matters have been
brought into this discussion, which only helped to confuse
the subject and made its solution so much more difficult.
One group of scientists (Pflüger, Rubner, Verworn, etc.)
assumed the existence of a special "live protein," "biogenic
molecule," etc. According to the ideas of these investigators
the molecules of the hypothetical compounds contain special atomic groupings, some peculiar radicles, which impart to the whole compound exceptional instability (lability) and chemical reactivity, which determine the metabolic
activity and all other vital properties of protoplasm. On
this supposition the phenomena of life can all be explained
by the definite arrangement of atoms in the molecule of
proteins present in the protoplasm. The origin of such a
hypothetical live protein molecule, endowed with specific
chemical structure, requires some very special and exclusive conditions, and the ideas of some scientists, especially
those of Verworn [35], are shrouded in a fog of mystery.

On the other hand, another group of investigators speaking of proteins have in mind the substances which have
been isolated from plant or animal sources. But even the
simplest of these substances represent extremely complex
compounds, containing many thousands of atoms of carbon,

hydrogen, oxygen, and nitrogen arranged in absolutely definite patterns, which are specific for each separate substance. To the student of protein structure the spontaneous formation of such an atomic arrangement in the protein molecule would seem as improbable as would the accidental origin of the text of Virgil's "Aeneid" from scattered letter type.

What we wish to consider here, however, does not concern itself with the origin in the protein molecule of some specific live grouping. Neither does the complete identity of primary proteins with substances, which could result only from a long evolutionary process in the organic world, claim our attention. We shall concern ourselves simply with the question whether protein substances, in the sense in which the term is understood by contemporary biochemists, could have arisen in the primitive hydrosphere together with other complex organic substances.

We still lack a definite conception of the structure of the protein molecule. Since the classical researches of E. Fischer it has been known that the amino acid components of the protein molecule are bound together through nitrogen atoms (polypeptide bonds), but other types of atomic arrangement have also been discovered in the course of subsequent numerous researches by Ssadikov and Zelinski[36], Abderhalden[37], Troensegaard[38], Gavrilov[39], etc. This problem is now a live topic of discussion in scientific literature. Summarizing this discussion, Kiezel[40] comes to the conclusion that the polypeptide structure of protein seems the best established and obvious, but by no means the only possible structure. Besides the ordinary chemical combinations, residual valences also play a very important part in the structure of the protein particle (as was demonstrated by the work of Meyer and Mark [41], and especially of Svedberg [42]). Separate amino acid chains and rings are united into large colloidal complexes by such residual valences.

Summing up briefly our present knowledge of the chemistry of the proteins it may be said that protein substances represent complex organic compounds built up from amino acids bound to each other by peptide linkages, as well as by other less well known bonds. The resulting molecular complexes are further bound together through residual valences into large colloidal particles. The formation of such organic compounds in the primitive hydrosphere of the Earth required no special or specific conditions apart from those already discussed in this chapter. The formation of the separate amino acids may follow the scheme proposed by Trier [43], according to which these compounds may result from the interaction of ammonia with oxy-acids, which are obtained by the Cannizzaro reaction from aldehydes. For instance, in the aldol condensation of formaldehyde, as was shown previously, glycol aldehyde is produced which, by an oxidation-reduction reaction, yields glycol and glycolic acid. The latter reacting with ammonia gives glycine, the simplest of the amino acids:

1. $2 CH_2OH \cdot COH + H_2O = CH_2OH \cdot CH_2OH + CH_2OH \cdot COOH$
   Glycol aldehyde   Glycol   Glycolic acid

2. $NH_3 + HO \cdot CH_2 \cdot COOH = NH_2 \cdot CH_2 \cdot COOH + H_2O$
   Ammonia   Glycolic acid   Glycine

Other amino acids are formed in a similar manner when different hydrocarbon derivatives are subjected to the above reactions. The combination of amino acids with each other to form polypeptide complexes has already been discussed. It results from polymerization and can, therefore, be easily accomplished under conditions prevailing in the primitive hydrosphere of the Earth. The other types of atomic grouping, which we must suppose also exist in the protein molecule, could likewise result from the previously mentioned reactions. Finally, the union between separate atomic chains and rings by residual valences is also easily accomplished in aqueous solutions of protein precursors.

Thus, the primary formation of compounds of the protein type is in no way unusual, exceptional, or different than the formation of other complex organic substances. It is a far more fundamental point to decide, why protein substances have come to play such an exclusive role in the further evolution of organic compounds and in the origin of living organisms. But it is hardly likely that an answer to this problem will be found in searching within the protein molecule for some unstable, labile atomic arrangement or radicle. The presence of basic amino groups and of acidic carboxyl groups imparts to amino acids, and to proteins built from them, very striking chemical properties. The amino acids and the proteins are so-called amphoteric electrolytes, or substances reacting with both acids and bases, which makes it possible for them to enter a number of different reactions with the elements of water or with organic substances present in the aqueous medium. At the same time, the ease with which separate amino acids become welded together and the ease with which the resulting complexes become united by their residual valences furnishes the necessary conditions for the creation of enormous hydrophil colloidal particles. The latter are in close relation to numerous molecules of water forming a diffuse aura about them. All these properties of proteins (extensive reactivity, tendency to form high-molecular complexes, etc.) lend to them, in comparison with other organic substances, by far the greatest capacity to attain a higher stage of organization and transition to a colloidal state, which bridges the gap between organic compounds and living things.

The carbon atom in the Sun's atmosphere does not represent organic matter, but the exceptional capacity of this element to form long atomic chains and to unite with other elements, such as hydrogen, oxygen and nitrogen, is the hidden spring which under proper conditions of existence has furnished the impetus for the formation of organic compounds. Similarly, protein is by no means living matter, but hidden in its chemical structure is the capacity for further organic evolution which, under certain conditions, may lead to the origin of living things. In this sense, it seems to us, we should interpret Engel's formula: "Life is a form of the existence of protein bodies."

CHAPTER VI

THE ORIGIN OF PRIMARY
COLLOIDAL SYSTEMS

IT WAS SHOWN PREVIOUSLY that the theories attempting to explain the properties of living matter on the basis of some specific radicles in the protein molecule are untenable. Attempts to deduce the specific properties of life from the manner of atomic configuration in the molecules of organic substance could be regarded as predestined to failure. The laws of organic chemistry cannot account for those phenomena of a higher order which are encountered in the study of living cells. The structure of the protein molecule, its amino and carboxyl radicles, polypeptide or other linkages, etc., determine only the ability of this material to evolve and change into a higher grade of organization, which depends not only on the arrangement of atoms in the molecule but also on the mutual relationship of molecules towards one another. But what paths did this evolution follow?

The idea has been frequently advanced that the evolution of organic substances and of proteins in particular must have proceeded as an unlimited growth of individual molecules. New atomic groups are supposed to unite continually with the small primary particle, either by main (homeopolar) valences or by supplementary (residual) valences, so that the particle or molecule grows larger and larger and its structure becomes more complicated. Finally it attains dimensions which correspond to those of the minutest living things. According to this idea, organisms represent such separate molecules with an infinite variety of atomic groupings which permit them to manifest the different vital functions. This viewpoint was discussed in detail in connection with the theories of spontaneous generation of ultramicrobes reviewed in the first chapter. But some investigators, like V. Kourbatov [1], apply this to all organisms, regarding every living cell as a "single chemical particle or, more correctly, as a colossal poly-ion."

At the present time such a conception of the living cell seems highly debatable since it is contradicted by a number of definitely established physico-chemical properties of the protoplasm. However, we must analyze carefully the possibility of such an evolutionary course of organic matter. This is especially necessary since the possibility of such an evolution, although only under definite artificial conditions, is to a certain degree supported by a series of recent experimental studies. From this standpoint the experiments of Staudinger [2] are of particular interest. This investigator studied a series of successive high molecular combinations obtained by successive polymerization of low molecular substances. Among these products he produced polyoxy-methylene-diacetates, which represent long chains formed from formaldehyde residues united to each other through oxygen atoms:

$$CH_3CO \cdot O \cdot CH_2O \ldots \ldots \ldots O \cdot CH_2O \cdot COCH_3$$

The number of formaldehyde residues in the chain may be gradually increased without limit. A tremendously interesting transformation takes place in the properties of polymeres produced by this method in that with the elongation of the chain and the increase of the molecular weight of the polymeres their solubility gradually diminishes and their density becomes progressively greater. Higher polymeres, composed of about fifty formaldehyde residues, already manifest a definite thread-like structure, and on roentgenological examination give the so-called Debye-Scherrer diagram, which indicates a definite orientation of their component parts.

Staudinger thinks that other *natural* and highly polymerized organic compounds, such as cellulose, silk, rubber, etc., have a similar type of structure, and accordingly these substances, like the artificial polymeres, result from repetitive additions of the same atomic groups, binding each other by basic or main valences and forming molecular chains of any desired length. Thus, for instance, cellulose represents fundamentally an extremely long chain made up of molecules of cellobiose united to each other by an oxygen.

Polanyi[3], Pringsheim[4], and Hess[5] have an entirely different idea of the nature of the structure of polymeres, and this view has been presented with great lucidity by Bergmann[6] in his famous report before the congress of naturalists in Düsseldorf in 1926. According to this view highly polymerized compounds consist of small molecules held together by associative forces. The principal factor in the formation of these high molecular complexes are thus not the main valences (which are generally indicated in structural formulas by dashes) but the forces of the side or residual valences, which not infrequently appear in atoms, groups of atoms or whole molecules after their usual main valences have been satisfied.

The chemical studies of Haworth[7] and especially the roentgenological investigations of Meyer and Mark[8] have shown that the truth is to be found somewhere between these opposite viewpoints. Particularly in the case of cellulose we are actually dealing with long chains of cellobiose molecules united to each other by oxygen atoms, but the length of these chains is not infinite. Mark's studies on the resistance of cellulose to tearing (tensile strength) demonstrate this especially clearly. If these molecular chains were infinitely long they would possess at least a ten-fold greater tensile strength than they actually possess. Haworth, studying the products of degradation of methylated cellulose, proved that the chain consists of approximately fifty cellobiose residues. Therefore the length of the molecular chains of which cellulose is made up has been fairly definitely established. According to Meyer's data this is equal to 500 Å [Å or Aengstrom unit is 0.1 millimicron; 250 million Aengstroms make up one inch] and 40-60 such chains are held together by residual valences in the form of bundles as crystallites or micels. The structure of such formations is determined, therefore, not only by the arrangement of the atoms as chains, the molecules, but also by the relation of these molecules to each other. Furthermore, the micels in the natural cellulose thread from different plants are also oriented in a definite manner.

Such orderly orientation of molecules in the micels and the arrangement of the micels themselves determines the structure of a large number of natural products composed of highly polymerized organic substances. Thus, for instance, the silk fiber, like cellulose, consists basically of micels oriented regularly and parallel to the axis of the thread, the micels themselves representing sheaves of molecular chains. However, in this instance the chains are made up not of carbohydrate but of amino acid residues. The chain evidently contains regularly alternating residues of glycine and alanine united by peptide linkages. In Figure 5 a schematic representation of these molecular structures is shown.

In the micels of silk, as well as of cellulose, each molecular chain is straight and extended, with its principal axis oriented parallel to the axis of the micel, but in hair or in wool more complicated patterns are encountered. Roentgenological investigation of natural hair and of hair subjected to stretching under the influence of steam shows that only in the latter are the molecular chains, which are made up of amino acid residues, arranged in a straight line. In the natural, unstretched hair these chains have a more complicated arrangement and instead of being in a straight line are in the form of a spiral, as is illustrated in Figure 6. In natural hair (a-keratin) NH and CO residues attract each other, causing the chain to become twisted into a spiral structure, with the result that the length of each link made from three amino acid residues is only 5.1 Å, but when the hair is stretched these atomic groups become separated. The chain straightens out and, as roentgenological studies show, the length of the chain becomes 10.2 Å (β-keratin).

It is actually possible to stretch hair to exactly double its length. Studying the molecular chains of natural hair,

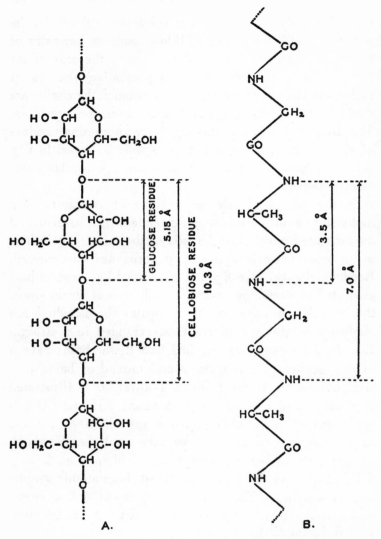

Fɪɢ. 5. Schematic structure of cellulose (A) and of silk fibroin (B).

we note for the first time the ability of proteins to form not only linear but more complicated chain configurations. Meyer and Mark remark that protein chains can exist in the extended linear shape only under special conditions,

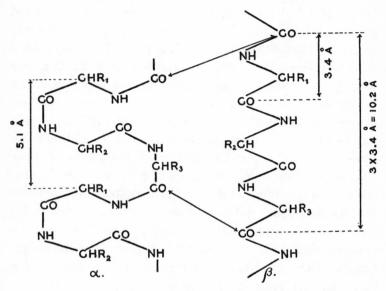

Fig. 6. Schematic structure of alpha and beta keratin.

while under ordinary circumstances they form twisted chains. This greatly complicates the inner structure of the proteins.

Such formations as we considered, i.e., cellulose, silk, hair possess a comparatively very simple organization represented by a more or less geometrically regular internal structure, which is essentially very close to the structure of a crystal. Their simplicity, constancy and static nature made these substances the favorite objects of investigation, because it is possible, even with the aid of our relatively crude methods, to unravel all the details of their structure. At the same time it must not be overlooked that this very simplicity and constancy of structure is associated with the fact that all these materials really represent only dead components of the cell. Numerous attempts to discover analogous structures in the living protoplasm have been without success. It can only be said that one is dealing here with some elusive reciprocal orientation of molecules, with the existence of some molecular swarms, whose structure cannot yet be elucidated with our comparatively crude means of investigation. To be sure, one can observe in protoplasm the reversible process of formation of fiber structures, of most delicate supporting threads, fibrils, etc., but it does not follow that such micellar structures actually preexist in the protoplasm and do not arise under the influence of some internal or external factors. This can be demonstrated by a very simple example. The investigations of Herzog[9], Katz[10], Procter and others have shown that collagen from tendon fibers and gelatin are very closely related to each other from the point of view of chemical composition and of the structure of their crystallites and micels. Whereas, however, the micels of collagen are regularly oriented in only one direction (along the fiber axis), those of gelatin are arranged without any recognizable plan. But dried and stretched gelatin gives the typical diagram of a fiber structure almost identical with that of collagen, i.e., under tension the gelatin micels orient themselves along the lines of force.

The fiber structure, therefore, does not preexist in gelatin but arises under external influences generated by the experimenter. Perhaps a different structure would result, if some other influence could be exerted. Under the manifest disorder in the arrangement of gelatin micels there lurks the possibility for the appearance of various micellar orientations and structures, and these structures can be modified by external influences. In the case of gelatin the possible variety of structure must be limited by the comparative simplicity of the structure of its micels. In this sense, protoplasm is endowed with incomparably greater potentialities. The preexisting molecular swarms and mixed micels, which as a rule are associations of different proteins and other organic compounds, may under proper external conditions form a great variety of very complex and, what is most important, labile structures. In this respect they differ fundamentally from the stable structures of cellulose, silk or hair, which were discussed previously, in which the orderly arrangement of the separate elements is fixed and definitive. Their structure even under extreme changes in the environment is most stable and permanent. The static order, the very perfection of their structure makes further evolution of these substances impossible. They are dead matter not only because they do not reveal any signs of life, but also because they are the blind ends in the evolutionary path of organic substance.

We shall indeed end up in blind alleys, if we follow the hypothesis of the evolution of organic substance mentioned in the beginning of this chapter. Unless we choose to indulge in chemical phantasies, instead of keeping our feet on firm ground of experimentally verified facts, it must be admitted that a successive growth of the molecule, by polymerization of link to link, will indeed result in compounds with definite structure, but these will be static and dead, either like those which Staudinger obtained in his syntheses or like cellulose, silk, etc.

But the evolution of organic matter along this path under the conditions discussed in the previous chapters is impossible anyway. Successive and repetitive polymerization of separate links can take place only in pure solutions and provided the polymerized substance is isolated. In complex mixtures of a great variety of organic substances this process follows an entirely different course. The primary hydrosphere of the Earth certainly was not a pure solution of some organic substance nor did it offer any possibility for the isolation of the formed products. Beyond any question one is dealing here with a complicated mixture of high molecular organic compounds, in which the infinite growth of chains made of the same type of molecule and the formation of uniform micels could not occur.

The chemist, and especially the physical chemist, always prefers to work with the isolated chemically pure substances, because only so can he study in detail their properties and nature. This accounts for the traditional contemptuous attitude of chemists to various mixtures or "dirty substances." Until quite recently it was still considered that the most essential thing for the chemist is to study the properties of individual compounds, and to regard the properties of mixtures as the sum of the properties of their components. Today such a view seems entirely untenable. Willstätter [11], in his remarkable Faraday lecture, lays special emphasis on the significance of investigating mixtures. "Until now it was taken for granted in chemistry that the properties of components in chemical compounds disappear but that in mixtures of substances they are retained. This is an antiquated viewpoint. . . . Mixtures may actually possess the nature of new chemical compounds. This similarity between mixtures and compounds can be explained in such a way that electrostatic and electromagnetic fields of force of separate components present in a mixture may act upon each other, whereby new means of attraction are produced." Thus, on mixing different substances new properties appear which were absent in the component parts of the mixture. This fact is of tremendous significance to every biochemist, since under natural conditions he never deals with pure substances. Sörensen [12] quite correctly points out that even in the preparation and isolation of proteins one never deals with individual substances. In a series of such preparations he demonstrated experimentally that they represent mixtures of components with different solubilities and different composition. Meyer and Mark [8] have shown that owing to their high content of the fat absorbing "lipophil groups" (phenyl, methyl, etc.) proteins manifest a very strong tendency to form molecular associations. Protein preparations are such associations of varied protein chains tied up somehow to each other. With our present technique of preparation it is not possible to separate the individual components of these associations and we are, therefore, dealing with more or less complex mixtures of different types of protein.

In dealing with protoplasm we are undoubtedly also confronted with such associations consisting of various proteins, but the situation here is even incomparably more complex owing to the fact that besides the proteins there is also present a great variety of other, non-protein components. The fat-like lipoid substances play a particularly outstanding role in this connection, forming intermolecular combinations with the proteins through their lipophil groups. On the other hand, by means of their so-called hydrophil groups (NH, OH, O, as well as the ionizable groups COOH and NH₂) the proteins can combine with molecules of water and with a number of water soluble substances. This complexity of the protoplasmic composition manifests itself strikingly in the study of its physicochemical properties.

Rubinstein [13] has shown that such properties of the protoplasm as heat coagulation, surface precipitation, permeability, electrical properties, etc., cannot be explained on the basis of the properties of some one protoplasmic component, like the proteins, lipids, etc., but are the resultant of correlation and reciprocal action of different colloidal systems, which make up the protoplasm. This alone compels us, in considering the evolution of organic substance, to rely not upon those alterations to which this or another isolated compound may be subjected, but to bear in mind alterations which take place in complex mixtures of various organic substances.

As is well known, the proteins, and other high molecular organic substances resembling them, form colloidal solutions in water. When one is dealing with a mixture of such colloidal systems the separation of any one component in pure condition, or its crystallization, is exceedingly difficult or even impossible to accomplish. But all the dissolved colloids can be separated from the solution simultaneously with comparative ease by means of coagulation. The mechanism of coagulation is very different for the hydrophobe and hydrophil colloids. The particles of hydrophobe colloids, which are principally inorganic, have no affinity for the solvent medium, the water, and are held in a dispersed state only by virtue of electrostatic forces. Bearing the same electrical charges, the colloidal particles repel each other and, being thus dispersed, cannot unite into complexes of greater or less size. But as soon as the charge upon the particles is decreased (for instance, by introducing electrolytes into the solution) the stability of the colloidal system is at once disturbed. The colloidal particles, having lost their electrical charge, commence to fuse together by the force of surface tension, forming large aggregates which finally separate as a precipitate.

The process is somewhat different in the case of hydrophil (organic) colloids. Here the stability of the colloidal system depends not only on electrostatic forces but also on the affinity of the colloidal particles for the molecules of water. Such radicles and groups as — NH, — OH, = O, etc., hold molecules of water by adsorption because of their affinity for the elements of water. The colloidal micels appear, therefore, as if they were swathed with a more or less thick membrane of water, which keeps the individual particles from clumping together. It is not enough to neutralize their electrical charge to coagulate such hydrophil colloids. It is also necessary to decrease their solvation, i.e., their ability to hold this surrounding water membrane. Upon the removal of these water membranes the hydrophil particles run together, forming a flocculent precipitate consisting of accidentally united colloidal micels.

But it has been known for a longe time [14] that in solutions

of hydrophil colloids, besides coagulation, another phenomenon of separation may be observed, which is perhaps
best described by the picturesque though unscientific word
"unscrambling" (Entmischung, the Germans call it). Under this condition the colloidal solution separates into two
layers, a fluid sediment, rich in colloidal substance, which
is in equilibrium with a liquid layer, free from colloids.
During the past several years this phenomenon has been
subjected to careful investigation by B. de Jong[15], who
designated it as *coazervation* in distinction to ordinary
coagulation. He calls the fluid sediment rich in colloidal
substances the *coazervate*, while the non-colloidal solution
he calls the *equilibrium liquid*. In a number of instances
this coazervate does not settle out as a continuous fluid
layer but remains in the form of minute microscopic droplets floating in the equilibrium liquid. The coazervate, unlike the coagulate, represents a fluid mass. Though in both
the coazervate and the equilibrium liquid the solvent is
water, nevertheless the droplets of coazervate are sharply
demarcated from the surrounding medium by a clearly
discernible surface. These droplets may fuse with each
other but they never mix with the equilibrium liquid. This
is strongly reminiscent of what one observes when lumps
of protoplasm are squeezed out from plant cells. Just as the
coazervate, protoplasm is also suffused with water but, in
spite of its fluid consistency, it does not mix with its surrounding medium and floats in the water in the form of
little balls sharply separated from the solvent medium.

At first glance such a sharp separation of two aqueous
solutions seems extremely strange, but de Jong arrived at a
very satisfactory explanation of this phenomenon on the

basis of a detailed analysis of its mechanism. As was noted
before, in hydrophil solutions (or sols, as they are termed)
the separate colloidal particles are surrounded by a membrane of hydration water which, as de Jong shows, is of a
diffuse nature. The molecules of water adsorbed directly

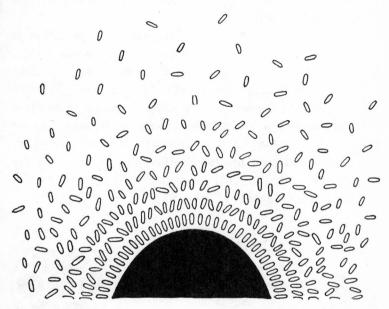

Fɪɢ. 7. Schematic arrangement of water molecules around the colloidal
particle of a hydrophile sol.

to the colloidal particles are attached very firmly and are
strictly oriented with regard to each other. But the water
molecules of the next layer are oriented less perfectly and
the farther they are removed from the colloidal particle the
less firmly are the molecules attached to each other. Finally
a zone is reached outside the colloidal particle where the

water molecules are no longer oriented and where they
move as the free molecules of the solution. Thus, the most
characteristic feature of the hydration membrane surrounding the colloidal particles of a sol is the complete absence
of any real delimitation between the water molecules of the
membrane and the water molecules of the solution. (See
illustration in Figure 7.)

On the other hand, the phenomenon of coazervation is
associated with the appearance of a definite delimitation.
The process of coazervation is nothing more than the dim-
inution in hydration of the colloidal particles; in other
words, their diminished ability to hold around themselves
a water membrane. The colloidal particles, however, do not
completely lose the water but retain those molecules which
are closest and most firmly adsorbed and are very rigidly
oriented towards the particle, as can be illustrated by the
accompanying diagram (Figure 8).

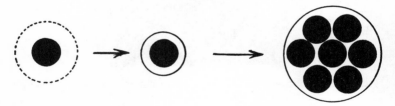

Fig. 8. Schematic representation of the transformation of a particle of
colloidal solution into a coazervate particle.

Thus the coazervate represents a special type of concentrated colloidal sol, in which the water molecules are
rigidly oriented with regard to the colloidal particle. A real
separation is thus brought about between the shell of

oriented water molecules and the free molecules of the equilibrium liquid.

The most varied colloidal systems may under certain conditions give rise to coazervation, but this happens most easily when two or more colloidal solutions having particles with opposite electrical charges are mixed together. As was already stated, the stability of hydrophil colloidal sols is determined partly by electrostatic and partly by hydration forces. Similarly charged particles repel each other and thus counteract the process of coagulation. But when oppositely charged colloidal particles are present in the same system the situation is quite different. Here the electrostatic and the hydration forces are antagonistic to each other, the hydration still promoting the stability of the sol, but the electrostatic forces, on the contrary, tending to bring the colloidal particles closer together. The mutual attraction of oppositely charged particles can, to a certain degree, overcome the effect of hydration. This so-called complex coazervate, resulting from the mixture of oppositely charged colloids, exists by virtue of the antagonistic action of the hydration and electrostatic forces, and the stability of the system is determined by the cooperation of two opposed but balanced influences. This imparts to the systems the property of extreme lability, making it possible for them to shift easily in either direction from the equilibrium under the influence of the smallest change in external conditions.

To illustrate this, let us consider an example of the formation of such complex coazervates. On mixing at 42° C. a dilute gelatin solution (0.67 percent) with a similar solution of gum arabic (0.67 percent) the mixture will appear as a clear, homogeneous liquid so long as the pH of the solution is above the isoelectric point* of gelatin (pH = 4.82), because under these conditions of actual acidity the particles of both colloidal components are negatively charged and, therefore, coazervation does not occur. But on making the solution somewhat more acid the gelatin, which is an amphoteric electrolyte, will change its electrical charge. At pH below 4.8 the electrical charge on the gelatin will become positive while the gum arabic particles will still be negatively charged. In this way coazervation will be induced and from the previously homogeneous solution droplets of the complex gelatin-gum arabic coazervate will now begin to separate out.

The stability of this complex coazervate is thus determined by the mutual attraction of colloidal particles, but the degree of attraction is a function of the product of the opposite electrical charges which the particles bear. On mixing solutions of gelatin and egg lecithin, the charge on the former at pH = 4.82 (the isoelectric point of gelatin) is zero and, although the lecithin particles are negatively charged, no coazervation takes place because the product of charges is also nil. Similarly, at pH = 2.7 (the isoelectric point of lecithin) the formation of a coazervate is still impossible, because the lecithin particles are devoid of electrical charge at that acidity. The greatest force of mu-

* The pH is a logarithmic scale for measuring the degree of acidity or of alkalinity of a solution, i.e. the concentration of its hydrogen and hydroxyl ions (H^+, OH^-). Theoretically this scale extends from 0 to 14 from the extreme acid to the extreme alkaline side, the value of pH = 7.0 corresponding to the exact neutral point. Certain substances such as the proteins (gelatin), etc., which have both acid and alkaline properties manifest these properties to a variable extent depending upon the pH of the solution. The pH at which these attain a minimal value is designated as the isoelectric point of the substance, because it is least ionized and does not migrate in an electric field at that point.

tual attraction between the particles of gelatin and lecithin is at an intermediate pH, for instance at pH = 3.6, at which acidity the coazervate is most stable. A shift in the concentration of hydrogen ions in either direction causes an increase in the hydration force with the resulting liquefaction of the coazervate. On approaching the isoelectric point of one or another component of the system the conditions for the existence of the coazervate disappear and the coazervate dissolves. Naturally, using mixtures of different components the maximum stability will likewise be within a different pH range. Thus, for instance, a mixture of gelatin with protamine, whose isoelectric point lies in an alkaline medium (pH = 10 — 11), may give a coazervate which is stable at pH = 8.9. The extreme sensitivity of coazervates to changes in the actual acidity of the solution beyond definite limits of tolerance is, therefore, clearly seen. But coazervates manifest such sensitivity not only towards hydrogen or hydroxyl ions (i.e., to changes in acidity or alkalinity) but also towards other electrolytes, and even towards neutral salts. Since the stability of the complex coazervates ultimately depends upon electrical forces of attraction between oppositely charged colloidal particles, every influence tending to diminish those forces must lead to a breaking up or a reversible dissolution of the coazervate. For this reason ions, which cause a discharge of the coazervate particles, bring about liquefaction of the coazervate system. However, a series of coazervate systems were found which are stable to neutral salts, as, for instance, the complex coazervates of clupein-nucleic acid or clupein-soya bean. lecithin. The behavior of coazervates under the action of a constant electrical current is also very interesting. Without going into details, not only by its external appearance but also by its physico-chemical mechanism this behavior is identical with the disintegration of protoplasm, which results when a constant current is passed for a long time through a medium containing living organisms.

As was already mentioned, the stability of a coazervate is greater the higher the product of the opposite electrical charges on its component particles, which is the stabilizing factor. On the contrary, the hydration of the particles, i.e., their ability to hold the membrane of water molecules, acts in the reverse direction and tends to dissolve the coazervate. But the hydration of the colloid depends greatly upon temperature, the hydration decreasing with rising temperature. This accounts for the fact that coazervates are not only sensitive to electrical but also to thermal influences. With rising temperature, owing to the decreased hydration of the colloids, the coazervate becomes condensed and squeezes out droplets of equilibrium liquid, but some of the latter may remain dispersed within the substance of the coazervate giving rise to vacuoles. This again suggests an analogy to the vacuolization of protoplasm. Vacuolization is an important characteristic which distinguishes protoplasm from most of the other colloidal systems.

B. de Jong describes many interesting physico-chemical properties of coazervates which may be compared to the properties of protoplasm, especially interesting correlations being obtained in experiments with coazervates made up of a large number of components, as, for instance, a coazervate of gelatin, gum arabic, nucleic acid, etc.

Obviously, such analogies must be considered with the

utmost caution and under no circumstances would it be permissible to look upon complex coazervates as an exact colloidal model of protoplasm. Nevertheless, a careful study of coazervates shows that one is dealing here not merely with an external resemblance, as was the case in the previously cited experiments of Leduc (Chapter III). The important thing is that a number of phenomena displayed by coazervates, as well as by protoplasm, are determined by the same physico-chemical causes and obey the same inner mechanism, so that a knowledge of the coazervates is a very essential landmark in the evolution of our appreciation of the physico-chemical properties of the protoplasm.

We must call attention especially to the following properties of the complex coazervates. In the first place, their marked capacity to adsorb various substances dissolved in the surrounding solution deserves mention. Before coazervation takes place, as was pointed out before, there is no real demarcation between the diffused molecules which make up the membrane surrounding the colloidal particles and the free molecules of the solvent. But in the process of coazervation a definite demarcation sets in, with the formation of an interface separating the coazervate from the equilibrium liquid. This demarcation leads to the development of new surface phenomena, particularly of adsorption by the coazervate of various substances dissolved in the surrounding medium. There are many organic compounds which are thus almost completely removed from the equilibrium liquid by the coazervates, even when these organic substances are in as low a concentration as 0.001 percent. Part of these adsorbed molecules is in the hydration membranes of the coazervate but part is actually attached to the colloidal particles themselves, not infrequently forming chemical compounds with them. As a result of this, the coazervate droplets may actually increase in size, growing at the expense of substances present in the equilibrium liquid, whereby even their chemical composition may undergo a radical change.

The second property of complex coazervates which merits attention is their ability to undergo secondary transformations. As was pointed out previously, the state of aggregation of complex coazervates makes them more or less mobile fluids. Depending upon external conditions (temperature, hydrogen ion concentration, presence of electrolytes, etc.) their viscosity may vary within wide limits. Under certain conditions directive forces arise in coazervates which alter their character of ideal solutions, thanks to which the coazervate particles acquire a regular orientation with regard to each other. In other words, something happens in the coazervate system similar to that which was previously described in the case of stretched gelatin. B. de Jong states that it is even possible to discern in coazervates a structural plan of a more or less regular crystalline form. He observed this in coazervates obtained from the proteins edestin and egg albumin. He likewise observed the formation of regular six-sided platelets in coazervates of which one component was starch. However, these structures appearing in coazervates differ materially from those rigid, static formations which characterize cellulose, silk, etc. These, on the contrary, are very unstable structures and even the friction of the cover glass can induce them to reverse back to the original droplet form. Thus a definite orientation of colloidal particles, i.e., a definite structure, may arise in coazervates, but this structure can be maintained only so long as the directive forces responsible for this orientation of the particles are operative. But as soon as these forces die out or are modified, the structure they helped to bring into being likewise disappears or changes.

After this long excursion into the domain of colloidal chemistry we may once more return to those organic substances which were dissolved in the original aqueous covering of the Earth. It is not likely that the chemical transformations of these substances could have followed some one definite direction, owing to the varied chemical potentialities with which the oxygen and nitrogen derivatives of hydrocarbons are endowed. According to the reactions described in the preceding chapter not a single, definite, individual substance must have appeared in the original hydrosphere of the Earth but a complex mixture of different high-molecular organic compounds of primary proteins, lipids, carbohydrates and hydrophil colloids. In other words, the formation of complex coazervates in the Earth's hydrosphere was unavoidable because their formation requires very simple conditions, merely the mixture of two or more high-molecular organic substances being necessary. In so far as we admit the possibility that such substances existed in the original aqueous envelope of the Earth, we have no reason for denying the possibility of formation of coazervates in the waters of the primitive seas and oceans. The relatively low concentration of these organic substances in the hydrosphere could not be an obstacle, since coazervation can take place even in highly diluted solutions. The waters of our present day sea and ocean contain only insignificant traces of organic compounds resulting from the de-

composition of dead organisms. In the great majority of
cases these compounds are used up by plankton organisms,
for which they serve as the basic food supply. However, in
some comparatively rare instances, in great depths of the
sea, under conditions precluding the development of microorganism, these substances may be preserved for a more
or less long time. Studies made on the ooze obtained from
such great depths indicate that under such conditions the
dissolved organic substances may form jelly sediments.
Such a phenomenon of colloidal precipitation from water
containing merely traces of organic substance has been also
observed not infrequently under experimental conditions,
when the action of microorganisms has been excluded.
Therefore, sooner or later complex coazervates were bound
to appear from the mixture of several different hydrophil
colloids in the original hydrosphere of the Earth.

The formation of coazervates was a most important event
in the evolution of the primary organic substance and in
the process of autogeneration of life. Before that event organic matter was indissolubly fused with its medium, being
diffused throughout the mass of the solvent. But with the
formation of coazervates organic matter became concentrated at different points of the aqueous medium and, at the
same time, sharp division occurred between the medium
and the coazervate. Previously the particles of hydrophil
sols, enveloped by hydration membranes and bound to their
dispersion medium, had no real boundary separating them
from this medium, but with the onset of coazervation organic substance became separated from the solution, was
set apart from the aqueous phase by a real, sharp boundary,

and in a certain sense became antagonistic to its surrounding, external environment.

This antagonism is a tremendously significant characteristic of living things. One cannot conceive of an organism which is completely dispersed in its surrounding medium. Every living thing is to a greater or less degree separated, more or less sharply differentiated from this medium. As a result of such a separation and of the existence of definite, sharp delimitation the chemical interactions between organism and its environment acquire a rather complex, peculiar character, which we designate as the material exchange between organism and its environment. In its primitive condition this exchange of matter must have been operative in the primary complex coazervate, because the coazervate was not suspended in pure water but in a very complicated mixture of various dissolved organic and inorganic compounds. Owing to the inherent ability of coazervates to adsorb, they must have picked out some of these substances not merely mechanically, by holding them fixed to the surface, but also by direct chemical reaction with the coazervate particle. In a word, there must have been a conversion of material derived from the environment into components of the colloid substance itself. According to the experiments of de Jong, this would result in an increase in size and weight of the primary coazervate; in other words, in its growth.

In the process of coazervate formation organic substance not only became concentrated at definite points in space but, to a certain degree, it also acquired structure. Where previously there was only a helter-skelter accumulation of moving particles, in the coazervates these particles are already to a certain extent oriented with regard to each other. True, this orientation is not yet stable and is preserved only so long as the directive forces within the coazervate are operating, nevertheless we witness here the origin of some, though still very labile, elementary organization. Thus, in coazervates the behavior is subject not only to the simplest laws of organic chemistry but also to the newly superimposed colloid-chemical order. However, even this higher order of relationship is still insufficient to secure the origin of primary living things. To initiate life, it was necessary for coazervates and similar colloidal systems to acquire, in the course of their evolution, properties of a yet higher order, properties subject to biological laws.

CHAPTER VII

ORIGIN OF PRIMARY ORGANISMS

So long as there was no delimitation between the organic substance and its aqueous environment; in other words, so long as it was still dissolved in the waters of the original hydrosphere of the Earth, the evolution of organic substance could be considered only in its entirety. But as soon as organic substance became spatially concentrated into coazervate droplets or bits of semi-liquid colloidal gels; as soon as these droplets became separated from the surrounding medium by a more or less definite border, they at once acquired a certain degree of individuality. The future history of coazervate droplets could now follow different courses. Their fate was now dependent not only on external conditions of the medium but also on their own specific physico-chemical structure or organization. To be able to trace the further course of this evolution of organic substances, we must first of all get a clear conception of the nature of this organization and of how this may affect the velocity and direction of the chemical processes.

As was already discussed in a previous chapter, the organic substances serving as material for the formation of colloidal structures can react with each other in a great variety of ways. They possess tremendous chemical potentialities, and we focused attention on these inherent chemical potentialities when the origin of high-molecular compounds in the primary hydrosphere of the Earth was considered. At that time we were little interested in the velocity of these processes because the evolution of organic substances undoubtedly took place over a very long period of time and even very slow chemical transformations could play a dominant role.

Indeed, it is very characteristic of organic substances to utilize their chemical potentialities extremely sluggishly, i.e., with very small velocity. There are various reactions which require months and even years for their completion. For this reason the organic chemist must always resort in his syntheses to powerful reagents, such as acids, alkalies, halogens, etc., with which to whip up and accelerate the progress of the chemical interaction between organic substances.

In modern chemical practice, both in the laboratory and in industry, special accelerators of chemical reactions and various catalysts have found wide application. By this we mean the introduction of substances which, when present in the reaction mixture even in very small amounts, increase tremendously the velocity of various reactions. It is characteristic for catalysts that they do not change the course of the reaction and are found in the same quantity at the conclusion as at the beginning of the reaction. The catalyst acts only by its presence, without becoming a part of the composition of the reaction products. For this reason a very small quantity of catalyst suffices to cause very large masses of substance to react very rapidly with each other.

Many different substances are used as catalysts and their number increases all the time as chemistry develops new demands for them. The ability to act as catalysts is undoubtedly characteristic for the majority, if not actually for all, substances. In particular, the various metals (platinum, mercury, copper, iron, cobalt, nickel, zinc, etc.) and their oxides; various ions, especially hydrogen and hydroxyl ions; halogens and a number of salts are widely used as catalysts in organic chemistry. All the reactions discussed in Chapter V, which are based on the interaction of organic substances with water, are greatly accelerated in the presence of various catalysts. Thus, for instance, the reaction of condensation of formaldehyde is catalyzed by the hydroxyl ion (OH^-) by the addition of lime or chalk. Hydrolysis is greatly accelerated by the presence of acids (hydrogen ions, H^+). The ions of iron and other metals also play an important role in oxidation-reduction reactions. There can be no doubt that in the transformation of organic substances in the primitive hydrosphere of the Earth the phenomenon of catalysis played an important part in so far, of course, as the waters always contained the enumerated substances, and the dissolved organic substances would always come in contact with every sort of mineral deposit.

In view of the exceptional theoretical and practical significance of catalysis, it is now attracting the attention of many investigators. However, to this day we have neither a well clarified conception nor a generally accepted theory as to the nature of this phenomenon. Perhaps no unified theory of catalysis is even possible, the acceleration of the reaction in different instances resulting from different causes. In particular, it is necessary to differentiate homogeneous catalysis, occurring in gases or in solutions, and heterogeneous catalysis, occurring on the surface of solid substances. In the first instance, the acceleration of the

reaction results from the formation of an unstable intermediate compound, the substrate-catalyst, which decomposes rapidly setting free the reaction end-products, while
the catalyst is restored in its original condition. In heterogeneous catalysis the adsorption of substrate on the catalyst
surface plays a very important part. Further transformation of the substrate takes place under the influence of specifically active centers of this surface. More detailed
information on catalysis will be found in P. Sabatier's[1]
book "Catalysis in Organic Chemistry" or in Rideal and
Taylor's[2] "Catalysis in Theory and Practice."

Chemical reactions between organic substances in the organism of animals and plants take place with very great
speed. Life could not proceed at such an overwhelming
tempo, as it actually does, were not these reactions so rapid.
In the last analysis, all vital phenomena such as nutrition,
respiration, growth, etc., result from the chemical transformation of organic substances. Outside the living organism, in the chemist's test tube or flask, these substances
react very slowly, indeed. The cause of the great velocity
of reaction in living cells is to be found in the great
variety of specifically acting catalyzers, the so-called
enzymes, present in the cell. The discovery of enzymes
dates far back and their enormous biological significance
was appreciated also a long time ago. Without enzymes
there can be no life. There is no living organism, no viable
cell which is not fitted out with a complete set of such
catalyzers. As soon as conditions become unfavorable for
enzymatic activity, the vital processes are either greatly in-
hibited (anabiosis) or even stop entirely.

It is easy to understand, therefore, that enzymes have

aroused great interest and received close attention from numerous investigators[3]. Enzymes have been obtained long ago from living cells either as aqueous extracts or as dry preparations, and under suitable conditions can be preserved for a considerable time. The dry preparations can be easily dissolved in water and in the form of solutions, without the aid of living cells, they manifest the same activity as in the organism. As a result of many researches by outstanding investigators it can be stated with certainty that enzymes are catalytically active substances. They differ from other catalysts, first, by their biological origin, and, secondly, by the specificity and exceptional vigor of their action. There are many inorganic and organic substances which can accelerate reactions just as the enzymes do, but there is no comparison between them so far as the effectiveness of the catalytic action is concerned. For instance, the hemoglobin pigment of blood catalyzes the oxidation of polyphenols by hydrogen peroxide, but Willstätter's peroxidase preparation is 30,000 times more powerful catalytically than an equal quantity of pure crystalline hemoglobin. The hydrogen ion hydrolyzes cane sugar just as the enzyme invertase does, but according to Euler yeast invertase splits the sugar ten million times as energetically as does the inorganic catalyst, the hydrogen ion (H^+). Such examples could be easily multiplied, but even these few will suffice to show that enzymes of living cells represent an exceptionally complete and extremely rational (if one may be permitted to describe it so) apparatus for the acceleration of chemical interactions between organic substances. In spite of the great advance in chemical technology, we have not as yet succeeded in creating such powerful accelerators as are at the disposal of living nature. What imparts to enzymes this exceptionally energetic activity and how did such a perfect apparatus come to exist in the living cell?

It is known from the practical application of inorganic catalysts that frequently a mixture of two or more catalysts acts much more powerfully than either one separately. Occasionally even the addition of substances, which themselves are very inactive, enhances greatly the activity of the catalysts. The effect of oxides added to metallic catalysts (iron, nickel, cobalt, etc.) of hydrogenation may serve as an example of such secondary catalyst-promoters. Similarly, in the catalytic oxidation of ammonia the oxide of iron if it is combined with the oxide of bismuth may give as good results as contact with platinum. The addition of cerium oxide to osmium-asbestos increases the catalytic activity of the latter many times. In the hydrolysis of pyridine the addition of cerium oxide increases more than ten-fold the catalysis of the oxidation of hydrogen by nickel. A mixture of oxides of copper and manganese promotes with exceptional energy the oxidation of carbon monoxide even in the cold, etc. The enormous theoretical and practical significance of promoters is responsible for the great interest aroused by this phenomenon, and there is a very extensive special literature dealing with this problem, but we cannot go into this matter in greater detail. We wish only to refer to the work of A. Mittasch's school, which has accumulated a tremendous amount of material on this question, based on the very long experience gained in the laboratory of the Baden Aniline and Soda Industry, and to the work of H. Taylor devoted to the theory of promoter activity.

According to information accumulated during the past

several years, the activity of promoters is the more energetic the more closely they are united with the basic catalysts. A simple mechanical mixture of promoter and
catalyst is generally not very effective. For instance, it was
shown that MnO must be mixed with Fe_2O_3 before the
higher oxides can be reduced. There are some indications
that promoters apparently become incorporated into the
crystal lattice of the catalyst, and that in some instances
catalyst and promoter become united into a single complex
substance.

At the Sixth Mendelejev Congress in Kharkov (1932)
the author[4] expressed the view that natural enzymes likewise represent some such complexes. The enzyme particle
is thought to represent a firm combination of separate catalysts and promoters in such a manner as to impart an extraordinarily high catalytic activity to the whole. This view
is based on the results of R. Willstätter's[5] brilliant work on
the isolation and purification of enzymes. This work was
begun by Willstätter back in 1920, and in his experiments
he proceeded on the assumption that enzymatic activity is
a property belonging to individual substances. It was his
opinion, therefore, that it is necessary, first of all, to isolate
the enzymes from the organism in a chemically pure condition, and then to study their chemical nature by the usual
methods employed in the investigation of other organic
compounds.

Willstätter devised very excellent new procedures for
isolating enzymes and for purifying them from various contaminating admixtures. In this way he succeeded in obtaining preparations possessing overwhelming, hitherto unknown catalytic activity. But his preparations were still

mixtures of substances rather than pure chemical compounds. Attempts at further purification of the preparations or of separating them into their components encountered insurmountable difficulties, inasmuch as each new step in this direction brought about a decrease in the total enzyme activity; in other words, purification resulted in an inactivation of the enzyme.

This perplexing fact is easily explained by the intricate structure of the enzymes. In living cells the separate components of the natural enzyme complex (catalysts and promoters) are intimately associated and in the usual procedures for separating enzymes from organisms or from their tissues the complex as a whole is obtained. In the process of isolation of this complex it can be freed to a certain degree from various accidental admixtures which have no catalytic effect. In this way Willstätter actually obtained highly active preparations. But as soon as the purification procedure is followed still further and the enzyme complex is broken up into its component parts, the activity of the system as a whole is lost or, at any rate, is very much decreased. In a number of instances the activity could be again restored by mixing the separated components. This, of course, is very easily accomplished where the complex is made up of chemically different substances, and particularly where one of the components is some inorganic compound or ion. For instance, the salivary amylase, an enzyme which converts starch to sugar, always contains a certain amount of inorganic salts, particularly of chlorides. In purifying this enzyme by the usual procedure, i.e., by precipitation with alcohol from aqueous solution, the inorganic component of the enzyme complex is fully retained even when the precipitation is repeated many times. However, the salt can be removed by other methods, such as dialysis (Bierry, Giaja et Henri[6]) or adsorption (Biedermann[7, 8]), in which case the amylase freed from the inorganic salts becomes entirely inactive. Its ability to split starch, however, is at once restored upon the addition to the organic moiety of the enzyme preparation of a small amount of sodium chloride or of some other chloride. According to Biedermann the inorganic salts of the amylase hydrolyze starch, though they do this very slowly, but the organic component of amylase by itself (i.e. without the chlorides) does not hydrolyze starch. The hydrolytic activity of the salts from the enzyme preparation is, however, increased many thousand times when they are combined with the organic component. Thus, the enzymatic activity belongs to a "chloride-amylase"[9] complex in which the catalyst proper is the inorganic salts, while the organic moiety increases tremendously, or promotes their action.

The complex nature of this enzyme is very obvious and can be easily demonstrated, but the situation is quite different where the enzymatic activity depends upon the combination of two or more substances, which are closely related by their chemical nature. The artificial separation of such a complex and especially its combination presents unwonted difficulties, as one can easily surmise. Still, in some instances this can be done under laboratory conditions. Then, again, there are instances where each component of the enzyme complex is produced by different cells and are, therefore, found separately under natural conditions.

An interesting example of this natural separation of components was discovered by Shepovalnikov[10] in the ac-

tivation of trypsin by enterokinase. Trypsin, the enzyme
from the pancreatic gland, cannot split native proteins
when it is obtained directly from the pancreatic juice, but
acquires this property on the addition to it of a substance
secreted by the mucous membrane of the small intestines
(enterokinase). According to the researches of Waldschmidt-Leitz[11], trypsin and enterokinase combine with
each other in definite proportions and a new enzyme complex results which now splits native proteins. This complex
is fairly stable but Waldschmidt-Leitz[12] succeeded in separating it again into its original components by means of
adsorption. The trypsin set free from the enterokinase, as
might have been expected, has lost its proteolytic activity.
Nevertheless, the activity can be restored once more by re-
combining the separate components, i.e., the trypsin and the
enterokinase. This experiment illustrates that, as a result
of combining two different substances, new enzymatic properties arise which are entirely absent when either component is used separately.

Theorell presented at the XV International Physiological
Congress in Leningrad (1935) an interesting example of
the formation of an enzyme from separate components. He
broke up the respiration enzyme into its component parts
and then regenerated the enzyme by combining the individual components.

It is interesting to compare these observations on natural enzymatic complexes with the various attempts described in recent years for creating artificial enzymatic
models, i.e., catalyzers which not only reproduce enzymatic
reactions qualitatively but actually resemble enzymes in the
specificity of their action. All these attempts deal primarily

with the construction of some more or less elaborate complex. For instance, Langenbeck[13] obtained a model for carboxylase, an enzyme which splits pyruvic acid into carbon dioxide and acetaldehyde. He showed that even the simplest amines exert a weak carboxylase effect which, however, can be increased manifoldly by successive and systematic introduction of new and very complex atomic groupings into their molecules. Recently, Bredig[14] and his collaborators constructed a new enzymatic model from diethyl-amino compounds adsorbed on cotton fibers. This artificial complex catalyzes the splitting of carbon dioxide from beta-keto-carbonic acids and aids in the synthesis of mandelic nitrile from hydrocyanic acid and benzaldehyde. It is interesting to note that Bredig obtained asymmetric reaction products (i.e., substances which rotate the plane of polarized light) with his enzyme model.

We have been dwelling at some length on these instances, because they illustrate quite clearly the idea of an inner chemical organization and how this may affect the velocity and direction of chemical transformations. So long as the separate components are scattered they exert very slight catalytic action, but when combined into a single complex they acquire extraordinary enzymatic activity. This activity depends not merely on the fact that these substances are spatially together, but is more or less determined by the position which they occupy with regard to each other, by the definite arrangement of the molecules in the crystal lattice as was shown to be the case for inorganic catalysts and promoters, or on the surface of protein colloidal carriers as in the case of enzymes.

We must, therefore, conclude that the naturally occurring

high-molecular enzymes of living cells are not individual chemical compounds but complexes made up of numerous catalysts and promoters. The tremendous power of enzymatic activity must be attributed exclusively to a favorable arrangement of components in this complex, which, of course, could not have arisen fortuitously but only as a result of a long evolution of living organisms. In this process ever new catalysts and promoters must have been gradually added on secondarily to the simple and not very active primitive catalyst. This greatly complicated the nature of the whole complex but, at the same time, endowed it with ever increasing activity and more perfect adaptation to the special function which enzymes fulfill in living cells. In this way the living cell acquired the ability to accomplish quickly and with very minute amounts of enzyme such transformations of matter, which previously could have been brought about only with very great quantities of catalyst. The inner chemical organization became strengthened in the process of natural selection, insuring a gradual evolution which finally culminated in those highly perfected enzyme systems existing at the present time. To a certain extent it is even possible to follow this evolutionary process by studying the enzymatic systems of the existing lower and higher organisms. Thus, according to Kuhn's [15] investigations, invertase obtained from various yeast manifests great differences in activity. The studies made on the natural proteolytic systems [16] from lower and higher plants and animals are likewise very interesting, since they show that proteases from lower forms are somewhat like prototypes of similar systems from the more highly developed organisms. It is, therefore, quite possible that the latter may have evolved from the former in the course of a very long evolution which involved a slow rearrangement between catalysts and promoters.

A study of enzymatic systems reveals how the more complicated biological phenomena are built up from the simplest chemical reactions. By their nature enzymes represent a certain combination of chemical compounds, but their origin is definitely biological. Enzymes are produced only by secretion from living cells and, what is even more important, these enzymatic systems could not have been formed anywhere else under natural conditions. To develop such perfect combinations of catalysts and promoters, as we now witness in the case of plant peroxidase or yeast invertase, a definite direction of evolutionary processes was needed, and a natural selective process was required, which destroyed the unsuccessful combinations, retaining for further development only such complexes as would fulfill their function with the greatest celerity and efficiency.

But enzymes represent merely the earliest and simplest form of chemical organization of living matter. Considered entirely as an isolated phenomenon, a single reaction catalyzed by this or that enzyme could not have any deciding significance in the internal chemical economy of living cells. It assumes significance, however, only in conjunction with the long chain of chemical transformations of the substances of protoplasm, of which the particular reaction is only a single link. The chain of transformations is determined by a strict coordination of the particular reaction with all the other chemical transformations.

The organic substances found in living cells rarely originate there as the products of a single reaction. Generally they are formed by a correlation of a number of chemical reactions following one another in a perfectly definite order. Such vital phenomena as respiration, fermentation, growth, etc., are always associated with a long succession of chemical transformations, the separate events of which are related to each other in a very definite manner. As was already pointed out in Chapter V, this orderly succession of separate reactions leads ultimately to the formation of one or another product, and every change in the succession is equivalent to a radical alteration of the process as a whole. A harmonious coordination of velocities of the different reactions is prerequisite for the existence of this orderly succession, and this is possible only under the condition of strict regulation of the activity of each enzyme catalyzing a particular reaction. If, for instance, one was to prepare an artificial mixture of all the enzymes which promote the separate reactions constituting the respiratory process, he would still fail to reproduce respiration by means of this mixture. Individual reactions, such as oxidation-reduction, or hydrolysis, etc., will take place in this mixture, but the entire process will not be accomplished for the simple reason that the reaction velocities will not be properly and mutually coordinated.

The same thing occurs when we destroy mechanically the integrity of the living protoplasm, as by grinding it finely. The mixture thus obtained contains all the enzymes which were present also in the living cells, and all the substances which were previously acted upon in the course of biological processes. Nevertheless, the mixture no longer reproduces the chemical transformations observed in the living cell because it lacks a definite physico-chemical organization. This has been long known and acknowledged as evidence that the enzymatic activity of living cells proceeds differently than that of destroyed cells.

F. Hofmeister [17] called attention to this fact back in 1901 and attempted to explain the regulating action of the protoplasm as being due to "the chemical organization of the living cell." He thought that such organization resulted from the foam structure of protoplasm. The possession of a definite protoplasmic structure, in his opinion, makes it possible for the enzymes to be localized spatially and for their actions to become coordinated. With the destruction of the protoplasm this coordination is disturbed and the character of the enzymatic reactions is therefore also altered.

The hypothesis of a foam or alveolar structure of protoplasm was finally discarded, but the conception of a regulatory action of the cell based upon this idea has been retained and is still found in the physiology text books. Thus, Jost [18] compares the living cell to a chemical factory, where all chemical processes must be strictly isolated from each other. Each product must pass through a consecutive series of departments (a series of separate chemical reactions) before it becomes the finished article of manufacture (final metabolic product). V. Palladin [19] interpreted the regulatory action of protoplasm as being due to the fact that, as the need for the separate enzymes ceases, they are changed to an inactive condition and are "locked up," so to speak, until they are again needed. The bound enzymes are released by the protoplasm as the need for them arises. Kostychev [20] compares the enzymes to actors and the protoplasm to the stage director who calls them upon the scene at the proper moment and thus insures the smooth running of a complicated play.

But these views, of course, are merely comparisons or analogies, which, apart from effectively visualizing the process, offer little of substantial value for understanding the essence of this phenomenon of regulation of the enzymatic activity within the living cell.

It is very difficult to conceive how any particular protoplasmic structure can influence the work of enzymes. At the same time many physiological observations show that enzymatic activity changes radically as soon as the protoplasmic structure is altered. It is not even necessary to have a far-reaching destruction of the protoplasm, since often what may appear as a slight external influence will alter seriously the regulating ability of the protoplasm. We may refer to the experiments of Iljin [21] for an illustration of such a profound change in enzymatic activity of living cells. Iljin studied the amylase * of stoma cells from leaves of different plants, which are very favorable for observing enzyme activity within the uninjured live cell. As the starch contained in these cells is hydrolyzed, the osmotic pressure of the cellular juice increases very much owing to the transformation of the colloidal starch to sugar, and the shape of the cell also changes because of the consequent absorption of water. It is possible, therefore, to determine exactly the progress of starch hydrolysis by following the changes in shape of the stoma cells. Placing whole leaves or small pieces of a leaf in salt solutions, Iljin was able to detect a

---

* Amylase is an enzyme which breaks up, or hydrolyzes the starch molecule into its sugar (maltose) components.

very definite influence of electrolytes* on the rate of the enzymatic process. The sodium and potassium ions (Na $^+$, K $^+$) especially increase markedly the hydrolytic action of amylase, whereas calcium ions (Ca $^{++}$) inhibit it. The acidity of the cellular juice likewise has great influence. Careful consideration of these experiments reveals that the changes in enzyme activity is conditioned by alterations in the colloidal properties of the protoplasm which these electrolytes induce. The same may be said of the action of narcotics or other surface active substances ** which have practically no *in vitro* effect on the action of enzymes in solution, whereas even minute traces alter the enzymatic function of the living cell. The interesting experiments of E. Lesser [22] on the influence of narcotics on the hydrolysis of glycogen (or animal starch) in the frog's liver may be offered as an illustration. Under the action of various surface tension lowering substances there is a sudden increase in the formation of sugar in the liver cells. Lesser even succeeded in establishing a definite relationship between the surface tension lowering effect of the substance investigated and its influence on the work of cellular enzymes. Similar observations have been made also on plant organisms as, for instance, the greatly increased enzymatic action (catalase, peroxidase, reductase, etc.) which F. Denny [23] obtained in

* Substances like salts, acids and bases whose molecules split up into fragments, called ions, conduct an electric current. They are therefore known as electrolytes. The ions, unlike the original molecule, are electrically charged, the cations bearing charges of positive and anions charges of negative electricity.

** Surface active substance or surface tension lowering substance are synonymous terms. Certain substances can decrease the tension at the surface of contact. Such substances, for instance soaps, tend to accumulate in the surface layer, this phenomenon being designated as adsorption. See note on p. 58.

potatoes by means of ethylene-chlorhydrine. This narcotic has no effect on the enzymatic activity of the pressed plant juice and acts only on the enzymes of living cells. N. Ivanov and his collaborators [24] reported recently similar results on the effect of ethylene on ripening fruit.

But the enzyme activity of living cells can be very much altered even without the aid of outside substances. A mere disturbance in water balance of green leaves from different plants brings about a very marked activation of many enzymes. H. Molisch [25] kept in the dark leaves that were cut in two, one half being somewhat wilted but the other half having normal turgor. After five hours in the dark he found that the starch of the wilted halves almost completely disappeared, whereas in the control halves with a normal water content there was only a very slight change in the starch content. A similar phenomenon was studied by D. Tollenaar [26] and was recently described also by Iljin [27] in tobacco leaves, and in our Institute in Moscow we [28] found the same thing to hold true for the enzymes invertase and β-glucosidase in wilted tea leaves.

These influences do not act directly on the enzymes themselves, and the results on wilted leaves depend upon the fact that in every instance the colloidal state of the protoplasm is altered and the enzyme activity rises and falls with the alteration in physico-chemical structure of the protoplasm. Recently we have shown in a number of experiments [29] that the regulating action of the protoplasm is very intimately associated with the phenomenon of adsorption. The protoplasmic colloids adsorb the enzymes whereby their hydrolytic activity is decreased. On the contrary, as the enzymes are freed again their original activity is restored. These changes in enzyme activity in relation to their adsorption by colloids can be easily demonstrated without living cells, as in experiments with protein precipitates. Thus, we [30] investigated the phenomenon of inactivation of amylase solutions by the addition of precipitates obtained from egg albumin with tannin, nucleic acid and other substances. The colloidal gels or coazervates thus formed adsorb the amylase. At the same time the hydrolytic action of the enzyme is greatly diminished or even stopped. On filtering or centrifuging off the precipitate the solution, which previously contained the enzyme, no longer splits starch. The amylolytic activity, or the enzyme amylase, of the solution has disappeared. The precipitate, however, acts quite differently. It does not have the ability to liquefy or saccharify starch because, as was pointed out previously, the adsorbed enzyme is in a sense inactivated. But by certain procedures it is possible to free the enzyme from the precipitate and to put it back again into solution, whereby its hydrolytic action is once more restored in its original strength.

It was possible to show, furthermore, that the most varied physical and chemical factors (shaking, warming, acidifying, etc.) can inactivate enzymes, provided they induce the formation of protein precipitates which can adsorb the amylase. It is the adsorption, or the change from a microheterogeneous to a macroheterogeneous state of the enzyme, which is responsible for the decrease or even loss of its hydrolytic action. It is not necessary that the protein precipitate should be formed in the enzyme solution, since inactivation can be brought about even by the addition to it of a ready precipitate. The important thing is that the conditions in the medium should be favorable for the adsorption of the enzyme by the protein precipitate.

Investigations carried out by A. Bach[31], V. Palladin[32], by myself[33], and others have shown that each living cell contains practically a constant amount of enzymes which is characteristic for the cell. However, only enzymes in the microheterogeneous condition exert hydrolytic activity, while that part of the enzyme which is adsorbed or bound to the protoplasmic colloids does not manifest hydrolytic action. Under the influence of various physical and chemical factors the colloidal state, particularly the degree of dispersion of substances in the living cell, is radically though reversibly altered. With such alteration in the colloids, the relation between the free and bound portions of the enzyme is also altered, leading to an increase or decrease in the free enzyme which, of course, results in an increase or decrease of the hydrolytic activity. This is the reason why every factor which alters the colloidal condition or structure of the protoplasm so markedly affects the enzymatic activity, too. Such factors, as the electrolyte composition, surface tension activity, dehydration of the protoplasm, whether by drying or freezing, etc., are all very important in producing a marked change in the hydrolytic activity of the cellular enzymes, because by their influence on the colloidal state of the protoplasm they alter the relationship between the adsorbed and the free moiety of the enzymes.

Subsequent extensive investigations on a great variety of plants carried out in our Institute by Kursanov, Rubin and by Sissakjan[34] have shown that not only the extent of enzyme activity but also the nature of this activity may be altered by adsorption or liberation of the enzyme. A large number of facts has convinced us that certain substances can be split by hydrolyzing enzymes only if the latter are in the free microheterogeneous state. In the adsorbed state, on the contrary, they not only lose the ability to promote hydrolysis but begin to manifest the opposite, or synthesizing action, whereby the formation of substances is now achieved which previously were decomposed by the enzyme.

Thus our investigations revealed that in every living cell the enzymes exist in two forms, a dissolved moiety which has a hydrolyzing action and a moiety adsorbed to the cellular structures which has a synthesizing action. Many physiological characteristics of different plants are intimately associated with the ratio which exists between the hydrolyzing and synthesizing moieties of the enzyme in the particular cell. This relationship between the enzymatic actions is determined primarily by the species and variety of a given plant. For instance, in the roots of the sugar beet almost all the invertase is adsorbed and exerts a synthesizing action, but in the common beet a considerable portion of this enzyme acts hydrolytically. By means of various influences it is possible to affect the state of the enzyme and thus to shift the equilibrium between hydrolytic and synthetic processes prevailing under natural conditions [35].

In the investigation of enzymes, these are ordinarily separated from cells and tissues by simple extraction with water. The enzymes in the aqueous extracts are, of course, in a free microheterogeneous state and consequently display their full hydrolytic activity. For this reason we are particularly well familiar with that side of their activity which results in the splitting or breaking up of various complex organic substances. But enzymes, like all catalysts, may also act in the reverse direction, accelerating the synthesis or formation of new high-molecular compounds. Their synthesizing action is especially clearly manifested in the living cells, where the enzymes are bound by adsorption to the protoplasmic colloids. Any influence, which aids in leaching out the enzyme from its combination and thus sets it free, increases its hydrolytic activity and at the same time decreases its synthetic action. This, of course, results in a preponderance of decomposition processes and leads to the cleavage of substances which make up the protoplasm. On the other hand, the increased adsorption of enzymes by cellular structures turns the resultant of the opposed forces in the direction of synthesis of new compounds, resulting in the growth of the cell through accumulation of substance.

Thus a change in the physico-chemical properties of protoplasmic colloids can affect in a very definite way the extent and the direction of enzymatic action. A definite colloidal structure of the living cell affects the work of enzymes and regulates their activity. However, it must not be assumed that adsorption and elution of the enzymes are the only mechanisms for the autoregulation of biochemical processes. We dwelt upon this aspect of the problem and discussed this phenomenon at some length because it throws light on the connection existing between protoplasmic structure and the force of enzymatic action.

One can mention, of course, several other factors affecting the velocity and the direction of chemical processes occurring in the protoplasm. In recent years the problem of

the influence of the electrical potential of oxidative processes, the so-called oxidation-reduction potential, on the
course of cleavage and synthesis of proteins has been carefully studied. It was established by the work of Willstätter [36],
Waldschmidt-Leitz [37], Grassmann [38], etc., that cathepsin, a
cellular proteolytic enzyme which splits native proteins,
can exert its action only under very definite conditions. Just
as trypsin from the pancreas can only act in the presence
of enterokinase, so does cathepsin hydrolyze native proteins only when activated by the special substance glutathione. Glutathione consists of three amino acids, one of
which is the sulfur containing cysteine or cystine. These
two amino acids differ from each other in that cysteine contains the sulfur in the reduced state as SH (sulfhydryl),
whereas in cystine the sulfur is in the oxidized S — S form,
the change from one to the other being reversible:

$$\underset{2\ SH}{\overset{R_1}{|}} \rightleftarrows \underset{S}{\overset{R_1}{|}} - \underset{S}{\overset{R_1}{|}} + 2\ H$$

The glutathione likewise may exist in two forms, the reduced (GSH) or oxidized (GS — SG):

$$\underset{2\ SH}{\overset{G}{|}} \rightleftarrows \underset{S}{\overset{G}{|}} - \underset{S}{\overset{G}{|}} + 2\ H$$

Only the reduced glutathione can activate cathepsin. If
the oxidation-reduction potential of a living cell is very
high, its glutathione will be entirely in the oxidized form,
the cathepsin will be inactive and the protoplasmic proteins, therefore, will not be hydrolyzed. On the contrary,
as the oxidative processes become weaker the glutathione
changes to the reduced form, which activates the enzymatic

cleavage of proteins. This in turn leads to a change or even destruction of protoplasmic structures. Other enzymes adsorbed on the proteins are set free and thus the hydrolytic activity with regard to a number of other substances is sharply increased. Ultimately all this may end in an extensive autolysis or self-digestion with the resulting dissolution of protoplasmic structures and complete destruction of the living cell. Such autolysis actually occurs in animal tissues when, for instance, their blood supply is cut off. This stops the respiration, which normally requires oxygen brought by the hemoglobin of the blood. The same may be also observed in plant cells and tissues whose oxidative processes are lowered or stopped by one means or another. In this respect the investigations of K. Mothes[39] are very interesting, because they demonstrate how the cleavage or synthesis of proteins in green leaves are regulated in this manner.

In the living, non-injured protoplasm phenomena of decomposition likewise occur to a certain extent, but their velocity is very definitely related to the velocity of constructive processes, which predominate and thus furnish the necessary conditions for a long and stable existence of the whole system. We wish to emphasize that the dynamic stability of living things should not be construed in the sense that there is no decomposition of organic compounds or destruction of colloidal structures. On the contrary, it is very well known that such decomposition does and must occur since the energy thereby set free is absolutely necessary for syntheses and for the formation of new substances. But in protoplasm, owing to the existence of a definite physico-chemical organization, the chemical processes are so reciprocally coordinated that a decomposed substance is at once replaced by a newly synthesized one, and a structure which had been destroyed is immediately restored. Thus, there is a constant exchange of substances, but synthesis always predominates over destruction, and this creates the dynamic stability of the system.

This type of stability is not to be confused with the static stability of crystals or similar formations. If a parallel can be drawn at all, it is with different types of simple dynamic systems whose very existence is determined by the movement of matter and by the energy changes associated with it. For instance, a stream of water under definite constant conditions may retain its form within certain limits for a certain length of time. The form depends upon a number of directive forces, which orient the movement of water molecules in this system in a definite manner. But the existence of the stream of water is determined by the circumstance that all the time new particles of water pass through it with a definite velocity. By quick freezing it is possible to fix the definite form of the stream, but the resulting mass of ice is no longer a dynamic system and its stability is purely static.

Analogous to the stream of water or to the flame of a gas burner, protoplasm also exists only so long as new matter and its chemical energy pass through it in an uninterrupted flow. A great variety of chemical substances enter the cell from the surrounding medium and are subjected to profound changes and transformations. The resulting molecules and particles become mutually oriented under the influence of definite directive forces and form mobile colloidal systems, which become part of the physico-chemical structure of the protoplasm. But alongside this assimilatory process there is also a breaking down of protoplasmic structures and substances which make up its composition, the products of destruction being eliminated back into the surrounding medium.

The enzymes merely accelerate the separate chemical reactions which take place there, making the entire system more dynamic. But they can equally well increase the constructive or the destructive processes. Thanks to the presence of a definite physico-chemical organization resulting from adsorption, permeability, etc., the separate chemical processes are brought into harmonious correlation, and the normal living cell is a dynamically stable system in which constructive processes predominate over the destructive processes. The cell is either maintained in a steady state or it actually grows. On the contrary, if the physico-chemical organization of the cell is disturbed, the destructive processes usually gain preponderance and the protoplasm begins to autolyze, its structure breaks up and its components dissolve.

The artificial coazervates, which we can obtain by mixing together different colloidal solutions, and the analogous formations, which have originated in the hydrosphere of the Earth, do not have and never have had the highly efficient physico-chemical organization described above. They lose their structure comparatively easily and go back to the solution state. One does not, therefore, find here any appreciable dynamic stability, but even in the instability of these coazervate systems exceptional possibilities for further evolution lie dormant.

Let us assume that in some archaic water basin on our planet coazervate droplets appeared as a result of the mixing of solutions of high-molecular organic substances. What would be the fate of such droplets? As was mentioned before, such colloidal formations are very unstable. Let the temperature of the surrounding medium undergo a substantial change, or let the hydrogen ion concentration approach the isoelectric point of one of the coazervate components, or let the salt composition in some part of the basin become unfavorable, and the coazervate droplet, after a more or less brief existence, will at once decompose, dissolve and change back to the primary sol, the molecules of the component colloids dispersing again in the surrounding solvent. The short-lived existence of the individual coazervate droplet will have come to a sudden end.

On the other hand, it is also possible that a situation may arise, where the external and internal conditions would be favorable for further and more or less durable existence of the droplet. Under given concrete conditions of the surrounding medium it would remain stable for a definite time. To understand the nature of this stability we must consider it in relation to the familiar artificial coazervates. As was pointed out in a previous chapter, such colloidal formations are usually obtained on mixing solutions of artificially purified and more or less distinct substances (gelatin, gum arabic, albumin, nucleic acid, etc.). These substances contain neither enzymes nor other sufficiently active catalysts and the chemical transformations within these artificial coazervates proceed at a very slow rate. During the comparatively brief period of observation no material chemical changes can take place within these co-azervates which, to a certain degree, lends them static character.

This static condition, however, is only apparent. Since the substances making up the coazervates do react with each other, even though very slowly, some chemical transformations must occur after long existence of these colloidal formations. This manifests itself especially strongly in coazervate droplets suspended not in pure water but in aqueous solutions of various substances. In that case it absorbs from the outside medium substances which react more or less rapidly with the materials constituting the coazervates, and the chemical composition of the coazervate must, therefore, gradually change.

These changes may contribute either to increased stability of the coazervate or, on the contrary, may cause the coazervate, even under constant external conditions, to lose its original structure, to break up and return to the original hydrophil sol state. At the same time the chemical processes within the coazervate may take the direction either towards assimilation or towards gradual degradation (by oxidation or hydrolysis) of the substances making up the coazervates. If the latter processes predominate, the coazervate will sooner or later disappear entirely. On the other hand, if the synthetic, assimilatory processes are the stronger, the coazervate will either keep its original mass or it may actually increase in size. In this case we may speak of a certain stability of the coazervate, but this stability is dynamic in character and is determined by a correlation between the velocities of the processes of assimilation and degradation.

This, of course, holds true for the natural coazervate

droplet which was suspended not in pure water but in solutions of a great variety of organic and inorganic substances. It absorbed these substances from the surrounding medium and, therefore, its composition must have been changing gradually. These changes were the more significant because the absorbed substances reacted with the coazervate substances, and though the interactions proceeded exceedingly slowly they would ultimately result in essential changes in the composition and structure of the droplet. The foundation was thus laid for the processes of assimilation and degradation. Coazervate droplets, in which the former counterbalanced or even overbalanced the latter, were the only ones which were stable under the existing environmental conditions. On the contrary, droplets in which the chemical forces worked chiefly in the direction of degradation were doomed to disappear sooner or later. The life history of such coazervates terminated rather quickly and they did not, therefore, play an important part in the further evolution of organic matter. In this way a natural selection of coazervates originated in its most primitive and simplest form, only the dynamically most stable colloidal systems securing for themselves the possibility of continued existence and evolution. Any deviation from this stability resulted in a more or less rapid loss and destruction of the individual system.

With the background of "natural selection" and by its strict control, further modifications in chemical organization of these colloidal formations must have proceeded along definite lines. To a certain extent, we may imagine that the origin of primitive enzyme systems followed a similar course of transformations. In naturally arising coazervate droplets, contrary to what happens in the artificial coazervates, inorganic catalysts, such as hydrogen ions, iron oxide, etc., undoubtedly assume an important part, accelerating the definite chemical changes within the coazervates. If these effects promote assimilatory processes the droplets containing catalysts gain a certain advantage as regards the speed of their growth. This advantage could be increased even much more if through absorption of new substances into the coazervates some inorganic or organic promoter became more or less successfully united to the catalysts and thus greatly increased their effectiveness. The enhanced speed of a given chemical reaction within the coazervate droplet made the colloidal system more highly dynamic.

Of course, the mere gain in dynamic force and the acceleration of chemical reactions within the coazervate could not determine the further evolution of such formations, but the increasing rate of chemical transformation was all the time regulated by a "natural selection" of newly arising formations. If the increase in the rate of a given reaction so affected the coordination between assimilation and degradation as to promote the latter, such an imperfect system would become mechanically unfitted for further evolution and would perish prematurely.

But we must not underestimate the enormous significance of the increase in dynamic force of coazervate systems in the process of their evolution. Previously, in discussing the resultant velocity of all the combined reactions, little attention had been paid to this factor. But in considering not the absolute amount of time required for a given phase of development but rather the relative velocity of reactions in isolated, individual systems, the coordination of the velocities assumes foremost significance, because this determines their dynamic stability. At a given stage of development the very process of evolution of organic systems depended upon the coordination of the growth velocities of separate individual coazervates. Each coazervate droplet increased in weight and volume the more rapidly the more perfectly its physico-chemical organization was adapted to this end. Every new change in this organization, if progressive in nature, in the sense that it promoted more rapid absorption of dissolved substances and consequent growth of the coazervate, furnished further impulses to more vigorous expansion. On the contrary, even stable coazervate droplets, in which the tempo of chemical transformation was slowed down, were retarded in their growth and became progressively less important in the total mass of coazervates. A peculiar competition had thus arisen among coazervate systems as regards the velocity of their growth.

Naturally, it must not be imagined that every coazervate droplet could grow indefinitely as a single system. Sooner or later this would have to break up into separate droplets or fragments simply under the influence of external mechanical forces, or this could result from the action of surface tension forces. Incidentally, such fragmentation would be advantageous from the point of view of further growth of the coazervate, since it would establish a more favorable relation between surface and mass and thus increase the absorption of dissolved substances. Therefore, a coazervate droplet endowed with an ability to divide had a certain definite advantage over the others.

The daughter droplets resulting from mechanical division have the same physico-chemical organization as the mother droplet, since they all represent portions of the same original system. They could each undergo changes which would either increase or decrease their chances in the growth competition. This would result not only in a gradual increase in the mass of organized substance on the Earth's surface, but, and this is even more important, the quality of the substance would change in a very definite direction.

The simplest organic coazervates with their unstable elementary structure were destined sooner or later to disappear from the face of the Earth, to disintegrate and to return to the original solution state. Their nearest descendants, too, although they have already developed some stability, will soon drop out of the procession unless they acquire the ability to accomplish chemical reactions quickly. Only those systems continue to grow and evolve whose structure has undergone profound changes and which have developed a complex enzymatic apparatus enabling them to transform chemically and to assimilate absorbed substances with extraordinary rapidity. At the same time, the coordination of enzymatic processes, upon which the high degree of dynamic stability depends, becomes more and more perfected. The separate chemical processes become so regulated that new substances immediately take the place of those destroyed, and new structures immediately replace those worn out. The process of "competition in growth velocity" results in a quantitative preponderance of such systems which are best adapted to their environmental conditions and possess the most perfect organization. But the further the growth process of organic matter advances and the less free organic material remains dissolved in the Earth's hydro-sphere, the more exacting "natural selection" tends to be-come. A straight struggle for existence displaces more and more the competition in growth velocity. A strictly biologi-cal factor now comes into play.

This new factor naturally raised the colloidal systems to a more advanced stage of evolution. In addition to the al-ready existing compounds, combinations and structures, new systems of coordination of chemical processes ap-peared, new inner mechanisms came into existence which made possible such transformations of matter and of en-ergy which hitherto were entirely unthinkable. Thus sys-tems of a still higher order, the simplest primary organisms, have emerged.

CHAPTER VIII

FURTHER EVOLUTION OF PRIMARY
ORGANISMS

WITH THE APPEARANCE of primary organisms the question of the origin of life on Earth is, properly speaking, closed. What follows now is a history of the evolution of living creatures which passes through a succession of stages, from the origin of cells to the formation of multicellular organisms, and finally, to the appearance of reasoning beings. The thing of special interest for us is the first stage in the development of the highly differentiated cell with its nucleus, chondriosomes, protoplasts and other organoids, since here one can learn something of the earliest steps in the evolution of primary organisms. Unfortunately, however, the problem of the origin of the cell is perhaps the most obscure point in the whole study of the evolution of organisms. This is easily understandable since the evolutionary history is founded upon the investigation and comparison of the structure of contemporary living things, aided by data derived from a study of fossils (paleontology) and of individual development (ontogeny). But neither from paleontology nor from ontology can one learn anything concerning the development of the simplest living things. Furthermore, our information as to the intimate structure of these organisms is very limited, inasmuch as the direct study of the inner structure is, for purely technical reasons, very difficult. We know only that some organisms, bacteria in particular, do not possess well differentiated separate structures, such as are found in a completely formed normal cell. But we know absolutely nothing as to how these structures were formed, how the nucleus originated, how the protoplasm became differentiated, etc., and on this score we can only advance general hypotheses of greater or less degree of probability.

Mention will be given to only a few of the most noteworthy views regarding the origin of the cell. Kozo-Poljanski[1] in his "Outline of a Theory of Symbiogenesis" develops the idea that the cell resulted from the symbiosis of simplest living organisms. In recent years Keller[2], discussing the problem of the origin of the cell, drew a parallel between the multicellular organisms and the cell. "The multicellular organism cannot be regarded simply as the sum total of cells, a mere congeries of unicellular organisms. The cells are more or less profoundly altered, having lost important old properties and acquired many new ones. . . . Similarly in the cell nucleus we have a system consisting of the residues of primitive living units which have been altered in an extraordinary way and highly specialized. . . . We are developing the view that at some distant time in its history the cellular nucleus passed through a stage when it existed as a colony of elementary living units similar to the colony stage through which the multicellular organism passed. Bacteriophages and genes are the remnants of those living units."

It is possible and, perhaps, even probable that the cell nucleus did originate from such primary living units not directly but through an intermediate stage of more complex living things, like the bacteria.

"Protoplasm perhaps still represents a drop of that organic medium in which the first beginnings of living things
appeared; to be sure, altered and modified to an extraordinary degree under the organizing influence of the cell nucleus. . . . Chlorophyll grains also must have been at one
time independent living units, simpler than the cell itself,
but containing the green substance, chlorophyll. Even now
we find organisms of this description, namely, the chloro-
bacteria." By way of summary Keller draws the following
picture of the development of a vegetable cell: "In the mass
of jelly which was to become the protoplasm a colony of
colorless living units existed which later was transformed
into the nucleus. Other living organisms, colored green by
a substance related to chlorophyll, likewise became incorporated into this mass. . . . This symbiosis of organisms,
which was at first accidental, gradually became elaborated
into a most intimate and permanent system in which the
previously independent organisms acquired the character
of organs of a single whole, the cell." In all these hypotheses the idea that the living cell, as a system of a higher
order, is compounded from the simplest living things, received fullest expression.

From the viewpoint developed in the preceding chapters
it seems much more probable that the origin of the isolated
nucleus, chondriosome, plastid, etc., is only the external visible expression of a gradual unfolding and perfection of an
inner physico-chemical structure and organization of colloidal formations. The very ephemeral initial orientation
of molecules could acquire by an evolutionary process a
more stable character and serve as the starting point for
the formation of complexes and structures more or less

easily distinguishable under the microscope. Differentiation of these complexes in the total protoplast mass came about gradually in the evolution of living organisms. Therefore, in our simplest organisms, for instance in bacteria, we find this still at a very low stage of development and comparatively poorly expressed. It is well known that the nuclear substance of bacteria is not concentrated into a single formation but is dispersed as very tiny particles throughout the protoplasm. Similarly, the structure of the nuclear apparatus of the blue-green algae is much less definite than of organisms at a higher stage of the evolutionary process. To a certain extent we can even follow the gradual elaboration of the cellular structure in the course of phylogenetic development of organisms (evolution of nucleus, plastid, etc.). *But we must not lose sight of the fact that these formations are but the visible reflections of the inner physico-chemical structures, which determine the course of vital processes and of the physiological behavior of the cell.* Only a comparative study of this inner physico-chemical structure could throw light on the course of the gradual development of primary living things. Unfortunately our present technique of investigation would not permit us to perceive directly this inner physico-chemical organization of the protoplast. This inability to observe directly is not only due to the fact that we are dealing with magnitudes approaching molecular sizes. The structures themselves are too complex and, what is even more important, too mobile to be actually directly perceivable. We must search, therefore, for other methods which will make it possible to penetrate the intimate inner structure of the simplest living things.

The comparative study of enzyme complexes and enzyme systems from different species of organisms seems to offer such a method, because the enzyme represents the primary elementary form of a biologically organized substance. As was pointed out previously, enzymes did not arise all at once but developed gradually in the evolutionary process by a coordination of catalysts and promoters. The degree of its perfection and the effectiveness of its action are determined by this coordination or organization. Therefore, the comparative investigation of the nature and activity of enzymes obtained from organisms at different stages of evolution can aid us, to a certain extent, in unraveling the changes which these elementary cellular "organs" undergo in the development of living things.

Unfortunately we possess only a few cursory bits of information on this subject. Grassmann [3] made a most interesting attempt at a comparative study of proteolytic systems (protein-splitting enzymes) of high and low organisms. These systems represent a combination of several enzymes such as proteinases, polypeptidases, aminopolypeptidases, dipeptidases, etc. The character of the action of these systems depends upon the mutual coordination of the separate enzymes as well as on the influence of additional substances, the activators. The study of this problem leads to the conclusion that the proteolytic systems of the lowest organisms are directly related to the protease systems of higher plants as well as to the proteolytic enzymes of animal cells. The constitution and functional division of the simplest proteolytic systems correspond to the more primitive development of lower organisms. On the contrary, the systems from higher organisms are correspondingly more highly organized, having resulted from a gradual perfection of the simplest proteolytic systems.

But the sum total of enzymes in the living cell does not, of course, reflect fully the inner physico-chemical structure of the simplest organisms, the enzymes representing merely their primary elementary structure. Therefore, the study of separate enzymes or of whole enzyme systems is not enough to comprehend the complexity of the inner physico-chemical structure of the protoplast. As was pointed out before, this structure determines the "regulatory action" of the protoplasm as a result of which the separate enzymatic reactions are correlated harmoniously into the long chain of chemical transformations constituting the processes of nutrition, fermentation, respiration, growth, etc. A disturbance of this organization disturbs also the connection between the separate chemical processes. Alteration of the inner physicochemical structure also changes the sequence in which one reaction follows the other and, therefore, changes the character of the entire biochemical process. It is in this manner that organization determines the course of vital phenomena. On the other hand, through the study of the biochemical processes in different organisms we can form some judgment of the inner physico-chemical organization and of its alterations in the process of evolution.

The comparative study of biochemical processes in living organisms allows one, to a certain extent, to perceive the gradual course of development of primary organisms. Just as the anatomist reconstructs the evolutionary development of animals by the comparative study of organs from different animals, so also can the biochemist form a conception of the consecutive stages passed by primary living things

in their evolution on the basis of chemical processes underlying various vital phenomena.

This comparative study of biochemical processes in living organisms is particularly significant from our point of
view because it furnishes a factual basis for testing the conclusions arrived at in previous chapters. All the intermediate forms of organization of substance transitional between primary organic compounds and simplest living
creatures have long since disappeared from the face of the
Earth as the result of a relentless natural selection. For this
reason we must make the constructions on the basis of a
study of physical and chemical properties of organic compounds and colloidal formations. We assumed that the external conditions, under which organic substances evolved
from the moment the Earth's hydrosphere was first formed,
differed little from contemporary conditions, as we observe
them in nature or can reproduce in our laboratories. This
idea appears entirely justifiable. It was only necessary to
establish firmly the primary mass evolution of organic substances on the Earth's surface, and this we attempted to do
in Chapter IV. But having reached definite conclusions as
to the gradual evolution of primary living things, it is very
interesting now to check these conclusions by a comparative
study of biochemical processes occurring in organisms living at the present time.

As was shown previously, primary organisms could exist
and grow only by virtue of absorption and assimilation of
organic substances dissolved in the surrounding aqueous
medium. The organization or inner chemical apparatus permitting assimilation of these substances must have existed,
therefore, from the very moment these primary organisms

came into existence. This must have inhered in the very foundation of their structure and consequently organisms living at the present time must still be endowed with that apparatus. Indeed, with few and readily explainable exceptions, the ability to use organic substances as nutriment is found in absolutely all living things, although many have long ago become adapted to independent nourishment with inorganic substances.

Most of the species of organisms now living are generally *heterotrophic,* i.e., they are capable of using only organic compounds for nourishment. Among them are found not only all the highest and the lowest animals but also the great majority of bacteria and all fungi. This fact in itself is extremely significant because it would be very difficult to imagine that the origin of such a multifarious assortment of living things was associated with a regression or loss of the ability for *autotrophic* nourishment (i.e., of the ability to form proteins, etc., from inorganic salts and CO_2). It must be noted, furthermore, that this loss had to be very thoroughgoing since in none of the species enumerated are there any signs or rudiments of an apparatus to be found indicating that at some time in the past they were able to nourish themselves on inorganic substances. Such a supposition seems extremely improbable.

On the other hand, an examination of typical autotrophic organisms, particularly of the green plants, shows that they have retained to a considerable degree the ability to use preformed organic substances for their nourishment. This ability is especially well developed in the lowest representatives of the plant kingdom, in the various species of algae. Although these living things are thoroughly capable of au-

totrophic existence, experiments have shown that nourishing
them artificially on organic substances acts very favorably
on their development. It was definitely established by these
experiments that they assimilate the organic substance directly[4]. This may run parallel with the assimilation of carbon dioxide, but in some instances the latter may be easily
excluded and the algae converted to an exclusively saprophytic mode of existence. Especially luxurious growth on
organic substance was secured in the case of the blue-green
algae, such as *Nostok*[5], diatoms, and even some of the green
algae *(Spirogyra)*. Some species of Spirogyra and a number of the blue-green algae utilize organic matter of pol-
luted waters even under natural conditions. In any event,
they develop especially luxuriantly in the presence of organic compounds. All this goes to show that the enumerated
organisms at first possessed the ability of using organic nu-
trients and that only in the later evolutionary process new
organizational forms were superimposed over the basic
mechanism, making it possible for the algae to assimilate
inorganic substances. That is the reason why, under proper
conditions, they can go back so easily to their primitive
mode of nourishment.

But this holds true even for the higher green plants which
long ago became specialized to assimilate carbon dioxide
by photosynthesis. Apart from the fact that a large variety
of cells from higher plants (cells of roots, stalks, etc.) generally depend entirely on organic substances for their nutrition, even the highly differentiated chlorophyll bearing
cells, with their perfectly organized assimilatory apparatus,
have preserved the ability to use preformed organic substances as nutriment. This has been corroborated by obser-

vations on sprouts and etiolated leaves [6] as well as in experiments with pure sterile cultures of higher plants [7], which have been reared through the entire vegetative cycle in the dark in solution of sugar or of closely related substances. Furthermore, with the aid of the method developed by Mothes of introducing solutions of organic substances through the stomata directly to the parenchyma of green leaves it was established that parenchyma cells can assimilate such substances. In our own laboratory A. Kursanov demonstrated that by this method of "feeding" green leaves with sugar a considerable increase in the protein content can be achieved, inorganic compounds serving as the source of nitrogen.

It was already mentioned that many investigators have accepted and still do accept the view that carbon first appeared on the Earth's surface in the form of carbon dioxide. If this were really so, it would follow inevitably that the primary living organisms must have been capable of independent autotrophic nutrition, assimilating carbon dioxide as the primary source of carbon. But such an assumption is radically contradicted by all the data gathered from a study of the lowest organisms. This contradiction has attracted the attention of many biologists for a number of years. The primary origin of green organisms capable of such assimilation seemed most improbable since it is easy to show that the operation of photosynthesis requires a very highly developed organization. The discovery that some bacterial species are capable of using mineral substances alone for their nutrition naturally attracted special attention because these organisms can utilize the energy of such exothermic reactions as the oxidation of ammonia to nitrous and nitric acid, of sulfur to sulfuric acid, or of ferrous to ferric oxide. The nitrifying bacteria, the sulfur bacteria, the iron bacteria were very quickly proclaimed as the type of organisms which was the first to appear on the Earth. S. Winogradski expressed this opinion when he found that nitrifying microbes, which he was the first to discover, can exist in the absence of organic substance [8]. The same idea was developed in greater detail by Osborn [9] in his book "The Origin and Evolution of Life", as well as by V. Omeljanski [10].

The idea that these bacteria represent primary living things is based exclusively on the supposed primitiveness of their metabolism. Careful analysis, however, reveals that their metabolism is far from being primitive. These autotrophic organisms can be compared in this respect to the green autotrophes, even to the simplest algae. Just as photosynthesis requires a sufficiently highly developed protoplast organization, so can the carbon dioxide assimilation through chemical synthesis (nitrification, oxidation of sulfur, iron, etc.) proceed only in the presence of a highly differentiated structure, and this could result only from a long evolution of living organisms. Therefore, nothing principally new is added by the assumption that nitrifying and similar bacteria have had a primary origin. One could equally well make the assumption that the green autotrophes are of primary origin, if one accepts the viewpoint that only carbon dioxide is the primary material used in building up living things. Such an assumption, however, does not in the least remove the contradiction between the hypothesis and the data from the systematics of lower organisms, according to which microorganisms capable of chemical synthesis could have arisen only as a side branch from the main stem of evolution followed by all other living organisms.

Lotsy's book "Studies on the History of Botanical Species" may be cited as an illustration of this. He starts with the assumption that all the carbon on the Earth's surface was originally in the form of carbon dioxide, but the enormous systematic material at his disposal forces him, nevertheless, to acknowledge that the progenitors of the entire organic kingdom could only be the simplest living beings capable of thriving exclusively on organic substances. Lotsy [11] himself does not attempt to resolve this contradiction. But it can be easily avoided by discarding the preconceived and, as shown before, totally unfounded notion that carbon dioxide was the sole possible source of carbon for the primary living organisms. In that case, of course, the basis for considering nitrifying and other autotrophic microorganisms as prototypes of primary living things is also destroyed. A number of considerations, to be discussed later, convince us that this fairly isolated group of living things must have arisen at a relatively much later period in the evolution of the organic kingdom, probably at the same time when the first autotrophes capable of photosynthesis appeared.

The study of contemporary forms of living things brings us, therefore, to the conclusion that the ability to assimilate dissolved organic substances is possessed by nearly all organisms and is inherent in their constitution. In full accord with the idea developed in the preceding chapter, contemporary living things even of the lowest organization are already endowed with a completely formed and quite perfect apparatus, enabling them to obtain and to assimilate organic substances with extreme rapidity. The study of many bacterial species demonstrates that these microorganisms can assimilate dissolved organic substances even when these are present in exceedingly small concentration. Under natural conditions a number of microorganisms belonging to the plankton exist at the expense of organic substances found as mere traces in their surrounding medium.

This is not surprising in view of the well known fact that these microorganisms possess an extremely well developed capacity to absorb organic substances. Many experiments show that bacteria absorb such substances exceptionally well and rapidly. The assimilation and transformation of absorbed substances by microorganisms proceeds likewise very rapidly. According to V. Vernadski's [12] calculations, a single coccus with a volume of 10^{-12} cc. could under favorable conditions cover the entire globe in less than thirty six hours by a process of cell-division. This magnitude of the "growth energy" indicates the great speed with which organic substance can be assimilated by these simplest of organisms. There can be no question, therefore, that they must possess a well adjusted internal physico-chemical apparatus. This could have been achieved only as a result of a long continued natural selection of colloidal systems, which have reached a high degree of perfection in this respect.

In the light of the newest findings with regard to the formation of so-called "secondary" bacterial cultures [15] it is interesting to consider the idea that the ability of assimilating organic substance inheres in the basic structure of modern living things. D'Herelle [13] already noted that when bacteriophage acts on dysentery bacilli the culture may be so completely destroyed (or lyzed) that no visible bacteria can be found in it. Occasionally, however, the solution becomes turbid after a lapse of some time and normal Shiga dysentery bacilli reappear. This phenomenon has been studied carefully by Handuroy [14], who concludes that under the influence of bacteriophage there is a breaking up or disaggregation of bacterial bodies into numerous fragments. Some of these fragments can pass through bacterial filters and represent the so-called invisible or filterable bacterial forms. Subsequently, normal bacteria (secondary cultures) are again formed from those fragments. It is most interesting that these separate "pieces" of bacteria are apparently able to grow in different organic media although many of the biochemical properties of the original cultures suffer material alterations from the fragmentation of bacteria.

Thus the proposition, that the inner physico-chemical organization which makes absorption and assimilation of organic substances possible must have appeared together with primary organisms, finds corroboration in a number of facts established by observation on organisms living at the present time. But assimilation of organic substances is always intimately associated with their degradation. Only in the case of simple adsorption can assimilation of organic substance proceed without decomposition. But as soon as the absorbed substance begins to undergo chemical transformation, it must be subjected to profound decomposition at least in part. This depends upon the fact that most syntheses represent endothermic reactions, i.e., processes requiring some energy for their accomplishment. In coazervates and in primary organisms this energy is derived from organic substances adsorbed from the environment. As was already pointed out, these substances are rich sources of potential energy and by coordinated reactions, principally oxidation-reduction reactions, this energy can be more or less utilized in the synthesis of substances for building up the organism.

It follows that assimilation of organic substances unaccompanied by a degradation process may occur only in primary coazervates representing an extremely simplified system. But rapid growth and development can occur only in colloidal systems in which the adsorbed organic substances are subjected to far-reaching chemical transformations. Consequently, in the course of evolution of coazervates and gels the ability must have developed very rapidly to utilize the hidden potential energy of organic substances for performing the endothermic synthetic reactions. In other words, an inner physico-chemical structure had to be developed which made it possible to bring about most complete degradation of adsorbed organic substance in order to utilize most fully its potential chemical energy.

The largest amount of potential energy can be released in the oxidation of organic substances by the oxygen of the air, i.e., by their "burning" to carbon dioxide and water as, for instance, in the oxidation of sugar according to the equation:

$$C_6H_{12}O_6 + 6\ O_2 = 6\ CO_2 + 6\ H_2O + 674\ Calories$$

A similar oxidation of carbohydrates actually occurs in the respiration of animals and plants. But, if the argument presented in previous chapters is valid, under no circumstances could this process have been realized in primary organisms, because free oxygen was completely lacking in the Earth's atmosphere of that epoch, and transformation of organic substances could take place only through interaction with the elements of water. The primitive apparatus of degradation must, therefore, have been such as to permit the oxidation of organic substance only by means of the hydroxyl (OH^-) of water.

To appreciate this we must consider the hypothesis proposed by Traube[16] at the close of the last century. Traube reasoned from the experimentally established fact that in the absence of water no oxidation can proceed even with the aid of free oxygen. Thus, for instance, metallic sodium retains its lustre in absolutely dry oxygen, i.e., this easily oxidizable metal fails to become oxidized. A carbon monoxide flame is immediately extinguished if it is introduced into oxygen completely free from water vapor. These observations led Traube to believe that substances are oxidized not by free gaseous oxygen of the air but by the bound oxygen of water.

The simplest instance of hydrolytic oxidation is presented by the decomposition of water by alkali metals, i.e., the oxidation by means of the hydroxyls of water with the liberation of a corresponding amount of hydrogen:

$$Na_2 + 2\,H_2O = 2\,NaOH + H_2$$

From thermodynamic considerations it is clear that only substances relatively rich in free energy, manifested in a strong affinity for the hydroxyl of water, can decompose water with the liberation of gaseous hydrogen. Such instances are comparatively rare, but the decomposition of water by the simultaneous action of two substances, of which one is oxidized by the hydroxyl (OH) of water while the other accepts the hydrogen (H) is much more common. This can be illustrated by the reaction first described by Engel [17] and later studied carefully by A. Bach [18]. The salts of hypophosphorous acid do not themselves decompose water with any measurable speed but, if a small amount of palladium black is introduced into an aqueous solution of such a salt, the hypophosphorous acid is immediately oxidized to phosphorous acid, the hydrogen being set free on the palladium (Pd) at the same time:

$$\underset{\substack{\text{Hypophosphorous}\\\text{Acid}}}{\overset{\displaystyle \underset{H}{\overset{H\quad O}{\diagdown\!\!\diagup}}P\diagdown\!\!\diagup}{\underset{H\quad OH}{}}} + \underset{\text{Water}}{\genfrac{}{}{0pt}{}{HOH}{HOH}} = \underset{\substack{\text{Phosphorous}\\\text{Acid}}}{\overset{\displaystyle \overset{H\quad O}{\diagdown\!\!\diagup}P}{\underset{HO\quad OH}{}}} + \boxed{\genfrac{}{}{0pt}{}{H_2}{Pd}} + H_2O$$

This reaction can be interpreted as follows: Water, as is well known, dissociates into hydroxyl and hydrogen ions (OH^-, H^+) to an extremely slight extent. Hydroxyl is a very powerful and universal oxidant which also oxidizes hypophosphorous acid very easily. However, if only the hydroxyls would disappear there would be no further dissociation of water and the reaction would come to an end from the very start. But the situation would be quite different if both the hydroxyl and hydrogen ions would disappear simultaneously, as this would disturb the equilibrium between the ionized and un-ionized molecules of water. The disappearing ions would be replaced by new hydrogen and hydroxyl ions resulting from the dissociation or ionization of water, and the reaction would proceed further. Therefore, the oxidation of hypophosphorous acid by the hydroxyl of water will proceed smoothly only in the event if the hydrogen of the water can be removed by one means or another. In the experiment referred to above the removal has been accomplished with the aid of palladium black.

The hydroxyl of water, which, as already pointed out, is a tremendously powerful oxidant, can oxidize a great variety of organic substances. A similar oxidation is generally observed at the anode in the electrolytic process, and Fichter oxidized a great variety of aliphatic and aromatic compounds at the anode. It is interesting to note in this connection that he found the same intermediate products of oxidation as are eliminated by living organisms.

Many investigations of recent years show unmistakably that the reaction of oxidation of organic substances by the hydroxyl of water is without exception the basis of all types of the energy metabolism of various living things. The only difference between them, as will be shown later, is in the methods of the hydrogen acceptance.

The detailed study of the respiratory process actually shows that fundamentally we are dealing here with anaerobic (i.e. without oxygen) transformations of organic substance. The inner physico-chemical mechanisms, which make the degradation of organic substance at the expense of the elements of water possible, are the primary mechanisms involved. On the contrary, the aerobic respiration by means of oxygen seems to be a supplementary overlayering of this process, and extra superstructure acquired at a later period. Indeed E. Pflüger [19], who discovered the anaerobic type of respiration in higher animals, expressed the thought that this process is neither pathological nor just a casual biological adaptation for surviving a brief oxygen deprivation. In Pflüger's opinion the ability to degrade carbohydrates anaerobically is the foundation of the whole respiratory process. Somewhat later Pfeffer [20] developed a similar view with regard to higher plants. He showed that plants deprived of atmospheric oxygen acquire the ability of so-called intramolecular respiration, which is entirely identical chemically with alcoholic fermentation. The still later investigations of V. Palladin and especially of S. Kostychev [21] have shown that in the great majority of cases normal respiration begins as an anaerobic cleavage or splitting of carbohydrates. However, on the admission of air the intermediate products of alcoholic fermentation are oxidized to carbon dioxide and water through the action of special oxidative mechanisms. On blocking free oxidation the process leads normally to the formation of alcohol and carbon dioxide. S. Kostychev [22] gives the following scheme to illustrate the coordination of these processes:

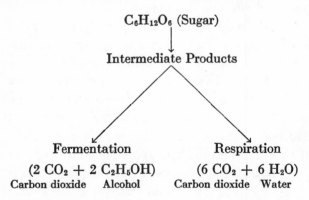

$C_6H_{12}O_6$ (Sugar)

Intermediate Products

Fermentation
(2 CO_2 + 2 C_2H_5OH)
Carbon dioxide   Alcohol

Respiration
(6 CO_2 + 6 H_2O)
Carbon dioxide   Water

Similarly the careful analysis of the chemistry of respiration of animals carried out principally by O. Meyerhof [23] and G. Embden [24] demonstrated that the process is based on an anaerobic lactic fermentation. All the early stages of muscle respiration coincide with the early stages of this fermentation, the oxidation by the free oxygen of air being superimposed only in the later stages.

Thus, just as absorption of organic substances is the basic primary process even in chlorophyll bearing autotrophes, while even the process of photosynthesis is secondary and of a much later origin, so also in the metabolism of energy lactic acid and alcohol fermentations are primary processes, while respiration by means of oxygen represents a much later supplementary superstructure. And just as in the matter of assimilation we can bring an organism back to its archaic, saprophytic mode of life, so also in the case of respiration it is possible to a certain extent to suppress the aerobic phase and to force higher organisms, at least for a short time, to return to the more archaic, primary method of metabolizing organic substances. At the same time we know large groups among the simplest organisms at the lower stage of development which have not yet become adapted to the oxidative respiration (i.e., to the use of oxygen) in the course of their evolution. These organisms still realize their energy metabolism by more archaic and less efficient methods: for instance, yeast by the typical alcohol fermentation and certain bacteria by lactic acid fermentation. These microorganisms, like their remote ancestors, can exist in the absence of oxygen, although oxygen is useful for their normal growth and multiplication, and in some instances is even indispensable.

In the anaerobic degradation of organic substances the end products are compounds still possessing considerable potential energy (alcohol, lactic acid) which can no longer be utilized by the organism without the aid of oxygen. The result, of course, is that fermentation processes have an incomparably smaller energy effect than respiration, as can be seen from the following equations:

$$C_6H_{12}O_6 + 6\ O_2 = 6\ CO_2 + 6\ H_2O + \underline{\underline{674\ \text{Calories}}}$$

Respiration

$$C_6H_{12}O_6 = 2\ CH_3CH_2OH + 2\ CO_2 + \underline{\underline{28\ \text{Calories}}}$$

Alcohol Fermentation

$$C_6H_{12}O_6 = 2\ CH_3CHOHCOOH + \underline{\underline{18\ \text{Calories}}}$$

Lactic Acid Fermentation

It is obvious from these equations that it would be necessary to subject 25 gram-molecules of sugar to alcohol fermentation or 37 gram-molecules to lactic acid fermentation in order to obtain as much energy (calories) as the oxidation of 1 gram-molecule of sugar yields by the respiratory process. This demonstrates clearly the inefficiency of fermentation as compared to respiration from the energy standpoint.

However, from the standpoint of inner biochemical adjustments the fermentation processes presuppose already a high degree of organization. As was already shown in Chapter V, both alcohol and lactic acid fermentation represent long chains of separate chemical reactions (hydrolysis, oxidation-reduction, cleavage of carbon bonds, etc.) which proceed at a definite and fairly great velocity owing to the presence in yeast and bacterial cells of specific enzymes. But the advanced inner physico-chemical organization of these cells manifests itself in this, that the velocities of the individual reactions are very strictly coordinated.

Intermediate products (triose, pyruvic acid, acetaldehyde, etc.) resulting from any of these reactions, just like every organic substance, possess large chemical potentialities and can undergo further transformation in a great variety of directions. But within the yeast or bacterial cell the velocities of different reactions constituting fermentation are so regulated that the products of one reaction are immediately subjected to further transformation in a definite direction by the next reaction. For instance, in alcohol fermentation pyruvic acid is split up into carbon dioxide and acetaldehyde by the action of the carboxylase enzyme. Acetaldehyde is a substance endowed with enormous biochemical potentialities and can be converted into a great variety of products. But in alcohol fermentation the acetaldehyde molecule resulting from the cleavage of pyruvic acid immediately undergoes an oxidation-reduction reaction and is thereby changed to ethyl alcohol. It gives rise to no extra by-products because there is no opportunity for it to undergo any other kind of chemical transformation.

The more highly perfected and coordinated the process becomes the fewer intermediate products and by-products are formed and the phenomenon acquires to an ever greater degree the character of a straight process. In yeast cells, because of their long adaptation to definite, specific environmental conditions, a fairly high type of physico-chemical organization has developed so that alcohol fermentation may serve as an example of an excellently regulated process. Under ordinary conditions only the initial and the final products of fermentation can be observed, since intermediate products do not accumulate to any appreciable extent, and the same holds true also for the by-products of this reaction. During fermentation sugar is converted in a strictly quantitative manner into alcohol and carbon dioxide so that the sugar concentration of a solution can be measured by the amount of carbon dioxide gas evolved by yeast. This orderliness of the fermentation process can be disturbed only by special means and then the yeast cell can be forced to realize its energy metabolism along different lines.

The lactic acid fermentation is a less perfect process than the alcohol fermentation both from the standpoint of the energy yield as well as of the effectiveness of regulation. When sugar is fermented by certain lactic acid bacilli, it is not uncommon for other products, particularly ethyl alcohol, acetic acid, etc., to be formed together with the lactic acid. Nevertheless, there are some species of these microorganisms whose inner physico-chemical mechanism for fermentation has already reached a high level of development. Thus, for instance, Bacterium lactis acidi Leichm. under favorable conditions of fermentation yields up to 98 percent of the theoretical amount of lactic acid. In other words, the separate reactions in these organisms are so integrated that the entire process runs off almost strictly in accordance with the equation:

$$C_6H_{12}O_6 \rightarrow 2\ C_3H_6O_3$$
$$\text{Sugar} \qquad \text{Lactic Acid}$$

practically all the sugar being changed to lactic acid [25].

Although both alcohol and lactic acid fermentation represent a more archaic and simpler type of energy metabolism than respiration, nevertheless a number of the microorganisms have attained a fairly high form of organization and a high degree of mutual adjustment of the separate links in the reaction chain of the process. Butyric acid fermentation, however, is associated with a very much lower stage of organization. Although there is good reason for believing that this represents one of the oldest fermentation types, it is carried on, on a colossal scale even at the present time under natural conditions. Kostychev [23] says that there is no ooze deprived of oxygen, no bog or swamp where butyric acid fermentation does not go on and, where oxidative activity is impossible, this process aids in the decomposition of the principal mass of organic substance.

Theoretically, the equation of butyric acid fermentation can be expressed as follows:

$$C_6H_{12}O_6 \rightarrow CH_3CH_2CH_2COOH + 2\ CO_2 + 2\ H_2 + \underline{\underline{15\ \text{Calories}}}$$
$$\text{Sugar} \qquad\qquad \text{Butyric Acid}$$

From the energetic standpoint this is even less efficient than the lactic acid fermentation but the primitive character of butyric fermentation manifests itself even more clearly in the poor adjustment of the separate chemical reactions partaking in this process. The regulation of the entire process in this case is at a much lower level of development than in the fermentations described earlier. As a matter of fact, a butyric acid fermentation corresponding exactly to the above equation has never been observed, and in addition to butyric acid, carbon dioxide and hydrogen there is also a long list of intermediate products formed such as ethyl alcohol, lactic acid, acetic acid, etc. Neither is the quantitative relationship between the separate reaction products constant, but varies greatly both with the genetic history of the microorganisms and with the external conditions of the fermentation. Not infrequently by-products such as acetic acid, which are formed during the first days of fermentation, are no longer found towards the end of the process, and vice versa. Frequently the by-products are found in such prodigious amounts that at times it is difficult to decide whether one is dealing with a butyric acid fermentation in which lactic acid is a by-product, or with a lactic acid fermentation complicated by butyric acid.

This variability, both quantitative and qualitative, of the products of butyric acid fermentation indicates that the organisms have not yet acquired that perfect physico-chemical organization which imparts an absolutely definite direction to the general course of the process by a strict integration of the velocities of its component chemical reactions. Here the intermediate products are not acted on in some one definite direction; they can enter a variety of chemical interactions resulting in different end products.

The chemistry of butyric acid fermentation has not been so well studied as that of lactic or alcoholic fermentation, because the process lacks constancy and its component reactions are very badly tangled up [26]. But one can say with certainty that at least the first stages of all these fermentations, even if not entirely identical, are quite similar. In every instance a molecule of hexose (a six carbon sugar) splits into two of triose (a three carbon sugar) molecules by a series of reactions. In butyric acid fermentation one molecule each of acetaldehyde, carbon dioxide and hydrogen result from the triose:

$$C_6H_{12}O_6 \rightarrow 2\ C_3H_6O_3$$
Hexose   Triose

$$C_3H_6O_3 \rightarrow CH_3CHO + CO_2 + H_2$$
Triose   Acetaldehyde

Naturally this splitting of the molecule does not take place in one step but is the outcome of a series of intermediate reactions, which have not yet been clarified in every detail.

In this process we must focus attention upon two extremely interesting points: the formation of acetaldehyde and the appearance of hydrogen which in butyric acid fermentation is liberated as a gas. Acetaldehyde is an extremely important biochemical product and within the living cell it may serve as the source of a great variety of substances. Actually the study of biochemical processes in cells shows that acetaldehyde is at the crossroads of a number of transformations in the living organism. It was already shown that it results from cleavage of pyruvic acid in the fermentation of alcohol, but in the yeast cell the chemical processes are so well regulated that the acetaldehyde is immediately reduced by the hydrogen (H) of water while the hydroxyl (OH) oxidizes the triose to glyceric acid, which later becomes converted to pyruvic acid (See Scheme of Alcohol Fermentation on p. 119):

$$C_3H_6O_3 \rightarrow C_3H_6O_4 \rightarrow C_3H_4O_3$$
$$\text{Triose} \quad \text{Glyceric Acid} \quad \text{Pyruvic Acid}$$

In butyric acid fermentation, where strict regulation of the processes is lacking, acetaldehyde can be changed in different directions. Fundamentally, it is transformed to acetaldol by an aldol condensation, as follows:

$$2\,CH_3CHO \rightarrow CH_3CHOH \cdot CH_2 \cdot CHO$$
$$\text{Acetaldehyde} \qquad \text{Acetaldol}$$

By an oxidation-reduction reaction at the expense of

water (inner Cannizzaro reaction) acetaldol is transformed to butyric acid, the basic product of this fermentation:

$$CH_3 \cdot CHOH \cdot CH_2 \cdot CHO \rightarrow CH_3 \cdot CH_2 \cdot CH_2 \cdot COOH$$
Acetaldol   Butyric Acid

However, together with butyric acid, as was already mentioned, other products may also be formed because, in the absence of a strong regulatory mechanism, acetaldehyde may react along other chemical paths as well. In particular, two acetaldehyde molecules may undergo a Cannizzaro oxidation-reduction reaction with the result that one molecule becomes reduced to alcohol while the other is oxidized to acetic acid:

$$2 CH_3CHO + HOH \rightarrow CH_3CH_2OH + CH_3COOH$$
Acetaldehyde   Water   Ethyl Alcohol   Acetic Acid

In this way other end products besides butyric acid may be formed in the fermentation process. Acetic acid may be formed even without ethyl alcohol in which case, however, hydrogen gas is set free. Furthermore, by the interaction of two acetic acid molecules, or directly from acetaldehyde, acetoacetic acid can be formed, which subsequently splits into acetone and carbon dioxide, as follows:

$$CH_3 \cdot CO \cdot CH_2 \cdot COOH \rightarrow CH_3 \cdot CO \cdot CH_3 + CO_2$$
Acetoacetic Acid   Acetone

The production of acetone is actually observed in ethyl-acetone or butyl-acetone fermentations, which are merely modifications of butyric acid fermentation.

The liberation of hydrogen in butyric acid fermentation is likewise a most noteworthy phenomenon, as it does not occur in other types of energy metabolism of the cell. In other types of fermentation the hydrogen of the water, set free when organic substance is oxidized by the hydroxyls, is immediately utilized for reduction processes either in the synthesis of protoplasmic substances or in the reduction of intermediate split products. But the butyric fermentation bacteria have not yet developed that powerful fermentative apparatus which would make such rapid reduction processes possible and, therefore, the hydrogen atoms in this case have the opportunity to unite into molecules and are liberated from the cell as a gas. Of course, from the standpoint of general energy economy of the cells this is very wasteful. For this reason butyric acid fermentation is characterized by a very low coefficient of utilization by living organisms even of the small amount of energy made available in this process.

However, in some types of butyric acid fermentation, for instance the butyl-acetone fermentation already mentioned, part of the hydrogen can be utilized for the reduction process. In this manner acetaldehyde becomes reduced to ethyl alcohol, butyric acid to butyl alcohol, while acetone is changed to iso-propyl alcohol:

$$CH_3 \cdot CHO + 2\,H \rightarrow CH_3 \cdot CH_2 \cdot OH$$
Acetaldehyde   Ethyl Alcohol

$$CH_3 \cdot CH_2 \cdot CH_2 \cdot COOH + 4\,H \rightarrow CH_3 \cdot CH_2 \cdot CH_2 \cdot CH_2 \cdot OH + H_2O$$
Butyric Acid   Butyl Alcohol

$$CH_3 \cdot CO \cdot CH_3 + 2\,H \rightarrow CH_3 \cdot CH(OH) \cdot CH_3$$
Acetone   Iso-propyl Alcohol

If we recall that lactic acid is also usually formed in butyric acid fermentation, it becomes clear that butyric acid bacteria are able to form a great variety of different end products. *Here, still in a chaotic and unregulated state, one finds the various physico-chemical mechanisms of fermentation, such as alcoholic, lactic acid, acetic acid, etc., which only later develop into perfect mechanisms.* If we follow Jost in comparing living cells to a chemical factory, bacteria performing butyric acid fermentation should be described as a handicraft industry, where different materials are fabricated as they are needed but without any plan or specialized tools, whereas the yeast cell is already like a well organized factory with highly specialized machinery and a strict balance sheet of production.

The study of butyric acid fermentation gives some conception of the poorly organized, insufficiently integrated energy metabolism prevailing among primary living things. Their different chemical reactions still lack strict coordination. Organic substances absorbed from the outside medium as well as intermediate products of metabolism undergo chemical transformations in a great variety of ways. Furthermore, because of the poor coordination of various processes the coefficient of utilization of the chemical energy of these reactions is still too low to permit secondary reactions of synthesis to proceed. Only gradually, and as a result of natural selection, mechanisms arise for the regulation of enzymatic action which coordinate more and more strictly the velocities of the separate reactions. The number of chemical possibilities for the formation of intermediate products is decreased, but the entire process is thereby improved and consequently the coefficient of useful activity is raised. The process becomes more direct and orderly, as is manifested in the more highly organized types of fermentation.

The detailed study of the chemistry of different fermentation types allows one, to a certain extent, to draw a picture of the gradual evolution of the internal chemical
organization of simplest living things. In all these fermentation types the basic phenomenon is the oxidation of triose
by the hydroxyl of water (OH). The fate of the liberated
hydrogen (H), however, differs according to the degree of
coordination of the velocities of reduction (hydrogen acceptance) and other simultaneous reactions. In butyric acid
fermentation the reduction reactions proceed extremely

slowly. The carbonyl groups $\left(\overset{\text{O}}{\underset{}{-\overset{\|}{C}-H}}\right)$ of the acetalde-

hyde, which could add on hydrogen, disappear instead,
with much greater speed, in condensation reactions whereby
butyric acid is formed, while the unaccepted hydrogen
atoms unite into molecules (H_2) which escape as gas bubbles. In lactic acid bacteria the reduction mechanism is already much perfected, so that hydrogen can no longer be
given off in molecular combination. It is rapidly accepted
by pyruvic acid which is thereby reduced to lactic acid. In
yeast, too, reduction reactions may proceed with great
speed but in this case they are strictly coordinated with the
action of carboxylase, an enzyme which the lactic acid
bacilli do not possess. This enzyme splits pyruvic acid
into carbon dioxide and acetaldehyde, the latter becoming
reduced to alcohol by the hydrogen of water. It is obvious,
therefore, that the processes of lactic acid and of alcohol
fermentation are outgrowths of butyric acid fermentation,
resulting from improved regulation, and that they represent
advanced types of fermentation which have been passed

on even to the more highly evolved organisms. Together with the oxidative processes by means of free oxygen these fermentative processes are now basic forms of energy metabolism of the higher plants and animals.

These fermentation types could be transformed into respiratory processes at a much later period but only after oxygen appeared on the Earth. *The primitive metabolism of energy was entirely anaerobic and depended on the interaction of organic substances with molecules of water.* But the supply of organic substance which could undergo fermentation must have been, therefore, decreasing in the primitive hydrosphere, being replaced by fermentation products, such as carbon dioxide, alcohol, lactic and butyric acid, etc. Sooner or later this process must have come to a natural end with the complete exhaustion of organic nutrient material and the death of all living things. That this did not actually happen is due to the fact that some microorganisms had acquired the ability to utilize light energy by virtue of their pigmentation.

The purple and green bacteria studied by G. Molisch[27] are interesting examples of such organisms capable of using light energy. Some species of these bacteria can be nourished only by means of organic substances since they have absolutely no power of photosynthesis. However, in some manner not yet clearly understood, light improves considerably the ability of these organisms to utilize organic compounds. There is, apparently, some increase in the coefficient of utilization of substances in the fermentation process. Van Niel[28] has recently made some very interesting investigations on the purple sulfur bacteria. These bacteria utilize hydrogen sulfide as a source of energy, oxidizing it to sulfur and even to sulfuric acid by means of the oxygen of air, according to the equation:

$$2 H_2S + O_2 = 2 H_2O + S_2$$
$$S_2 + 2 H_2O + 3 O_2 = 2 H_2SO_4$$

Van Niel's experiments show that in the light these bacteria oxidize hydrogen sulfide even in the complete absence of free oxygen. By virtue of photochemical processes they can thus use for their oxidative reactions the bound oxygen of water (OH) while the hydrogen is used in a number of reducing reactions, particularly in the reduction of carbon dioxide.

It seems most probable that the primary utilization of light by pigmented organisms was not a photosynthesis but only a "rationalization" of the process of degradation of organic substances and of the energy metabolism of cells in the complete absence of oxygen. Unfortunately this subject has been studied very little so far, but the supposition does not seem baseless that the light energy absorbed by organisms could contribute to a more thorough and more "rational" oxidation of organic substance.

It is a well known fact that ultraviolet rays promote the dissociation of water into its ions (H^+, OH^-). The recent investigation of many photochemists show that the dissociation can be brought about even by rays of the visible spectrum provided proper sensitizers are employed. In other words, radiant energy may be used to dissociate water just as electrical energy is used in electrolysis. Weigert [29] offers the following scheme of the photochemical reaction of the dissociation of water:

$$\text{Sensitizer} + hv \text{ (quantum)} = \text{Sensitizer}^+ + e \text{ (electron)}$$
$$e + H_2O = H_2O^- = H + OH^-$$
$$OH^- + \text{Sensitizer}^+ = \text{Sensitizer} + OH$$

$$H_2O + hv = H + OH$$

Microorganisms which, through the formation of pigment-sensitizers, have acquired the ability to dissociate water by some such photochemical reactions have an enormous advantage in the matter of a more "rational" utilization of organic substances serving as sources of nutrition. As was already pointed out on several occasions, in all types of fermentation organic substance is oxidized by means of the hydroxyls of water. The liberation of the hydroxyls by the decomposition of water molecules is, therefore, an essential preliminary step in the process. This can be brought about by the simultaneous action of the oxidizable substance and of a hydrogen acceptor, just as in Bach's experiments of the oxidation of hypophosphorous acid to phosphorous acid in the presence of palladium black. A very considerable amount of chemical energy produced in the oxidation of organic substances is dissipated in dissociating the water and consequently the coefficient of utilization of nutritive material cannot be very large. But in photolysis this dissociation of water is accomplished with the aid of outside energy derived from the Sun's rays and the coefficient of utilization of organic substances can be increased many times. This is the real significance of light for the purple bacteria of Molisch, which are capable of nourishing themselves only on organic matter.

It may, therefore, be supposed that the first organisms possessing pigment benefited from light as a supplementary means for the more efficient utilization of organic substances and that only at a later period they developed the accessory ability for photochemical assimilation of carbon dioxide. This view is supported also by the circumstance that, according to the results of a number of investigators, photolysis of water is the primary reaction in the process of photosynthesis.

This hypothesis was first formulated at the close of the last century by A. Bach [30], who attempted to support it with his experiments on the photochemical reduction of carbon dioxide in the presence of uranium salts. Much later O. Warburg [31] applied the quantum theory to photosynthesis and came to the conclusion that carbon dioxide cannot be decomposed directly by the action of the Sun's rays, its transformation to formaldehyde being a secondary and purely chemical process. The hypothesis was developed further by T. Thunberg [32], who showed that the first act in the assimilation of carbon dioxide is the dissociation of water by the light. Subsequently this hypothesis was repeatedly subjected to criticism but even the most recent experimental work argues in favor of a primary photolysis of water in the photosynthetic process. One may also recall Wurmser's [33] theory according to which carbon dioxide does not even partake in the primary photochemical reaction. By the aid of chlorophyll as sensitizer the energy of a certain substance A is raised to the level A_1 by an expenditure of radiant energy. The substance A_1 passes from the chlorophyll grains into the stroma of the protoplasts where it meets the carbon dioxide, the latter becoming reduced in a coupled reaction. Wurmser assumes that the transformation of A to A_1 represents the primary photochemical dissociation of water. A. Stoll [34] likewise presupposes the dissociation of water with the absorption of light energy in developing, on the basis of extensive researches, his recent theory of photosynthesis. According to this theory, the hydrogen necessary for the reduction of carbon dioxide comes from a preliminary hydration of chlorophyll and a subsequent photolysis of the hydrate. The activated hydrogen acts further on the carbon dioxide bound to the chlorophyll molecule while the hydroxyl (OH) is transformed to hydrogen peroxide (H_2O_2). The enzyme catalase sets free oxygen from the latter:

$$2\ H_2O_2 \rightarrow 2\ H_2O + O_2$$

A similar liberation of oxygen must have taken place in the photochemical reaction of pigmented organisms which still feed on organic substances and are not able to assimilate carbon dioxide. The liberation of an oxygen molecule played an outstanding biological role. The appearance of oxygen immediately disturbed the chemical equilibrium which has already come into existence. Let us for a moment survey the environment of that epoch. Organic substance forming suitable raw material for the anaerobic metabolism is already to a considerable extent exhausted. The atmosphere is enriched with carbon dioxide, hydrogen, methane, and other gaseous products of fermentation. Products, such as ethyl alcohol, organic acids and carbonates, are dissolved in the waters of the seas and oceans, together with many reduced inorganic compounds, particularly ammonia in the form of its salts, ferrous iron in the form of its carbonate ($FeCO_3$) and, finally, hydrogen sulfide.

In the absence of free oxygen all these substances are entirely unavailable for the animals of that epoch, but with the advent of oxygen the possibility of their utilization as sources of energy has been realized. In the first place, this must have stimulated the evolution of organisms capable of oxidative fermentation, like acetic acid fermentation. The basic physico-chemical mechanisms necessary for accomplishing this process in its simplest form was already possessed by organisms performing butyric acid fermentation. We already noted there the formation of acetic acid and the problem was merely one of creating some superstructure which would make it possible to oxidize the hydrogen by means of molecular oxygen. The evolution of such a mechanism even in a very imperfect form markedly increased the coefficient of utilization of organic substances which yield energy. At the same time, this widened considerably the range of available substances which could serve as sources of energy. For instance, ethyl alcohol which previously was a totally useless by-product of alcoholic fermentation, could now be used for acetic acid fermentation [35]:

$$CH_3CH_2OH + O_2 = CH_3COOH + H_2O + 117 \text{ Calories}$$

But even such by-products of primitive fermentation were found on the Earth's surface in limited quantities. The acute shortage of organic nutriment at that epoch in the world's history makes it quite intelligible why the change in the evolution of living organisms took place in the direction of utilization of inorganic substances (ammonia, hydrogen sulfide, ferrous iron). The development of nitrifying bacteria, of sulfur bacteria, of iron bacteria must be referred to this particular epoch in the Earth's history, because these processes require for their realization molecular oxygen which previously was not present in the atmosphere of our planet [36]:

$$2 \, NH_3 + 3 \, O_2 = 2 \, HNO_2 + 2 \, H_2O$$
$$2 \, HNO_2 + O_2 = 2 \, HNO_3$$
$$2 \, H_2S + O_2 = 2 \, H_2O + S_2$$
$$S_2 + 2 \, H_2O + 3 \, O_2 = 2 \, H_2SO_4$$
$$2 \, FeCO_3 + 3 \, H_2O + O = Fe_2(OH)_6 + 2 \, CO_2$$

The same holds true, with a high degree of probability, for the origin of bacteria which oxidize hydrogen, methane and carbon monoxide.

The luxuriant development of these organisms with an extremely specialized type of energy metabolism was greatly aided by the specific conditions existing during that epoch, namely, *the shortage of organic nutriment and the great abundance of inorganic sources of energy.* This epoch could not have been of a very long duration. In the first place, the supply of inorganic sources of energy could not have been unlimited and was gradually exhausted with the development of autotrophic organisms capable of chemical synthesis. Replenishment of the supply from the deep layers of the Earth's crust could have taken place only very slowly. Besides, the supply of organic nutrient materials must have been gradually increasing at the same time, owing to the rapid development of the process of carbon dioxide assimilation.

The pigment which appeared in primitive organisms and enabled them to perform the photolysis of water had no direct relation to carbon dioxide assimilation in the sense as we now understand this process. The ability to employ radiant energy for a more rational utilization of organic substances created enormous odds for further rapid growth and evolution in favor of the pigmented organisms. The endowment with pigment put these organisms ahead of the rest of the Earth's population. In the dissociation of water by radiant energy active hydrogen is formed which is available not only for reduction processes associated with synthesis of "living substance" but for a number of other reduction reactions as well. Therefore, photolysis itself furnishes a basis for accomplishing the reduction of carbon dioxide. As soon as new supplementary mechanisms for binding carbon dioxide have arisen in the evolution of pigmented organisms, the actual assimilation of the carbon dioxide commenced immediately.

We are still very much in the dark as to the chemistry of carbon dioxide assimilation and cannot, therefore, trace the sequence of events in the development of this process. One thing, however, is certain, namely, that the assimilation of carbon dioxide is made up of a series of reactions proceeding in the light or in the dark in a strictly coordinated fashion. R. Willstätter and A. Stoll[37] in 1918 worked out a scheme of photosynthesis according to which the assimilation of carbon dioxide is a diphasic process. At first the carbon dioxide combines with the magnesium of a chlorophyll molecule forming a complex salt. Then the primary photochemical reaction really occurs, the carbon dioxide bound by the chlorophyll being converted to aldehyde peroxide through the absorption of large quantities of radiant energy. This compound rich in energy but easily decomposable now undergoes a series of transformations ending in the liberation of oxygen. Willstätter and Stoll assumed that first one, then the other oxygen atom is freed by the action of a catalase-like enzyme, with the formation first of formic acid, then of formaldehyde, which is split off from the chlorophyll. The freed chlorophyll is ready to react again with a molecule of carbon dioxide.

Chlorophyll   Chlorophyll formaldehyde peroxide

Carbon dioxide

Formaldehyde   Oxygen

Chlorophyll

According to this scheme the first step in this process is a photochemical reaction associated with absorption of light energy. The second step, involving the decomposition of the peroxide, is an enzymatic reaction which occurs even in the dark. The later and very extensive researches of O. Warburg corroborated this subdivision of the reactions into those which proceed in the light and those which proceed in the dark.

The weak point in the Willstätter-Stoll scheme is the splitting off of oxygen. Recently, in an investigation already referred to, Stoll elaborates this point by suggesting that a primary photolysis of water occurs, the dissociation of H_2O into $H + OH$ initiating the photosynthetic process. At first the chlorophyll becomes hydrated (i.e., it takes up a molecule of water) then the hydrate decomposes: $H_2O \rightarrow H + OH$, under the action of light energy.

The hydroxyls formed in this process are converted to hydrogen peroxide which is decomposed into water and oxygen by the enzyme catalase. Thus, the oxygen produced in photosynthesis does not originate from the carbon dioxide but from water (H_2O) which was changed to peroxide (H_2O_2) by the absorbed energy. The hydrogen of the water reduces the carbon dioxide, but before this can happen the latter must be first activated. According to the Willstätter-Stoll hypothesis carbon dioxide unites with the chlorophyll and is changed by the action of solar energy to a peroxide. The hydrogen from water acts upon this peroxide with the result that the carbon dioxide is reduced to formaldehyde, which serves as the material for the subsequent synthesis of carbohydrates.

According to the researches of Wurmser, Kautsky [38], Ostwald [39] and others the separate light and dark reactions must occur in different phases of the chlorophyll granule (the lipid and aqueous phase) and are coordinated not only in time but also in space. This may explain why neither pure chlorophyll nor ground-up leaves can affect the assimilation of carbon dioxide since a definite organization, even a certain architectonic of the constituent colloids, is necessary in order that the process should be accomplished [40].

Thus the acquisition of pigment does not yet by itself insure that an assimilatory process will take place. For this a complex physico-chemical organization is also required, including a number of special enzyme complexes which regulate in a definite manner the course and velocity of the different reactions. This, of course, could not have just happened all at once. Highly developed organisms, capable of perfecting their inner organization, must have already been in existence and furnished a solid basis for such an evolution. It would be most instructive to compare the assimilatory systems found in plants at different stages of evolution. In all probability a similar sequence could be established in the organization of these biochemical processes as was done for the different forms of fermentation. At any rate, even the little we know of carbon dioxide assimilation allows one to imagine how this process could have developed from heterotrophic nutrition by means of organic substances.

The origin of photosynthesis was an extremely important phase in the process of evolution of the organic kingdom on our planet, which modified radically all the hitherto existing relationships. Alongside with the accumulation of oxygen the amount of organic substance, which could be drawn into the cycle of energy metabolism, was also increasing, and this made it possible for the basic evolutionary current to return to its primitive bed, developing organisms adapted to feed on organic substances. The epoch of acute shortage of organic nutriment had been relegated to the past. The only biological reminiscence of this epoch is to be found now in the small group of autotrophic organisms capable of chemosynthesis, and this represents merely an insignificant rivulet in the main evolutionary stream.

But once photosynthesis came into play, the further evolution of organisms adapted to feed on organic matter proceeded on an altogether different biochemical basis. The presence of a considerable amount of free oxygen enabled even organisms without pigment to evolve in the direction of greater rationalization of their energy metabolism. Speaking broadly, this consisted in the oxidation by atmospheric oxygen of hydrogen resulting from the hydrolytic oxidation of organic substances. In this way the archaic apparatus of fermentation was fully preserved but new physico-chemical structures were added to it, enabling organisms to utilize more fully the chemical energy of nutritive substances. Therefore, as was already pointed out, respiration is still based upon the oxidation by means of hydroxyl from water, as was also the case in the archaic forms of energy metabolism. But, whereas in alcohol or lactic acid fermentation, for instance, the hydrogen is accepted by organic substances, under the new conditions the hydrogen unites with the oxygen of the air. This opens up the possibility for complete oxidation to carbon dioxide and water with the liberation of the full energy content of the substance, according to the equation:

$$C_6H_{12}O_6 + 6\,O_2 = 6\,CO_2 + 6\,H_2O + \underline{\underline{674\ Calories}}$$

It must not be supposed, however, that oxidation by atmospheric oxygen proceeds very easily. On the contrary, molecular oxygen is, generally speaking, a fairly inert gas. Organic substances serving as sources of energy for living organisms (carbohydrates, fats, proteins, etc.) do not at ordinary temperatures or in the presence of water undergo oxidation by oxygen of the air with any measurable velocity. To bring about this oxidation, a very complex apparatus is needed for the activation of the molecular oxygen.

According to the researches of A. Bach[41], V. Palladin[42], and myself[43], the respiratory process of contemporary higher plants is accomplished by the following inner physico-chemical mechanism: The plant cells contain a very powerful system of strictly specific oxidative enzymes (oxidases and peroxidases) which activate the molecular oxygen. However, even in their presence oxygen cannot oxidize carbohydrates, fats or proteins, but acts only on certain substances of the polyphenol type. Such substances, always found in plant cells, have been designated by V. Palladin as the "respiratory chromogens". The oxidation of these substances by oxygen of the air catalyzed by oxidase and peroxidase proceeds according to the following equations:

Chromogen   Active Oxygen   Respiratory Pigment   Hydrogen Peroxide

Oxidase Action

Chromogen   Hydrogen Peroxide   Respiratory Pigment   Water

Peroxidase Action

It can be seen, therefore, that oxygen activated by the enzymes removes hydrogen from the polyphenols forming two molecules of water and two molecules of a quinone compound, the so-called "respiratory pigment", which functions as an excellent hydrogen acceptor. By adding to itself two atoms of hydrogen from two molecules of water it is once more reduced to the original condition of "respiratory chromogen", while the hydroxyls thus set free from the water oxidize various organic substances. The entire process of aerobic oxidation proceeds, therefore, according to the following scheme:

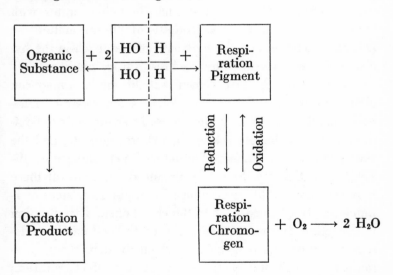

The oxygen of the air activated by the oxidase system oxidizes the "respiratory chromogens", which give up hydrogen and are transformed into "respiratory pigments" which, in turn, act as hydrogen acceptors. By the action of oxidation-reduction enzymes (already discussed in connection with the fermentation problem) a coupled oxidation-reduction reaction takes place as a result of which various organic substances are oxidized by the hydroxyl of water, while the hydrogen reduces the "respiratory pigment" back to the "chromogen" condition.

In respiration with the aid of carbohydrates the phenomenon also begins with a splitting of the sugar molecules just as in the process of alcohol fermentation. In ordinary alcohol fermentation the trioses are oxidized by the hydroxyls of water to pyruvic acid while the acetaldehyde is reduced by the hydrogen of water to alcohol. But in respiration the hydrogen is intercepted by the "respiratory pigment" and the liberated acetaldehyde either unites with some other substances in a synthesis of "living matter" or is further oxidized by the hydroxyl of water while the hydrogen is again accepted by the "respiratory pigment".

Our experiments have shown that this process may run along uninterruptedly only so long as the separate reactions remain very exactly integrated. In living cells the oxidation of polyphenols (chromogens) to pigments, and the reverse reaction of their reduction to the chromogen condition, are extremely delicately balanced. As a result there is never any notable accumulation of pigment, since it is immediately reduced back to the chromogen. The situation is altogether different, however, when the cell has been destroyed by cutting or grinding, which disturbs the regulation of the separate reactions. At first the effect manifests itself in a marked preponderance of oxidation over reduction processes which results in an accumulation of a certain amount of respiratory pigment. This substance, however, can be either reduced again to the chromogen state or it may be oxidized further, forming a stable brown pigment which cannot longer be reduced reversibly, and represents, therefore, a final end-product of the reaction.

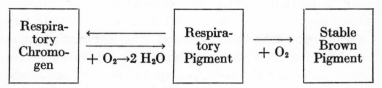

Scheme of oxidation in the destroyed cell.

Under the influence of the oxidase enzyme the chromogen is oxidized by atmospheric oxygen to the respiratory pigment which in turn is oxidized to the stable brown compound. Since the latter is incapable of accepting hydrogen the respiratory cycle is broken. The oxidation of organic substances by the hydroxyl of water ceases and the whole respiratory process thus comes to a stop.

This illustration shows that in the course of evolution a relatively complex mechanism must have developed in the living cell, which enabled it to oxidize organic substances to carbon dioxide and water and to utilize fully their potential chemical energy. It shows, furthermore, that such a complex physico-chemical apparatus can function only if the separate processes, constituting the links of a complicated chain of events in the transformation of substances, are delicately regulated and integrated.

The chemistry of respiration of animal cells has not been so clearly established. The basic respiratory mechanisms so well defined in the higher plants are either entirely lacking or play only a subordinate role. For one thing, the animal cell does not possess the tremendously active peroxidase system characteristic for the plant cell, nor are the specific respiratory chromogens present there. According to the view developed in the last few years by O. Warburg[44], the fundamental physico-chemical apparatus governing the respiration of animal cells is the "respiratory enzyme" which he has discovered. This enzymatic system consists of a combination of iron with a pigment of the pyrrol structure. The latter is a special form of hemin, the basic structural nucleus of the red pigment of blood, hemoglobin.

In recent years D. Keilin[45] described a different oxidation system. He thinks that the entire process of oxidation is accomplished by means of special intermediate catalysts and a specific enzyme responsible for the oxidation. This enzyme differs from Warburg's respiratory enzyme. It is not a hemin compound but a special kind of oxidase containing heavy metals. Keilin's intermediate catalyst is cytochrome, a reversible oxidation-reduction system consisting of pyrrol compounds which are closely related to the protohemins. It is very probable that there are also other oxidative systems functioning in the animal cell.

At any rate, the inner physico-chemical mechanisms responsible for respiration in higher plants and in higher animals are entirely distinct. This, of course, is quite understandable since the oxidative process originated at a comparatively late phase in the evolution of organisms, when the two principal branches of organic life (animal and plant) had already become widely separated from each other.

We purposely narrowed down the discussion of biochemical processes in contemporary living organisms to a few essential problems of metabolism. Unfortunately, even these problems have not yet been studied sufficiently and our information is punctuated by many blank spaces. But what little we do know is enough to sketch a more or less definite picture of the gradual evolution of the inner physico-chemical organization of the protoplast. In the simplest organisms we find a fairly well adjusted apparatus, which permits them to obtain quickly and to assimilate easily organic substances. But we still find evidence of an inner organization of a very low degree of evolution so far as the metabolism of energy is concerned. There are many enzymatic systems for carrying out different reactions with the aid of the elements of water, but the delicate adjustment and strict coordination of the separate reactions is still lacking. The whole process of metabolism still bears the marks of being somewhat chaotic, its different parts still lacking quantitative correlation. But gradually out of this chaotic metabolic activity strictly interrelated systems have evolved, which brought definite order and integration into the current of chemical reactions. These reactions became the separate links in well regulated metabolic processes. Thus, for instance, alcohol and lactic acid fermentation have evolved from the primitive, basic process of butyric acid fermentation.

The appearance in the protoplast of a new chemical factor, the pigment, and its noncomitant effect, the photolysis of water, created conditions for a more rational utilization of organic substances as a source of energy. Under the conditions of a general shortage of such materials, this introduced new forms of existence and led to an elaboration of new inner mechanisms permitting the assimilation of carbon dioxide. The abundance of organic substance resulting from the introduction of photosynthesis gave a new impetus to the evolution of heterotrophic organisms. This evolution followed the line of utilization of atmospheric oxygen for a more rationalized and, from the point of view of energy made available, a more effective oxidation of organic substances. Thus, new mechanisms were created, a new apparatus for intracellular respiration and for energy metabolism came into existence.

The evolution of the inner physico-chemical apparatus of the protoplasm consists, on the one hand, of the creation of new substances (pigments, etc.) and new enzymatic systems, and, on the other hand, of the refinement of regulation of separate enzyme reactions and the organization of strictly coordinated processes, such as fermentation, respiration, etc. It is quite clear that this evolution was not limited only to the brief period which the organisms existing at the present time make it possible for us to study. From what has been said in the preceding chapters it is obvious that the evolution commenced very much earlier. But studying the separate stages in the gradual development of contemporary organisms we may, with a certain measure of probability, draw analogous conclusions also with regard to the course of evolution even before living organisms appeared. Undoubtedly, the evolutionary process which molded the inner physico-chemical structure of the protoplast still operates even at the present time. Even now, whenever a new race or variety originates, it is possible to demonstrate that it possesses new biochemical properties and that its metabolism of matter and energy is somewhat different from that of its ancestors. This indicates that some changes must have occurred in the inner structure, that new combinations of substances and enzymes have been formed, that new physical and chemical systems and new relations have been introduced. From our point of view, therefore, the modern process of evolution of living organisms is fundamentally nothing more than the addition of some new links to an endless chain of transformations of matter, a chain the beginning of which extends to the very dawn of existence of our planet.

CHAPTER IX

CONCLUSION

Summarizing what has been discussed in the preceding chapters, one must first of all categorically reject every attempt to renew the old arguments in favor of a sudden and spontaneous generation of life. It must be understood that no matter how minute an organism may be or how elementary it may appear at first glance it is nevertheless infinitely more complex than any simple solution of organic substances. It possesses a definite dynamically stable structural organization which is founded upon a harmonious combination of strictly coordinated chemical reactions. It would be senseless to expect that such an organization could originate accidentally in a more or less brief span of time from simple solutions or infusions.

However, this need not lead us to the conclusion that there is an absolute and fundamental difference between a living organism and lifeless matter. Everyday experience enables one to differentiate living things from their nonliving environment. But the numerous attempts to discover some specific "vital energies" resident only in organisms invariably ended in total failure, as the history of biology in the nineteenth and twentieth centuries teaches us.

That being the case, life could not have existed always. The complex combination of manifestations and properties so characteristic of life must have arisen in the process of evolution of matter. A weak attempt has been made in these pages to draw a picture of this evolution without losing contact with the ground of scientifically established facts.

The gaseous mass which had once separated from the Sun, owing to a cosmic catastrophe, furnished the material out of which our planet was formed. Carbon together with other elements of the solar atmosphere passed into this gaseous mass which ultimately was destined to form our Earth. Carbon is distinguished among all the chemical elements by its exceptional ability to form atomic associations, and is found invariably in all living things. Even at temperatures similar to those prevailing on the Sun's surface its atoms are united in pairs, and on further cooling it tends to form molecules with even greater numbers of atoms (type C_n). Therefore, in the process of formation of our planet from the original incandescent mass of gas, heavy clouds of carbon must have very quickly condensed into drops or even solid particles and entered the primitive nucleus of the Earth in the form of a carbonaceous rain or snow. There the carbon came into immediate contact with the elements of heavy metals forming the nucleus, primarily with iron which constitutes such an essential component of the central core of our present Earth.

Mixed with the heavy metals, the carbon reacted chemically as the Earth gradually cooled off, whereby carbides were produced, which are the carbon compounds most stable at high temperatures. The crust of primary igneous rocks which were formed subsequently separated the carbides from the Earth's atmosphere. The atmosphere at that period differed materially from our present atmosphere in that it contained neither oxygen nor nitrogen gas but was filled instead with superheated aqueous vapor. The crust separating the carbides from this atmosphere still lacked rigidity to resist the gigantic tides of the inner molten liquid mass, caused by the attractive forces of Sun and Moon. The thin layer of igneous rock would rupture during these tides and through the crevices so formed the molten liquid mass from the interior depths would spread over the Earth's surface. The superheated aqueous vapor of the atmosphere coming in contact with the carbides reacted chemically giving rise to the simplest organic matter, the hydrocarbons, which in turn gave rise to a great variety of derivatives (alcohols, aldehydes, ketones, organic acids, etc.) through oxidation by the oxygen component of water. At the same time these hydrocarbons also reacted with ammonia which appeared at that period on the surface of the Earth. Thus amides, amines and other nitrogenous derivatives originated.

Thus it came about, when our planet had cooled off sufficiently to allow the condensation of aqueous vapor and the formation of the first envelope of hot water around the Earth, that this water already contained in solution organic substances, the molecules of which were made up of carbon, hydrogen, oxygen and nitrogen. These organic substances are endowed with tremendous chemical potentialities, and they entered a variety of chemical reactions not only with each other but also with the elements of the water itself. As a consequence of these reactions complex, high-molecular organic compounds were produced similar to those which at the present time compose the organism of animals and plants. By this process also the biologically most important compounds, the proteins, must have originated.

At first these substances were present in the waters of seas and oceans in the form of colloidal solutions. Their molecules were dispersed and uniformly distributed in the solvent, but entirely inseparable from the dispersing medium. But as the colloidal solutions of various substances were mixed new and special formations resulted, the so-called coazervates or semiliquid colloidal gels. In this process organic substance becomes concentrated in definite spatial arrangements and separated from the solvent medium by a more or less distinct membrane. Inside these coazervates or gels the colloidal particles assume a definite position towards each other; in other words, the beginnings of some elementary structure appear in them. Each coazervate droplet acquires a certain degree of individuality and its further fate is now determined not only by the conditions of the external medium but also by its own specific internal physico-chemical structure. This internal structure of the droplet determined its ability to absorb with greater or less speed and to incorporate into itself organic substances dissolved in the surrounding water. This resulted in an increase of the size of the droplet, i.e., they acquired the power to grow. But the rate of growth depends upon the internal physico-chemical structure of a given colloidal system and is greater the more this is adapted for absorption and for the chemical transformation of the absorbed materials.

In such manner a peculiar situation had arisen which may be described as the growth competition of coazervate gels. However, the physico-chemical structure of gels during growth did not remain unaltered but tended constantly to change owing to the addition of new substances, to chemical interaction, etc. These transformations could either result in a further perfection of the organization or, on the contrary, induce the degradation and loss of structure. In other words, it could bring about self-destruction and resolution of the coazervate droplet which was itself responsible for starting the process. Only such changes in the structure of colloidal systems which enabled the gel to adsorb dissolved substances more rapidly and thus to grow better; in other words, only changes of a progressive kind acquired importance for continued existence and development. A peculiar selective process had thus come into play which finally resulted in the origin of colloidal systems with a highly developed physico-chemical organization, namely, the simplest primary organisms.

This brief survey purports to show the gradual evolution of organic substances and the manner by which ever newer properties, subject to laws of a higher order, were superimposed step by step upon the erstwhile simple and elementary properties of matter. At first there were the simple solutions of organic substances, whose behavior was governed by the properties of their component atoms and the arrangement of those atoms in the molecular structure. But gradually as a result of growth and increased complexity of the molecules new properties have come into being and a new colloid-chemical order was imposed upon the more simple organic chemical relations. These newer properties were determined by the spatial arrangement and mutual relationship of the molecules. Even this configuration of organic matter was still insufficient to give rise to primary living things. For this, the colloidal systems in the process of their evolution had to acquire properties of a still higher order, which would permit the attainment of the next and more advanced phase in the organization of matter. In this process biological orderliness already comes into prominence. Competitive speed of growth, struggle for existence and, finally, natural selection determined such a form of material organization which is characteristic of living things of the present time.

Natural selection has long ago destroyed and completely wiped off the face of the Earth all the intermediate forms of organization of primary colloidal systems and of the simplest living things and, wherever the external conditions are favorable to the evolution of life, we find countless numbers of fully developed highly organized living things. If organic matter would appear at the present time it could not evolve for very long because it would be quickly consumed and destroyed by the innumerable microorganisms inhabiting the earth, water and air. For this reason, the process of evolution of organic substance, the process of formation of life sketched in the preceding pages cannot be observed directly now. The tremendously long intervals of time separating the single steps in this process make it impossible to reproduce the process as it occurred in nature under available laboratory conditions.

There still remains, however, the problem of the artificial synthesis of organisms but for its solution a very detailed knowledge of the most intimate, internal structure of living things is essential. Even the synthesis of comparatively simple organic combinations can be accomplished only when one possesses a more or less complete understanding of the atomic arrangement of their molecules. This, of course, would apply even more so in the case of such complex systems as organisms. We are still too far removed from such a comprehensive knowledge of the living organism to even dream of attempting their chemical synthesis. For the present research into the origin of life must, therefore, be restricted to studies of a purely analytical character.

We are faced with a colossal problem of investigating each separate stage of the evolutionary process as it was sketched here. We must delve into the properties of proteins, we must learn the structure of colloidal organic systems, of enzymes, of protoplasmic organization, etc. The road ahead is hard and long but without doubt it leads to the ultimate knowledge of the nature of life. The artificial building or synthesis of living things is a very remote, but not an unattainable goal along this road.

BIBLIOGRAPHY

CHAPTER I

1. E. LIPPMANN, Urzeugung und Lebenskraft. Berlin, 1933.
2. E. RODEMER, Lehre von der Urzeugung bei den Griechen und Römern. Dissert. Giessen, 1928.
3. A. MAKOVELSKI, The Pre-Socratians, 1914 (Russian).
4. P. TANNERY, The first steps in ancient Greek science. St. Petersburg, 1902 (Russian).
5. T. GOMPERZ, Griechische Denker. Berlin und Leipzig, 1908.
6. A. DEBORIN, Readings in the history of philosophy. Vol. 1. Moscow, 1924 (Russian).
7. E. ZELLER, Die Philosophie der Griechen, Leipzig, 1923.
8. H. MEYER, Geschichte der Lehre von den Keimkraften. Bonn, 1914.
9. A. TSCHIRCH, Handbuch der Pharmakognosie. Leipzig, 1909.
10. E. DARMSTAEDTER, Acta Paracelsica. München, 1931.
11. W. BULLOCH, History of Bacteriology in "A System of Bacteriology," Vol. I. London, 1930.
12. T. MEYER-STEINEG and K. ZUDGOV, History of Medicine, 1925 (Russian).
13. I. LAMARCK, Philosophie zoologique. Ch. Martin, 1873.
14. V. OMELJANSKI, Principles of Microbiology, 1922 (Russian).
15. L. JOBLOT, Descriptions et usages de plusieurs nouveaux microscopes. Paris, 1718.
16. E. NORDENSKIÖLD, Die Geschichte der Biologie, Jena, 1926.
17. T. NEEDHAM, Philos. Transactions, No. 490, 1749.
18. L. SPALLANZANI, Saggio di osservazioni microscopiche concernenti il systema della generazione dei sig. di Needham e Buffon, Modena. 1765.
19. L. GAY-LUSSAC, Ann. Chimie, 76, 245, 1810.
20. T. SCHWANN, Ann. physik. Chemie, 41, 184, 1837.

21. FR. SCHULZE, Ann. physik. Chemie, 39, 487, 1836.
22. H. SCHRÖDER und TH. VON DUSCH, Ann. Chem. Pharmacie, 89, 232, 1854.
23. F. POUCHET, Compt. rend., 47, 979, 1858; 48, 148, 546, 1859; 57, 765, 1863;
    Hétérogénie ou traité de la génération spontanée, basé sur de nouvelles experiences. Paris, 1859.
24. L. PASTEUR. Compt. rend., 50, 303, 675, 849, 1860; 51, 348, 1860; 55, 734, 1863;
    Ann. sci. nat. 16, 51, 1861;
    Ann. de chim. et de phys., 3, 64, 1862;
    Études sur la bière, Paris, 1876.
25. H. BASTIAN, The beginnings of life. London, 1872.
26. A. GARDNER, Microbes and ultramicrobes, 1935 (Russian).

CHAPTER II

1. F. ENGELS, Dialectics of nature. Partizdat, 1933 (Russian).
2. W. PREYER, Die Hypothesen über den Ursprung des Lebens. Berlin, 1880.
3. H. RICHTER, Zur Darwinschen Lehre. Schmidts Jahrb. ges. Med., 126, 1865; 148, 1870.
4. J. LIEBIG, Letters on Chemistry, translated by Alexejev, 1861 (Russian).
5. H. VON HELMHOLTZ, Ueber die Entstehung des Planetensystems. Vorträge und Reden. Braunschweig, 1884.
6. H. VON HELMHOLTZ, Handbuch der theoretischen Physik. Introduction by Thompson and Tait. Braunschweig, 1874.
7. CH. LIPMAN, Am. Museum Novitates, 588, 1932.
8. S. ARRHENIUS, Lehrbuch der kosmischen Physik, 1903.
    Worlds in the making. The evolution of the Universe. 1908.
    The fate of the Planets, 1912 (Russian ed.).
9. S. KOSTYCHEV, The appearance of life on the earth. Gosizdat, 1921 (Russian).

10. J. JEANS, Contemporary development of cosmic physics. Smithsonian Bull., 1927.

The Stars in their Courses. Cambridge, 1931.

11. J. LEWIS, The Physical Review, 46, 1934.

CHAPTER III

1. H. BASTIAN, The beginnings of life. London, 1872.

Studies in heterogenesis, London, 1903.

2. FR. DARWIN, Life and letters of Ch. Darwin, London, 1887.

3. A. WEISMANN, Vorträge über die Deszendenztheorie. Jena, 1902.

4. E. HAECKEL, Generelle Morphologie der Organismen. Berlin, 1866.

5. E. HAECKEL, Natürliche Schöpfungsgeschichte. Berlin, 1878.

6. E. PFLÜGER, Ueber die physiologische Verbrennung in den ledendigen Organismen. Arch. gesam. Physiol., 10, 1875.

7. E. ABDERHALDEN, Handbook of physiological Chemistry. (Russian ed. 1934).

8. F. ALLEN, What is Life? Proc. Birmingham Natural History and Philosophical Soc., 11, 1899.

9. H. OSBORN, The origin and evolution of life. London, 1918.

10. V. OMELJANSKI., Principles of microbiology, 1922 (Russian).

11. M. TRAUBE, Zbl. med. Wiss., 95, 609, 1864; 97, 113, 1866; Arch. physiol., 87, 129, 1867.

12. O. BÜTSCHLI, Untersuchungen über microscopische Schäume und das Protoplasma. Leipzig, 1892.

13. L. RHUMBLER, Ergebn. Anat. Entwichklungsgesch., 15, 1906.

14. S. LEDUC, Les bases physiques de la vie, Paris, 1907.

G. BOSSE, From inanimate to animate, Vologda 1925 (Russian).

15. —. KUCKUCK, Lösung des Problems der Urzeugung. Leipzig, 1907.

16. W. PREYER, Die Hypothesen über den Ursprung des Lebens. Berlin, 1880.

17. S. Kostychev, The appearance of life on earth. Gosizdat, 1921 (Russian).

CHAPTER IV

1. The Henry Draper Catalogue, Ann. Harv. Obs., 91-99, 1918–1924;
   The Henry Draper Extension, Ann. Harv. Obs., 100, 1925.
2. J. S. Plaskett, Publ. Dominion Astrophys. Obs., Victoria, II, No. 16, 1924.
3. H. N. Russell, Publ. Am. Astr. Soc., 3; 22, 1918.
   Russell, Steward, Dugan, Astronomy Vol. II.
4. F. Henroteau and J. P. Henderson, Publ. Dominion Obs., 5, No. 1, 1920; No. 8, 331, 1921.
5. E. P. Waterman, Lick Obs. Bull., 8, No. 243, 1913.
6. W. Rufus, Publ. Astr. Obs., Univ. Mich. 2, 103, 1915;
   R. Sanford, Publ. Astr. Soc. Pacific, 41, 271, 1929.
7. H. von Klüber, Das Vorkommen der chemischen Elemente im Kosmos, Leipzig, 1931.
8. H. Newall, F. Baxandal and C. Butler, Monthly Notices Royal Astr. Soc., 76; 640, 1916;
   F. Lowater, Pop. Astr., 25; 179, 1917.
9. A. Fowler and C. Gregory, Phil. Trans., 213, 351, 1919.
10. C. Rafferty, Phil. Mag., 32; 546, 1916.
11. F. Baldet, Ann. de l' Obs. d'Astr. phys. de Paris, VII, 1926;
    F. Hogg, J. Astr. Soc. Canada, 1929.
12. H. Russell, Nature, No. 3406, 9, II, 1935.
13. A. Adel and V. Slipher, Physic. Rev., 46; 902, 1934.
14. I. Zaslavski, Priroda, No. 3, 219, 1931; No. 8, 754, 1931; No. 6, 17, 1935 (Russian).
15. A. Fersman, Geochemistry, Vols. I-II, Onti, Leningrad, 1934 (Russian).
16. J. and W. Noddack, Die Naturwissenschaften, 35, 1930.
17. —. Melikov and —. Erzizhanovski, J. Chem. Soc., I, 651, 1896 (Russian).
18. V. Vernadski, Outlines of Geochemistry, 1934 (Russian).

19. V. VERNADSKI, Bull. Acad. Sc., I, 174, 1914 (Russian).

20. J. JEANS, Origin of the solar system, Mirovedenje, 21, 1932 (Russian).

21. H. JEFFREYS, Origin of the solar system, Mirovedenje, 19, 1930 (Russian).

22. H. ROWLAND, Preliminary Table of Solar Spectrum Wave Lengths, Chicago, 1896; Revised Table, Carnegie Inst. Washington, 1928.

23. C. ST. JOHN, Mt. Wilson Obs. Contrib., 4, 157, 1913; 117, 348, 1928.

24. M. NEUMAYER, History of the Earth, 1897.

25. L. DE LAUNAY, Gîtes minereaux et metallifique, 1913.

26. S. ARRHENIUS, Life course of a planet. Gosizdat, 1923 (Russian).

27. V. VERNADSKI, Problems of Biogeochemistry. Acad. Sc. Ed., 1935 (Russian).

28. V. VERNADSKI, Bull. Acad. Sc., VII, No. 5, 633, 1931 (Russian).

29. D. MENDELEJEV, Principles of chemistry, I. Gosizdat, 1927 (Russian).

30. S. CLOEZ, Compt. Rend., 86, 1248, 1878.

31. H. HAHN, Liebigs Ann., 129, 57, 1864.

32. K. HARITCHKOV, J. chem. Soc., 825, 1896; 162, 1897 (Russian).

33. B. IPATJEV, Naphtha and its origin, 1922 (Russian).

34. A. GAUTIER, Ann. des miner., 10; 350, 563, 1906.

35. K. KEYSER and A. MOSER, Nitrogen of the Air and its utilization, Moscow, 1929 (Russian); also contributions of the Commissions on Fixed Nitrogen, 1925 (Russian).

CHAPTER V

1. E. HAECKEL, Generelle Morphologie der Organismen. Berlin, 1866.

2. H. F. OSBORN, The origin and evolution of life. London, 1918.

3. V. L. Omeljanski, Principles of Microbiology, 1922 (Russian).

4. A. E. Tchitchibabin, First principles of organic chemistry. Vol. I. 1932 (Russian).

5. A. E. Tchitchibabin, J. Russian physico-chem. Soc., 47, 703, 1915.

6. Ch. Würtz, Compt. Rend., 74, 1361, 1872; 76, 1165, 1873.

7. E. Abderhalden, Textbook of physiological chemistry, 1934. K. Oppenheimer, Chemical bases of living processes, 1934 (Russian ed. Biomedgiz).

8. A. M. Butlerov, Compt. Rend., 53, 145, 1861.

9. C. Neuberg und E. Simon, Ergeb. Enzymforsch., 2, 118, 1933.

10. E. Fischer, Untersuchungen über Aminosäuren, Polypeptide und Proteine. Vols. I-II, Berlin, 1923.

11. S. Cannizzaro, Liebig's Ann. 88, 129, 1853.

12. M. Traube, Ber. Deutsch. Chem. Ges., 15, 659, 2421, 2434; 16, 123, 1883; 18, 1877–1890, 1885.

13. A. Bach, Compt. Rend. 124, 951, 1897; J. Russian physico-chem. Soc., 44, 1, 1912.

14. H. Wieland, Mechanismus der Oxydation und Reduction in lebender Substanz, Hndb. Biochemie, II, 252, 1923.

15. O. Meyerhof, Ergeb. Enzynforsch. 4, 208, 1935.

16. E. Fischer, Ber. Deutsch. Chem. Ges., 22, 97, 1889.

17. O. Löw, J. Prakt. Chem., 33, 321, 1886; Ber. Deutsch. chem. Ges., 22, 475, 1889.

18. H. und A. Euler, Ber. Deutsch. chem. Ges., 39, 45, 1906.

19. Th. Curtius, Ber. Deutsch. chem. Ges., 37, 1904.

20. A. Bach, Personal communication, unpublished results.

21. P. Sabatier, Catalysis in organic chemistry, 1932 (Russian ed.).

22. L. Pasteur, Ostwalds Klassiker, No. 28.

23. W. Marcwald, Ber. Deutsch. chem. Ges., 37, 349, 1368, 1904.

24. A. McKenzie, J. Chem. Soc., 85, 1249, 1904; 87, 1373, 1905; 89, 365, 688, 1906; 91, 1215, 1907.

25. G. BREDIG und F. GERSTNER, Biochem. Z., 250, 414, 1932.
    K. FAJANS, Z. physiol. Chem., 73, 25, 1910.
26. G. BREDIG und M. MINAJEV, Biochem. Z., 249, 241, 1932.
27. F. R. JAPP, Nature, 58, 452, 1898.
28. L. PASTEUR, Revue Sc., 3, 7, 1884.
29. J. H. VAN'T HOFF, Die Lagerung der Atome im Raume, 1894.
30. W. KUHN und BRAUN, Naturwiss., 14, 227, 1929; 18, 183, 1930.
31. ST. MITCHELL, J. Chem. Society, London, 1829, 1930.
32. A. SEMENTZOV, Chemical progress, II, 225, 1933 (Russian).
33. V. VERNADSKI, Bull. Acad. Sc., No. 5, 633, 1931 (Russian).
34. F. ENGELS, Anti-Düring. Moscow 1934 (Russian).
35. M. VERVORN, General Physiology, 1911 (Russian ed.).
36. V. SSADIKOV und N. ZELINSKI, Biochem. Z., 136, 241, 1923; 179, 326, 1926.
37. E. ABDERHALDEN, Z. physiol. Chem., 143, 128, 1925; Fermentforsch., II, 44-119, 1929.
38. N. TROENSEGAARD, Z. physiol. Chem., 112, 86, 1921.
39. N. GAVRILOV, The Protein Problem, 1934 (Russian).
40. A. KIEZEL, The Protein Problem, 1934 (Russian).
41. K. MEYER und H. MARK, Ber. Deutsch. Chem. Ges., 61, 593, 1928.
42. T. SVEDBERG, Z. physiol. Chem., 121, 65, 1926.
43. G. TRIER, Ueber einfache Pflanzenbasen, 1912.

CHAPTER VI

1. V. KURBATOV, Collection of works on applied physiology, Vol. II, 1930 (Russian).
2. H. STAUDINGER, Ber. Deutsch. chem. Ges., 44, 2212, 1911; 53, 1073, 1920; 60, 1782; 61, 2427, 1928; 61, 2575, 1928; 62, 222, 1929; 63, 717, 1930; 63, 921, 1930.
3. M. POLANYI, Naturwiss., 9, 228, 1921.
4. H. PRINGSHEIM, Ber. Deutsch. chem. Ges., 59, 3008, 1926.
5. K. HESS und E. MESSMER, Liebig Ann., 435, 14, 1923.
6. M. BERGMANN, Ber. Deutsch. chem. Ges., 59, 2973, 1926.

7. W. HAWORTH, Ber. Deutsch. chem. Ges., 65 (A), 43, 1932.

8. K. MEYER and G. MARK, The Structure of highly polymerized organic natural compounds. Goschimtechizdat, 1932 (Russian).

9. R. O. HERZOG und W. JANCKE, Ber. Deutsch. chem. Ges., 53, 1920.

10. J. R. KATZ, Chem. Ztg., 49, 1925.

11. R. WILLSTÄTTER, Naturwiss., 15, 585, 1927.

12. S. SÖRENSEN, Kolloid Z., 53, 102, 306, 1930.

13. D. RUBINSTEIN, The Protein Problem. Biomedgiz, 1934 (Russian).

14. Wo. OSTWALD, Kolloid Z., 43, 131, 1927.

15. BUDENBERG DE JONG, Protoplasma, 15, 110, 1932; 235, 174, 1931; 248, 131, 335, 1932.

CHAPTER VII

1. P. SABATIER, Catalysis in organic chemistry, 1932 (Russian ed.).

2. E. K. RIDEAL and H. S. TAYLOR, Catalysis in theory and practice, 1933 (Russian ed.).

3. C. OPPENHEIMER, Die Fermente und ihre Wirkungen. Leipzig, 1925–29.

4. A. OPARIN, Progress of Chemistry, Vol. II, 334, 1933.

5. R. WILLSTÄTTER, Untersuchungen über Enzyme, Berlin, 1928.

6. A. BIERRY, J. GIAJA et V. HENRI, Compt. Rend., 143, 300, 1906; C. r. soc. biol., 60, 479, 1906; 62, 432, 1907; Biochem. Z., 40, 357, 1912.

7. W. BIEDERMANN, Fermentforsch. 4, 258, 1921.

8. W. BIEDERMANN, Biochem. Z., 129, 282; 137, 35, 1923.

9. L. MICHAELIS und PECHSTEIN, Biochem. Z., 59, 77, 1914.

10. N. SCHAPOVALNIKOV, Dissertation. St. Petersburg, 1899 (Russian).

11. E. WALDSCHMIDT-LEITZ, Z. physiol. Chem., 132, 181, 1924.

12. E. WALDSCHMIDT-LEITZ und K. LINDERSTRÖM-LANG, Z. physiol. Chem., 166, 227, 1927.

13. W. LANGENBECK, Ergeb. Enzymforsch., 2, 314, 1933.

14. G. BREDIG und F. GERSTNER, Biochem. Z., 250, 414, 1932.

15. R. KUHN, Z. physiol. Chem., 125, 28, 1923.

16. W. GRASSMANN, Ergeb. Enzymforsch., 1, 129, 1932.

17. F. HOFMEISTER, Die chemische Organization der Zelle, 1901.

18. L. JOST, Lectures on the physiology of plants, 1912 (Russian).

19. V. PALLADIN, Plant physiology, 1912 (Russian).

20. S. KOSTYCHEV, Plant physiology, 1924 (Russian).

21. W. ILJIN, Biochem. Z., 132, 494, 511, 526, 1921.

22. E. LESSER, Biochem. Z., 102, 304, 1920; 119, 108, 1921.

23. F. DENNY, J. Soc. Chem. Ind., 47, 239, 1928; Am. J. Bot., 16, 326, 1929; 17, 483, 1930.

24. N. IVANOV, S. PROKOSCHEV, and M. GARBUNJA, Contributions to practical Botany, 1, 25, 1931 (Russian).

25. H. MOLISCH, Ber. Deutsch. Bot. Gesel., 39, 339, 1921.

26. D. TOLLENAAR, Omzet van Koolhydrat in het Blad van nicot. Tabac. Wageningen, 1925.

27. W. ILJIN, Planta, 10, 170, 1930.

28. "Biochemistry of the Tea Production" 1935 (Russian).

29. A. OPARIN, Ergeb. Enzymforsch., 3, 57, 1934.

30. A. OPARIN und A. KURSANOV, Biochem. Z., 209, 181, 1929; 256, 190, 1932.
    A. OPARIN, S. MANSKAJA und I. GLASUNOW, Biochem. Z., 272, 21, 1934.

31. A. BACH, A. OPARIN und R. WAHNER, Biochem. Z., 180, 363, 1927.

32. V. PALLADIN und E. POPOV, Biochem. Z., 128, 487, 1922.

33. A. OPARIN und A. BACH, Biochem. Z., 148, 476, 1924.
    A. OPARIN und S. RISSKINA, Biochem. Z., 252, 8, 1932.

34. A. KURSANOV, Biochemia, 1, 269, 411, 1936 (Russian).
    B. RUBIN, Biochemia, 1, 467, 1936; 2, 423, 1937 (Russian).
    N. SISSAKJAN, Biochemia, 2, 263, 1937 (Russian).

35. A. OPARIN, Enzymologia, 4, 13, 1937.

36. R. WILLSTÄTTER und E. BAMANN, Z. physiol. Chem., 180, 127, 1928.
37. E. WALDSCHMIDT-LEITZ, Naturwiss., 18, 644, 1930.
38. W. GRASSMANN, Erg. Enzymforsch., 1, 129, 1932.
39. K. MOTHES, Ber. Deutsch. Bot. Gesel., 51, 31, 1933.

CHAPTER VIII

1. B. KOZO-POLJANSKI, Outline of a Theory of Symbiogenesis, 1924 (Russian).
2. B. KELLER, Botany on a physiological basis. Selkhozgiz, 1933 (Russian).
3. W. GRASSMANN, Ergeb. Enzymforsch., 1, 129, 1932.
4. A. PASCHER, Ber. Deutsch. Bot. Gesel., 33, 427, 1915.
   O. RICHTER, Ber. Deutsch. Bot. Gesel., 21, 494, 1903.
   CHARPENTIER, Compt. rend. 134, 672, 1902.
5. K. HARDER, Z. Bot., 9, 145, 1917.
6. V. PALLADIN, Rev. génér. Bot., 6, 201, 1894; 8, 225, 1896; 13, 18, 1901; Ber. Deutsch. Bot. Gesel., 20, 1902.
   LINDET, Compt. rend. 152, 775, 1911.
7. J. BOEHM, Bot. Z., 41, 54, 1883; I. LAURENT, Compt. rend., 125, 887, 1897; 135, 870, 1902; MOLLIARD, Compt. rend., 141, 389, 1905; 142, 49, 1906; LJUBIMENKO, Compt. rend., 143, 130, 516, 1906; G. PETROV, Nitrogen assimilation by higher plants in the light and in the dark, 1917 (Russian).
8. S. VINOGRADSKI, Ann. Inst. Pasteur, 4, 213, 257, 760, 1890; 5, 92, 577, 1891; Cbl. Bakt. 2, 415, 1896.
9. H. F. OSBORN, The origin and evolution of life. London, 1918.
10. V. OMELJANSKI, Principles of Microbiology, 1922 (Russian).
11. I. LOTSY, Vorträge über botanische Stammgeschichte, Vol. I. Jena, 1907.
12. V. VERNADSKI, Biosphere. Leningrad, 1926 (Russian).

13. F. D'HERELLE, The bacteriophage and its behavior. London, 1926.

14. P. HANDUROY, Les ultravirus et les formes filtrantes des microbes. Paris, 1929.

15. D. NOVOGROUDSKJI, Priroda No. 12, 31, 1934 (Russian).

16. M. TRAUBE, Ber. Deutsch. Chem. Gesel., 15, 659, 2421, 2434; 16, 123, 1883; 18, 1877, 1890, 1885.

17. R. ENGEL, Compt. rend., 110, 786, 1890.

18. A. BACH, Ber. Deutsch. chem. Gesel., 42, 4463, 1909.

19. E. PFLÜGER, Arch. ges. Physiol., 10, 251, 1875.

20. N. PFEFFER, Landw. Jahrb., 7, 805, 1878.

21. S. KOSTYCHEV, Studies on the anaerobic respiration of plants, 1907 (Russian).

22. S. KOSTYCHEV, The physiology of plants, I, 1933.

23. O. MEYERHOF, Chemical dynamics of living phenomena, 1926.

24. G. EMBDEN und F. KRAUS, Biochem. Z., 45, 1, 1912.

25. O. MEYERHOF, Ergeb. Enzymforsch., 4, 208, 1935.

26. A. KLUYVER, Ergeb. Enzymforsch, 4, 230, 1935; K. BERHAUER, Grundzüge der Chemie und Biochemie der Zuckerarten, Berlin, 1933.

27. H. MOLISCH, Die Purpurbakterien, 1907.

28. C. VAN NIEL, Contributions to Marine Biology (Stanford Univ.), 161, 1930.

29. F. WEIGERT, Z. physik. Chem., 106, 313, 383, 1923.

30. A. BACH, Arch. sc. phys. et. natur., 5, 1898.

31. O. WARBURG, Katalytische Wirkung der lebender Substanz. Berlin, 1928

32. T. THUNBERG, Z. physik. Chem., 106, 305, 1923.

33. R. WURMSER, Bull. Soc. Chim. Biol., 5, 305, 1923; Arch. Phys. Biol., 1, 33.

34. A. STOLL, Naturwiss., 995, 1932.

35. A. BERTHO, Die Essiggärung, Ergeb. Enzymforsch., I, 231, 1932; K. BERNHAUER, Biochemie der oxydativen Gärungen, Ergeb. Enzymforsch., 3, 185, 1934.

36. O. MEYERHOF, Arch. gesam. Physiol., 164, 353, 1916.

37. R. WILLSTÄTTER und A. STOLL, Untersuchungen uber die Assimilation der kohlensäure. Berlin, 1918.
38. H. KAUTSKY, Ber. Deutsch. Chem. Gesel., 65, 1762, 1932.
39. W. OSTWALD, Kolloid Z., 33, 356, 1932.
40. K. NOACK, Photosynthese. Hndb. Naturwiss., 1932.
41. A. BACH, Chemistry of the respiratory processes. J. Russian physico-chem. Soc., 1912 (Russian).
42. V. PALLADIN, Ber. Deutsch. bot. Gesel., 30, 104, 1912; Z. Gärungsphysiol., 1, 91, 1912.
43. A. OPARIN, Biochem. Z., 182, 155, 1927.
44. O. WARBURG, Nobelvortrag, Angew. Chem. 1, 1932.
45. D. KEILIN, Ergeb. Enzymforsch., 2, 239, 1933.

INDEX OF NAMES

INDEX OF SUBJECTS

CATALOGUE OF DOVER BOOKS

Nature

AN INTRODUCTION TO BIRD LIFE FOR BIRD WATCHERS, Aretas A. Saunders. Fine, readable introduction to birdwatching. Includes a great deal of basic information on about 160 different varieties of wild birds—elementary facts not easily found elsewhere. Complete guide to identification procedures, methods of observation, important habits of birds, finding nests, food, etc. "Could make bird watchers of readers who never suspected they were vulnerable to that particular virus," CHICAGO SUNDAY TRIBUNE. Unabridged, corrected edition. Bibliography. Index. 22 line drawings by D. D'Ostilio. Formerly "The Lives of Wild Birds." 256pp. 5⅜ x 8½.   T1139 Paperbound **$1.00**

LIFE HISTORIES OF NORTH AMERICAN BIRDS, Arthur Cleveland Bent. Bent's historic, all-encompassing series on North American birds, originally produced under the auspices of the Smithsonian Institution, now being republished in its entirety by Dover Publications. The twenty-volume collection forms the most comprehensive, most complete, most-used source of information in existence. Each study describes in detail the characteristics, range, distribution, habits, migratory patterns, courtship procedures, plumage, eggs, voice, enemies, etc. of the different species and subspecies of the birds that inhabit our continent, utilizing reports of hundreds of contemporary observers as well as the writings of the great naturalists of the past. Invaluable to the ornithologist, conservationist, amateur naturalist, and birdwatcher. All books in the series contain numerous photographs to provide handy guides for identification and study.

LIFE HISTORIES OF NORTH AMERICAN BIRDS OF PREY. Including hawks, eagles, falcons, buzzards, condors, owls, etc. Index. Bibliographies of 923 items. 197 full-page plates containing close to 400 photographs. Total of 907pp. 5⅜ x 8½. Vol. I: T931 Paperbound **$2.50**
Vol. II: T932 Paperbound **$2.50**
The set Paperbound **$5.00**

LIFE HISTORIES OF NORTH AMERICAN SHORE BIRDS. Including 81 varieties of such birds as sandpipers, woodcocks, snipes, phalaropes, oyster catchers, and many others. Index for each volume. Bibliographies of 449 entries. 121 full-page plates including over 200 photographs. Total of 860 pp. 5⅜ x 8½. Vol. I: T933 Paperbound **$2.35**
Vol. II: T934 Paperbound **$2.35**
The set Paperbound **$4.70**

LIFE HISTORIES OF NORTH AMERICAN WILD FOWL. Including 73 varieties of ducks, geese, mergansers, swans, etc. Index for each volume. Bibliographies of 268 items. 106 full-page plates containing close to 200 photographs. Total of 685pp. 5⅜ x 8½.
Vol. I: T285 Paperbound **$2.50**
Vol. II: T286 Paperbound **$2.50**
The set Paperbound **$5.00**

LIFE HISTORIES OF NORTH AMERICAN GULLS AND TERNS. 50 different varieties of gulls and terns. Index. Bibliography. 93 plates including 149 photographs. xii + 337pp. 5⅜ x 8½.
T1029 Paperbound **$2.75**

LIFE HISTORIES OF NORTH AMERICAN GALLINACEOUS BIRDS. Including partridge, quail, grouse, pheasant, pigeons, doves, and others. Index. Bibliography. 93 full-page plates including 170 photographs. xiii + 490pp. 5⅜ x 8½.   T1028 Paperbound **$2.75**

THE MALAY ARCHIPELAGO, Alfred Russel Wallace. The record of the explorations (8 years, 14,000 miles) of the Malay Archipelago by a great scientific observer. A contemporary of Darwin, Wallace independently arrived at the concept of evolution by natural selection, applied the new theories of evolution to later genetic discoveries, and made significant contributions to biology, zoology, and botany. This work is still one of the classics of natural history and travel. It contains the author's reports of the different native peoples of the islands, descriptions of the island groupings, his accounts of the animals, birds, and insects that flourished in this area. The reader is carried through strange lands, alien cultures, and new theories, and will share in an exciting, unrivalled travel experience. Unabridged reprint of the 1922 edition, with 62 drawings and maps. 3 appendices, one on cranial measurements. xvii + 515pp. 5⅜ x 8.   T187 Paperbound **$2.00**

THE TRAVELS OF WILLIAM BARTRAM, edited by Mark Van Doren. This famous source-book of American anthropology, natural history, geography is the record kept by Bartram in the 1770's, on travels through the wilderness of Florida, Georgia, the Carolinas. Containing accurate and beautiful descriptions of Indians, settlers, fauna, flora, it is one of the finest pieces of Americana ever written. Introduction by Mark Van Doren. 13 original illustrations. Index. 448pp. 5⅜ x 8.   T13 Paperbound **$2.00**

COMMON SPIDERS OF THE UNITED STATES, J. H. Emerton. Only non-technical, but thorough, reliable guide to spiders for the layman. Over 200 spiders from all parts of the country, arranged by scientific classification, are identified by shape and color, number of eyes, habitat and range, habits, etc. Full text, 501 line drawings and photographs, and valuable introduction explain webs, poisons, threads, capturing and preserving spiders, etc. Index. New synoptic key by S. W. Frost. xxiv + 225pp. 5⅜ x 8.   T223 Paperbound **$1.45**

LIFE HISTORIES OF NORTH AMERICAN MARSH BIRDS. A wealth of data on 54 different kinds of marsh bird (flamingo, ibis, bittern, heron, egret, crane, crake, rail, coot, etc.). Index. Bibliography. 98 full-page plates containing 179 black-and-white photographs. xiv + 392pp. 5⅜ x 8½. T1082 Paperbound **$2.75**

LIFE HISTORIES OF NORTH AMERICAN DIVING BIRDS. Thirty-six different diving birds including grebe, loon, auk, murre, puffin, and the like. Index. Bibliography. 55 full-page plates (92 photographs). xiv + 239pp. 5⅜ x 8½. T1091 Paperbound **$2.75**

LIFE HISTORIES OF NORTH AMERICAN WOOD WARBLERS. Covers about 58 types. Index. Bibliography. 83 full-page plates containing 125 black-and-white photographs. xi + 734pp. of text. 5⅜ x 8½.
Vol. I: T1153 Paperbound **$2.50**
Vol. II: T1154 Paperbound **$2.50**
The set Paperbound **$5.00**

LIFE HISTORIES OF NORTH AMERICAN FLYCATCHERS, LARKS, SWALLOWS, AND THEIR ALLIES. Complete information on about 78 different varieties. Index. Bibliography. 70 full-page plates (117 photographs). xi + 555pp. of text. 5⅜ x 8½. T1090 Paperbound **$2.75**

AMERICAN WILDLIFE, AND PLANTS: A GUIDE TO WILDLIFE FOOD HABITS, A. C. Martin, H. S. Zim, A. L. Nelson. Result of 75 years of research by U. S. Fish and Wildlife Service into food and feeding habits of more than 1,000 species of birds and mammals, their distribution in America, migratory habits, and the most important plant-animal relationships. Treats over 300 common species of birds, fur and game animals, small mammals, hoofed browsers, fish, amphibians, reptiles by group, giving data on their food, ranges, habits and economies. Also focuses on the different genera of plants that furnish food for our wildlife, animals that use them, and their value. Only thorough study of its kind in existence. "Of immense value to sportsmen, naturalists, bird students, foresters, landscape architects, botanists," NATURE. "Undoubtedly an essential handbook," SCIENTIFIC MONTHLY. Unabridged republication of 1951 edition. Over 600 illustrations, maps, etc. Classified bibliography. Index. x + 500pp. 5⅜ x 8. T793 Paperbound **$2.50**

HOW TO KNOW THE WILD FLOWERS, Mrs. Wm. Starr Dana. A Guide to the names, haunts, and habits of wild flowers. Well-known classic of nature lore. Informative and delightful. Plants classified by color and season of their typical flowers for easy identification. Thorough coverage of more than 1,000 important flowering, berry-bearing and foliage plants of Eastern and Central United States and Canada. Complete botanical information about each important plant. Also history, uses, folklore, habitat, etc. Nomenclature modernized by C. J. Hylander. 174 full-page illustrations by Marion Satterlee. xii + 481pp. 5⅜ x 8½. T332 Paperbound **$2.00**

HOW PLANTS GET THEIR NAMES, L. H. Bailey. Introduction to botanical nomenclature for the horticulturist and garden-lover. Discussions of Carl Linnaeus, "father of botany," and analysis of his definitions of genus and species, a brief history of the science before Linnaean systematization, a chapter on plant identification, a mine of information on the rules of nomenclature and Latin stems and word-endings used in botanical nomenclature, with pronunciation guides. An important section contains a full list of generic terms of horticultural literature and common Latin words and their English botanical applications and meanings. "Written with knowledge and authority, charm and eloquence and poetic imagination on the varied aspects of the author's specialty," New York Times. 11 illustrations. vi + 181pp. 5⅜ x 8½. T796 Paperbound **$1.25**

THE CACTACEAE: DESCRIPTIONS AND ILLUSTRATIONS OF PLANTS OF THE CACTUS FAMILY, N. L. Britton and J. N. Rose. Definitive study of plants of the Cactus Family. The authors devoted more than 15 years of research to this monumental task and produced an exhaustive, rigorously scientific account never likely to be superseded. 3 major classifications, or tribes, are recognized, under which they arrange and describe in full detail 124 genera and 1,235 species of cactus from all over the world. Complete data on each species: leaves, flowers, seeds, fruit, distribution, growth, spines, stem structure, economic uses, etc. In addition, 125 keys facilitate identification of genera and species. For teachers and students of botany and forestry, naturalists, conservationists, and nature lovers, this is an indispensable work. Unabridged republication of second (1937) edition. First edition originally published under the auspices of the Carnegie Institution, Washington, D.C. 4 vols. bound as 2. 1279 illustrations, photographs, sketches, etc. 137 plates. Total of xxvii + 1039pp. 8 x 10¼. T771 Clothbound, 2-volume set **$20.00**

GUIDE TO SOUTHERN TREES, Elwood S. and J. George Harrar. A handy, comprehensive 700-page manual with numerous illustrations and information on more than 350 different kinds of trees, covering the entire area south of the Mason-Dixon line from the Atlantic Ocean to the Florida Keys and western Texas. Descriptions range from the common pine, cypress, walnut, beech, and elm to such rare species as Franklinia, etc. A mine of information on leaves, flowers, twigs, bark, fruit, distribution etc. of each kind of tree. Eminently readable, written in non-technical language, it is an indispensable handbook for all lovers of the outdoors. Revised edition. Index. 81-item bibliography. Glossary. 200 full-page illustrations. ix + 709pp. 4⅝ x 6⅜. T945 Paperbound **$2.35**

WESTERN FOREST TREES, James B. Berry. For years a standard guide to the trees of the Western United States. Covers over 70 different subspecies, ranging from the Pacific shores to western South Dakota, New Mexico, etc. Much information on range and distribution, growth habits, appearance, leaves, bark, fruit, twigs, etc. for each tree discussed, plus material on wood of the trees and its uses. Basic division (Trees with needle-like leaves, scale-like leaves, and compound, lobed or divided, and simple broadleaf trees), along with almost 100 illustrations (mostly full-size) of buds, leaves, etc., aids in easy identification of just about any tree of the area. Many subsidiary keys. Revised edition. Introduction. 12 photos. 85 illustrations by Mary E. Eaton. Index. xii + 212pp. 5⅜ x 8.
T1138 Paperbound **$1.35**

MANUAL OF THE TREES OF NORTH AMERICA (EXCLUSIVE OF MEXICO), Charles Sprague Sargent. The magnum opus of the greatest American dendrologist. Based on 44 years of original research, this monumental work is still the most comprehensive and reliable sourcebook on the subject. Includes 185 genera and 717 species of trees (and many shrubs) found in the U.S., Canada, and Alaska. 783 illustrative drawings by C. E. Faxon and Mary W. Gill. An all-encompassing lifetime reference book for students, teachers of botany and forestry, naturalists, conservationists, and all nature lovers. Includes an 11-page analytical key to genera to help the beginner locate any tree by its leaf characteristics. Within the text over 100 further keys aid in easy identification. Synopsis of families. Glossary. Index. 783 illustrations, 1 map. Total of 1 + 891pp. 5⅜ x 8.
T277 Vol. I Paperbound **$2.25**
T278 Vol. II Paperbound **$2.25**
The set **$4.50**

TREES OF THE EASTERN AND CENTRAL UNITED STATES AND CANADA, W. M. Harlow, Professor of Wood Technology, College of Forestry, State University of N. Y., Syracuse, N. Y. This middle-level text is a serious work covering more than 140 native trees and important escapes, with information on general appearance, growth habit, leaf forms, flowers, fruit, bark, and other features. Commercial use, distribution, habitat, and woodlore are also given. Keys within the text enable you to locate various species with ease. With this book you can identify at sight almost any tree you are likely to encounter; you will know which trees have edible fruit, which are suitable for house planting, and much other useful and interesting information. More than 600 photographs and figures. xiii + 288pp. 4⅝ x 6½.
T395 Paperbound **$1.35**

FRUIT KEY AND TWIG KEY TO TREES AND SHRUBS (FRUIT KEY TO NORTHEASTERN TREES, TWIG TREE TO DECIDUOUS WOODY PLANTS OF EASTERN NORTH AMERICA), W. M. Harlow. The only guides with photographs of every twig and fruit described—especially valuable to the novice. The fruit key (both deciduous trees and evergreens) has an introduction explaining seeding, organs involved, fruit types and habits. The twig key introduction treats growth and morphology. In the keys proper, identification is easy and almost automatic. This exceptional work, widely used in university courses, is especially useful for identification in winter, or from the fruit or seed only. Over 350 photos, up to 3 times natural size. Bibliography, glossary, index of common and scientific names, in each key. xvii + 125pp. 5⅝ x 8⅜.
T511 Paperbound **$1.25**

HOW TO KNOW THE FERNS, F. T. Parsons. Ferns, among our most lovely native plants, are all too little known. This modern classic of nature lore will enable the layman to identify any American fern he is likely to come across. After an introduction on the structure and life of ferns, the 57 most important ferns are fully pictured and described (arranged upon a simple identification key). Index of Latin and English names. 61 illustrations and 42 full-page plates. xiv + 215pp. 5⅜ x 8.
T740 Paperbound **$1.35**

OUR SMALL NATIVE ANIMALS: THEIR HABITS AND CARE, R. Snedigar, Curator of Reptiles, Chicago Zoological Park. An unusual nature handbook containing all the vital facts of habitat, distribution, foods, and special habits in brief life histories of 114 different species of squirrels, chipmunks, rodents, larger mammals, birds, amphibians, lizards and snakes. Liberally sprinkled with first-hand anecdotes. A wealth of information on capturing and caring for these animals: proper pens and cages, correct diet, curing diseases, special equipment required, etc. Addressed to the teacher interested in classroom demonstrations, the camp director, and to anyone who ever wanted a small animal for a pet. Revised edition, New preface. Index. 62 halftones. 14 line drawings. xviii + 296pp. 5⅜ x 8⅛.
T1022 Paperbound **$1.75**

INSECT LIFE AND INSECT NATURAL HISTORY, S. W. Frost. Unusual for emphasizing habits, social life, and ecological relations of insects, rather than more academic aspects of classification and morphology. Prof. Frost's enthusiasm and knowledge are everywhere evident as he discusses insect associations, and specialized habits like leaf-mining, leaf-rolling, and casemaking, the gall insects, the boring insects, aquatic insects, etc. He examines all sorts of matters not usually covered in general works, such as: insects as human food; insect music and musicians; insect response to electric and radio waves; use of insects in art and literature. The admirably executed purpose of this book, which covers the middle ground between elementary treatment and scholarly monographs, is to excite the reader to observe for himself. Over 700 illustrations. Extensive bibliography. x + 524pp. 5⅜ x 8.
T517 Paperbound **$2.45**

Biological Sciences

AN INTRODUCTION TO GENETICS, A. H. Sturtevant and G. W. Beadle. A very thorough exposition of genetic analysis and the chromosome mechanics of higher organisms by two of the world's most renowned biologists, A. H. Sturtevant, one of the founders of modern genetics, and George Beadle, Nobel laureate in 1958. Does not concentrate on the biochemical approach, but rather more on observed data from experimental evidence and results . . . from Drosophila and other life forms. Some chapter titles: Sex chromosomes; Sex-Linkage; Autosomal Inheritance;; Chromosome Maps; Intra-Chromosomal Rearrangements; Inversions—and Incomplete Chromosomes; Translocations; Lethals; Mutations; Heterogeneous Populations; Genes and Phenotypes; The Determination and Differentiation of Sex; etc. Slightly corrected reprint of 1939 edition. New preface by Drs. Sturtevant and Beadle. 1 color plate. 126 figures. Bibliographies. Index. 391pp. 5⅜ x 8½.   S306 Paperbound **$2.00**

THE GENETICAL THEORY OF NATURAL SELECTION, R. A. Fisher. 2nd revised edition of a vital reviewing of Darwin's Selection Theory in terms of particulate inheritance, by one of the great authorities on experimental and theoretical genetics. Theory is stated in mathematical form. Special features of particulate inheritance are examined: evolution of dominance, maintenance of specific variability, mimicry and sexual selection, etc. 5 chapters on man and his special circumstances as a social animal. 16 photographs. Bibliography. Index. x + 310pp. 5⅜ x 8.   S466 Paperbound **$2.00**

THE ORIENTATION OF ANIMALS: KINESES, TAXES AND COMPASS REACTIONS, Gottfried S. Fraenkel and Donald L. Gunn. A basic work in the field of animal orientations. Complete, detailed survey of everything known in the subject up to 1940s, enlarged and revised to cover major developments to 1960. Analyses of simpler types of orientation are presented in Part I: kinesis, klinotaxis, tropotaxis, telotaxis, etc. Part II covers more complex reactions originating from temperature changes, gravity, chemical stimulation, etc. The two-light experiment and unilateral blinding are dealt with, as is the problem of determinism or volition in lower animals. The book has become the universally-accepted guide to all who deal with the subject—zoologists, biologists, psychologists, and the like. Second, enlarged edition, revised to 1960. Bibliography of over 500 items. 135 illustrations. Indices. xiii + 376pp. 5⅜ x 8½.   T786 Paperbound **$2.25**

THE BEHAVIOUR AND SOCIAL LIFE OF HONEYBEES, C. R. Ribbands. Definitive survey of all aspects of honeybee life and behavior; completely scientific in approach, but written in interesting, everyday language that both professionals and laymen will appreciate. Basic coverage of physiology, anatomy, sensory equipment; thorough account of honeybee behavior in the field (foraging activities, nectar and pollen gathering, how individuals find their way home and back to food areas, mating habits, etc.); details of communication in various field and hive situations. An extensive treatment of activities within the hive community—food sharing, wax production, comb building, swarming, the queen, her life and relationship with the workers, etc. A must for the beekeeper, natural historian, biologist, entomologist, social scientist, et al. "An indispensable reference," J. Hambleton, BₑES. "Recommended in the strongest of terms," AMERICAN SCIENTIST. 9 plates. 66 figures. Indices. 693-item bibliography. 252pp. 5⅜ x 8½.   T1137 Paperbound **$2.00**

BIRD DISPLAY: AN INTRODUCTION TO THE STUDY OF BIRD PSYCHOLOGY, E. A. Armstrong. The standard work on bird display, based on extensive observation by the author and reports of other observers. This important contribution to comparative psychology covers the behavior and ceremonial rituals of hundreds of birds from gannet and heron to birds of paradise and king penguins. Chapters discuss such topics as the ceremonial of the gannet, ceremonial gaping, disablement reactions, the expression of emotions, the evolution and function of social ceremonies, social hierarchy in bird life, dances of birds and men, songs, etc. Free of technical terminology, this work will be equally interesting to psychologists and zoologists as well as bird lovers of all backgrounds. 32 photographic plates. New introduction by the author. List of scientific names of birds. Bibliography. 3-part index. 431pp. 5⅜ x 8½.   T1128 Paperbound **$2.00**

THE SPECIFICITY OF SEROLOGICAL REACTIONS, Karl Landsteiner. With a Chapter on Molecular Structure and Intermolecular Forces by Linus Pauling. Dr. Landsteiner, winner of the Nobel Prize in 1930 for the discovery of the human blood groups, devoted his life to fundamental research and played a leading role in the development of immunology. This authoritative study is an account of the experiments he and his colleagues carried out on antigens and serological reactions with simple compounds. Comprehensive coverage of the basic concepts of immunolgy includes such topics as: The Serological Specificity of Proteins, Antigens, Antibodies, Artificially Conjugated Antigens, Non-Protein Cell Substances such as polysaccharides, etc., Antigen-Antibody Reactions (Toxin Neutralization, Precipitin Reactions, Agglutination, etc.). Discussions of toxins, bacterial proteins, viruses, hormones, enzymes, etc. in the context of immunological phenomena. New introduction by Dr. Merrill Chase of the Rockefeller Institute. Extensive bibliography and bibliography of author's writings. Index. xviii + 330pp. 5⅜ x 8½.   S299 Paperbound **$2.00**

CATALOGUE OF DOVER BOOKS

CULTURE METHODS FOR INVERTEBRATE ANIMALS, P. S. Galtsoff, F. E. Lutz, P. S. Welch, J. G. Needham, eds. A compendium of practical experience of hundreds of scientists and technicians, covering invertebrates from protozoa to chordata, in 313 articles on 17 phyla. Explains in great detail food, protection, environment, reproduction conditions, rearing methods, embryology, breeding seasons, schedule of development, much more. Includes at least one species of each considerable group. Half the articles are on class insecta. Introduction. 97 illustrations. Bibliography. Index. xxix + 590pp. 5⅜ x 8. S526 Paperbound **$3.00**

THE BIOLOGY OF THE LABORATORY MOUSE, edited by G. D. Snell. 1st prepared in 1941 by the staff of the Roscoe B. Jackson Memorial Laboratory, this is still the standard treatise on the mouse, assembling an enormous amount of material for which otherwise you spend hours of research. Embryology, reproduction, histology, spontaneous tumor formation, genetics of tumor transplantation, endocrine secretion & tumor formation, milk, influence & tumor formation, inbred, hybrid animals, parasites, infectious diseases, care & recording. Classified bibliography of 1122 items. 172 figures, including 128 photos. ix + 497pp. 6⅛ x 9¼. S248 Clothbound **$6.00**

MATHEMATICAL BIOPHYSICS: PHYSICO-MATHEMATICAL FOUNDATIONS OF BIOLOGY, N. Rashevsky. One of most important books in modern biology, now revised, expanded with new chapters, to include most significant recent contributions. Vol. 1: Diffusion phenomena, particularly diffusion drag forces, their effects. Old theory of cell division based on diffusion drag forces, other theoretical approaches, more exhaustively treated than ever. Theories of excitation, conduction in nerves, with formal theories plus physico-chemical theory. Vol. 2: Mathematical theories of various phenomena in central nervous system. New chapters on theory of color vision, of random nets. Principle of optimal design, extended from earlier edition. Principle of relational mapping of organisms, numerous applications. Introduces into mathematical biology such branches of math as topology, theory of sets. Index. 236 illustrations. Total of 988pp. 5⅜ x 8. S574 Vol. 1 (Books 1, 2) Paperbound **$2.50** / S575 Vol. 2 (Books 3, 4) Paperbound **$2.50** / 2 vol. set **$5.00**

ELEMENTS OF MATHEMATICAL BIOLOGY, A. J. Lotka. A pioneer classic, the first major attempt to apply modern mathematical techniques on a large scale to phenomena of biology, biochemistry, psychology, ecology, similar life sciences. Partial Contents: Statistical meaning of irreversibility; Evolution as redistribution; Equations of kinetics of evolving systems; Chemical, inter-species equilibrium; parameters of state; Energy transformers of nature, etc. Can be read with profit even by those having no advanced math; unsurpassed as study-reference. Formerly titled ELEMENTS OF PHYSICAL BIOLOGY. 72 figures. xxx + 460pp. 5⅜ x 8. S346 Paperbound **$2.45**

THE BIOLOGY OF THE AMPHIBIA, G. K. Noble, Late Curator of Herpetology at the Am. Mus. of Nat. Hist. Probably the most used text on amphibia, unmatched in comprehensiveness, clarity, detail. 19 chapters plus 85-page supplement cover development; heredity; life history; speciation; adaptation; sex, integument, respiratory, circulatory, digestive, muscular, nervous systems; instinct, intelligence, habits, environment, economic value, relationships, classification, etc. "Nothing comparable to it," C. H. Pope, Curator of Amphibia, Chicago Mus. of Nat. Hist. 1047 bibliographic references. 174 illustrations. 600pp. 5⅜ x 8. S206 Paperbound **$2.98**

STUDIES ON THE STRUCTURE AND DEVELOPMENT OF VERTEBRATES, E. S. Goodrich. A definitive study by the greatest modern comparative anatomist. Exceptional in its accounts of the ossicles of the ear, the separate divisions of the coelom and mammalian diaphragm, and the 5 chapters devoted to the head region. Also exhaustive morphological and phylogenetic expositions of skeleton, fins and limbs, skeletal visceral arches and labial cartilages, visceral clefts and gills, vacular, respiratory, excretory, and peripheral nervous systems, etc., from fish to the higher mammals. 754 illustrations. 69 page biographical study by C. C. Hardy. Bibliography of 1186 references. "What an undertaking . . . to write a textbook which will summarize adequately and succinctly all that has been done in the realm of Vertebrate Morphology these recent years," Journal of Anatomy. Index. Two volumes. Total 906pp. 5⅜ x 8. Two vol. set S449-50 Paperbound **$5.00**

A TREATISE ON PHYSIOLOGICAL OPTICS, H. von Helmholtz, Ed. by J. P. C. Southall. Unmatched for thoroughness, soundness, and comprehensiveness, this is still the most important work ever produced in the field of physiological optics. Revised and annotated, it contains everything known about the subject up to 1925. Beginning with a careful anatomical description of the eye, the main body of the text is divided into three general categories: The Dioptrics of the Eye (covering optical imagery, blur circles on the retina, the mechanism of accommodation, chromatic aberration, etc.); The Sensations of Vision (including stimulation of the organ of vision, simple and compound colors, the intensity and duration of light, variations of sensitivity, contrast, etc.); and The Perceptions of Vision (containing movements of the eyes, the monocular field of vision, direction, perception of depth, binocular double vision, etc.). Appendices cover later findings on optical imagery, refraction, ophthalmoscopy, and many other matters. Unabridged, corrected republication of the original English translation of the third German edition. 3 volumes bound as 2. Complete bibliography, 1911-1925. Indices. 312 illustrations. 6 full-page plates, 3 in color. Total of 1,749pp. 5⅜ x 8. Two-volume set S15, 16 Clothbound **$15.00**

INTRODUCTION TO PHYSIOLOGICAL OPTICS, James P. C. Southall, former Professor of Physics in Columbia University. Readable, top-flight introduction, not only for beginning students of optics, but also for other readers—physicists, biochemists, illuminating engineers, optometrists, psychologists, etc. Comprehensive coverage of such matters as the Organ of Vision (structure of the eyeball, the retina, the dioptric system, monocular and binocular vision, adaptation, etc.); The Optical System of the Eye (reflex images in the cornea and crystalline lens, Emmetropia and Ametropia, accommodation, blur circles on retina); Eye-Glasses; Eye Defects; Movements of the Eyeball in its Socket; Rod and Cone Vision; Color Vision; and other similar topics. Index. 134 figures. x +426pp. 5⅜ x 8.   S924 Paperbound **$2.25**

LIGHT, COLOUR AND VISION, Yves LeGrand. A thorough examination of the eye as a receptor of radiant energy and as a mechanism (the retina) consisting of light-sensitive cells which absorb light of various wave lengths—probably the most complete and authoritative treatment of this subject in print. Originally prepared as a series of lectures given at the Institute of Optics in Paris, subsequently enlarged for book publication. Partial contents: Radiant Energy—concept, nature, theories, etc., Sources of Radiation—artificial and natural, the Visual Receptor, Photometric Quantities, Units, Calculations, Retinal Illumination, Trivariance of Vision, Colorimetry, Luminance Difference Thresholds, Anatomy of the Retina, Theories of Vision, Photochemistry and Electro-physiology of the Retina, etc. Appendices, Exercises, with solutions. 500-item bibliography. Authorized translation by R. Hunt, J. Walsh, F. Hunt. Index. 173 illustrations. xiii + 512pp. 5⅜ x 8½.   S979 Clothbound **$10.00**

FINGER PRINTS, PALMS AND SOLES: AN INTRODUCTION TO DERMATOGLYPHICS, Harold Cummins and Charles Midlo. An introduction in non-technical language designed to acquaint the reader with a long-neglected aspect of human biology. Although a chapter dealing with fingerprint identification and the systems of classification used by the FBI, etc. has been added especially for this edition, the main concern of the book is to show how the intricate pattern of ridges and wrinkles on our fingers have a broader significance, applicable in many areas of science and life. Some topics are: the identification of two types of twins; the resolution of doubtful cases of paternity; racial variation; inheritance; the relation of fingerprints to body measurements, blood groups, criminality, character, etc. Classification and recognition of fundamental patterns and pattern types discussed fully. 149 figures. 49 tables. 361-item bibliography. Index. xii + 319pp. 5⅝ x 8⅜.   T778 Paperbound **$1.95**

Classics and histories

ANTONY VAN LEEUWENHOEK AND HIS "LITTLE ANIMALS," edited by Clifford Dobell. First book to treat extensively, accurately, life and works (relating to protozoology, bacteriology) of first microbiologist, bacteriologist, micrologist. Includes founding papers of protozoology, bacteriology; history of Leeuwenhoek's life; discussions of his microscopes, methods, language. His writing conveys sense of an enthusiastic, naive genius, as he looks at rainwater, pepper water, vinegar, frog's skin, rotifers, etc. Extremely readable, even for non-specialists. "One of the most interesting and enlightening books I have ever read," Dr. C. C. Bass, former Dean, Tulane U. School of Medicine. Only authorized edition. 400-item bibliography. Index. 32 illust. 442pp. 5⅜ x 8.   S594 Paperbound **$2.25**

THE GROWTH OF SCIENTIFIC PHYSIOLOGY, G. J. Goodfield. A compact, superbly written account of how certain scientific investigations brought about the emergence of the distinct science of physiology. Centers principally around the mechanist-vitalist controversy prior to the development of physiology as an independent science, using the arguments which raged around the problem of animal heat as its chief illustration. Covers thoroughly the efforts of clinicians and naturalists and workers in chemistry and physics to solve these problems—from which the new discipline arose. Includes the theories and contributions of: Aristotle, Galen, Harvey, Boyle, Bernard, Benjamin Franklin, Palmer, Gay-Lussac, Priestley, Spallanzani, and many others. 1960 publication. Biographical bibliography. 174pp. 5 x 7½.   T1066 Clothbound **$3.00**

MICROGRAPHIA, Robert Hooke. Hooke, 17th century British universal scientific genius, was a major pioneer in celestial mechanics, optics, gravity, and many other fields, but his greatest contribution was this book, now reprinted entirely from the original 1665 edition, which gave microscopy its first great impetus. With all the freshness of discovery, he describes fully his microscope, and his observations of cork, the edge of a razor, insects' eyes, fabrics, and dozens of other objects. 38 plates, full-size or larger, contain all the original illustrations. This book is also a fundamental classic in the fields of combustion and heat theory, light and color theory, botany and zoology, hygrometry, and many other fields. It contains such farsighted predictions as the famous anticipation of artificial silk. The final section is concerned with Hooke's telescopic observations of the moon and stars. 323pp. 5⅜ x 8.   T8 Paperbound **$2.00**

CATALOGUE OF DOVER BOOKS

Medicine

CLASSICS OF MEDICINE AND SURGERY, edited by C. N. B. Camac. 12 greatest papers in medical history, 11 in full: Lister's "Antiseptic Principle;" Harvey's "Motion in the Heart and Blood;" Auenbrugger's "Percussion of the Chest;" Laënnec's "Auscultation and the Stethoscope;" Jenner's "Inquiry into Smallpox Vaccine," 2 related papers; Morton's "Administering Sulphuric Ether," letters to Warren, "Physiology of Ether;" Simpson's "A New Anaesthetic Agent;" Holmes' "Puerperal Fever." Biographies, portraits of authors, bibliographies. Formerly "Epoch-making Contributions to Medicine, Surgery, and the Allied Sciences." Introduction. 14 illus. 445pp. 5⅜ x 8. S539 Paperbound **$2.25**

A WAY OF LIFE, Sir William Osler. The complete essay, stating his philosophy of life, as given at Yale University by this great physician and teacher. 30 pages. Copies limited, no more than 1 to a customer. Free.

SOURCE BOOK OF MEDICAL HISTORY, compiled, annotated by Logan Clendening, M.D. Unequalled collection of 139 greatest papers in medical history, by 120 authors, covers almost every area: pathology, asepsis, preventive medicine, bacteriology, physiology, etc. Hippocrates, Gain, Vesalius, Malpighi, Morgagni, Boerhave, Pasteur, Walter Reed, Florence Nightingale, Lavoisier, Claude Bernard, 109 others, give view of medicine unequalled for immediacy. Careful selections give heart of each paper save you reading time. Selections from non-medical literature show lay-views of medicine: Aristophanes, Plato, Arabian Nights, Chaucer, Molière, Dickens, Thackeray, others. "Notable . . . useful to teacher and student alike," Amer. Historical Review. Bibliography. Index. 699pp. 5⅜ x 8. T621 Paperbound **$2.75**

EXPERIMENTS AND OBSERVATIONS ON THE GASTRIC JUICE AND THE PHYSIOLOGY OF DIGESTION, William Beaumont. A gunshot wound which left a man with a 2½ inch hole through his abdomen into his stomach (1822) enabled Beaumont to perform the remarkable experiments set down here. The first comprehensive, thorough study of motions and processes of the stomach, "his work remains a model of patient, persevering investigation. . . . Beaumont is the pioneer physiologist of this country." (Sir William Osler, in his introduction.) 4 illustrations. xi + 280pp. 5⅜ x 8. S527 Paperbound **$1.50**

AN INTRODUCTION TO THE STUDY OF EXPERIMENTAL MEDICINE, Claude Bernard. 90-year-old classic of medical science, only major work of Bernard available in English, records his efforts to transform physiology into exact science. Principles of scientific research illustrated by specific case histories from his work; roles of chance, error, preliminary false conclusions, in leading eventually to scientific truth; use of hypothesis. Much of modern application of mathematics to biology rests on the foundation set down here. New foreword by Professor I. B. Cohen, Harvard Univ. xxv + 266pp. 5⅜ x 8. T400 Paperbound **$1.50**

A WAY OF LIFE, AND OTHER SELECTED WRITINGS, Sir William Osler, Physician and humanist, Osler discourses brilliantly in thought provoking essays and on the history of medicine. He discusses Thomas Browne, Gui Patin, Robert Burton, Michael Servetus, William Beaumont, Laënnec. Includes such favorite writings as the title essay, "The Old Humanities and the New Science," "Creators, Transmitters, and Transmuters," "Books and Men," "The Student Life," and five more of his best discussions of philosophy, religion and literature. 5 photographs. Introduction by G. L. Keynes, M.D., F.R.C.S. Index. xx + 278pp. 5⅜ x 8. T488 Paperbound **$1.50**

THE HISTORY OF SURGICAL ANESTHESIA, Thomas E. Keys. Concise, but thorough and always engrossing account of the long struggle to find effective methods of eliminating pain during surgery, tracing the remarkable story through the centuries to the eventual successes by dedicated researchers, the acceptance of ether, the work of men such as Priestley, Morton, Lundy, and many, many others. Discussions of the developments in local, regional, and spinal anesthesia, etc. "The general reader as well as the medical historian will find material to interest him in this fascinating story," U.S. QUARTERLY BOOKLIST. Revised, enlarged publication of original edition. Introductory essay by C. D. Leake. Concluding chapter by N. A. Gillespie. Appendix by J. F. Fulton. 46 illustrations. New preface by the author. Chronology of events. Extensive bibliographies. Index. xxx + 193pp. 5⅜ x 8½. T1122 Paperbound **$2.00**

A SHORT HISTORY OF ANATOMY AND PHYSIOLOGY FROM THE GREEKS TO HARVEY, Charles Singer. Corrected edition of THE EVOLUTION OF ANATOMY, classic work tracing evolution of anatomy and physiology from prescientific times through Greek & Roman periods, Dark Ages, Renaissance, to age of Harvey and beginning of modern concepts. Centered on individuals, movements, periods that definitely advanced anatomical knowledge: Plato, Diocles, Aristotle, Theophrastus, Herophilus, Erasistratus, the Alexandrians, Galen, Mondino, da Vinci, Linacre, Sylvius, others. Special section on Vesalius; Vesalian atlas of nudes, skeletons, muscle tabulae. Index of names, 20 plates. 270 extremely interesting illustrations of ancient, medieval, Renaissance, Oriental origin. xii + 209pp. 5⅜ x 8. T389 Paperbound **$1.75**

Books Explaining Science and Mathematics

WHAT IS SCIENCE?, N. Campbell. The role of experiment and measurement, the function of mathematics, the nature of scientific laws, the difference between laws and theories, the limitations of science, and many similarly provocative topics are treated clearly and without technicalities by an eminent scientist. "Still an excellent introduction to scientific philosophy," H. Margenau in PHYSICS TODAY. "A first-rate primer . . . deserves a wide audience," SCIENTIFIC AMERICAN. 192pp. 5⅜ x 8.   S43 Paperbound **$1.25**

THE NATURE OF PHYSICAL THEORY, P. W. Bridgman. A Nobel Laureate's clear, non-technical lectures on difficulties and paradoxes connected with frontier research on the physical sciences. Concerned with such central concepts as thought, logic, mathematics, relativity, probability, wave mechanics, etc. he analyzes the contributions of such men as Newton, Einstein, Bohr, Heisenberg, and many others. "Lucid and entertaining . . . recommended to anyone who wants to get some insight into current philosophies of science," THE NEW PHILOSOPHY. Index. xi + 138pp. 5⅜ x 8.   S33 Paperbound **$1.25**

EXPERIMENT AND THEORY IN PHYSICS, Max Born. A Nobel Laureate examines the nature of experiment and theory in theoretical physics and analyzes the advances made by the great physicists of our day: Heisenberg, Einstein, Bohr, Planck, Dirac, and others. The actual process of creation is detailed step-by-step by one who participated. A fine examination of the scientific method at work. 44pp. 5⅜ x 8.   S308 Paperbound **75¢**

THE PSYCHOLOGY OF INVENTION IN THE MATHEMATICAL FIELD, J. Hadamard. The reports of such men as Descartes, Pascal, Einstein, Poincaré, and others are considered in this investigation of the method of idea-creation in mathematics and other sciences and the thinking process in general. How do ideas originate? What is the role of the unconscious? What is Poincaré's forgetting hypothesis? are some of the fascinating questions treated. A penetrating analysis of Einstein's thought processes concludes the book. xiii + 145pp. 5⅜ x 8.   T107 Paperbound **$1.25**

THE NATURE OF LIGHT AND COLOUR IN THE OPEN AIR, M. Minnaert. Why are shadows sometimes blue, sometimes green, or other colors depending on the light and surroundings? What causes mirages? Why do multiple suns and moons appear in the sky? Professor Minnaert explains these unusual phenomena and hundreds of others in simple, easy-to-understand terms based on optical laws and the properties of light and color. No mathematics is required but artists, scientists, students, and everyone fascinated by these "tricks" of nature will find thousands of useful and amazing pieces of information. Hundreds of observational experiments are suggested which require no special equipment. 200 illustrations; 42 photos. xvi + 362pp. 5⅜ x 8.   T196 Paperbound **$2.00**

*MATHEMATICS IN ACTION, O. G. Sutton. Everyone with a command of high school algebra will find this book one of the finest possible introductions to the application of mathematics to physical theory. Ballistics, numerical analysis, waves and wavelike phenomena, Fourier series, group concepts, fluid flow and aerodynamics, statistical measures, and meteorology are discussed with unusual clarity. Some calculus and differential equations theory is developed by the author for the reader's help in the more difficult sections. 88 figures. Index. viii + 236pp. 5⅜ x 8.   T440 Clothbound **$3.50**

SOAP-BUBBLES: THEIR COLOURS AND THE FORCES THAT MOULD THEM, C. V. Boys. For continuing popularity and validity as scientific primer, few books can match this volume of easily-followed experiments, explanations. Lucid exposition of complexities of liquid films, surface tension and related phenomena, bubbles' reaction to heat, motion, music, magnetic fields. Experiments with capillary attraction, soap bubbles on frames, composite bubbles, liquid cylinders and jets, bubbles other than soap, etc. Wonderful introduction to scientific method, natural laws that have many ramifications in areas of modern physics. Only complete edition in print. New Introduction by S. Z. Lewin, New York University. 83 illustrations; 1 full-page color plate. xii + 190pp. 5⅜ x 8½.   T542 Paperbound **95¢**

THE STORY OF X-RAYS FROM RÖNTGEN TO ISOTOPES, A. R. Bleich, M.D. This book, by a member of the American College of Radiology, gives the scientific explanation of x-rays, their applications in medicine, industry and art, and their danger (and that of atmospheric radiation) to the individual and the species. You learn how radiation therapy is applied against cancer, how x-rays diagnose heart disease and other ailments, how they are used to examine mummies for information on diseases of early societies, and industrial materials for hidden weaknesses. 54 illustrations show x-rays of flowers, bones, stomach, gears with flaws, etc. 1st publication. Index. xix + 186pp. 5⅜ x 8.   T622 Paperbound **$1.35**

SPINNING TOPS AND GYROSCOPIC MOTION, John Perry. A classic elementary text of the dynamics of rotation — the behavior and use of rotating bodies such as gyroscopes and tops. In simple, everyday English you are shown how quasi-rigidity is induced in discs of paper, smoke rings, chains, etc., by rapid motions; why a gyrostat falls and why a top rises; precession; how the earth's motion affects climate; and many other phenomena. Appendix on practical use of gyroscopes. 62 figures. 128pp. 5⅜ x 8.   T416 Paperbound **$1.00**

SNOW CRYSTALS, W. A. Bentley, M. J. Humphreys. For almost 50 years W. A. Bentley photographed snow flakes in his laboratory in Jericho, Vermont; in 1931 the American Meteorological Society gathered together the best of his work, some 2400 photographs of snow flakes, plus a few ice flowers, windowpane frosts, dew, frozen rain, and other ice formations. Pictures were selected for beauty and scientific value. A very valuable work to anyone in meteorology, cryology; most interesting to layman; extremely useful for artist who wants beautiful, crystalline designs. All copyright free. Unabridged reprint of 1931 edition. 2453 illustrations. 227pp. 8 x 10½.   T287 Paperbound **$3.00**

A DOVER SCIENCE SAMPLER, edited by George Barkin. A collection of brief, non-technical passages from 44 Dover Books Explaining Science for the enjoyment of the science-minded browser. Includes work of Bertrand Russell, Poincaré, Laplace, Max Born, Galileo, Newton; material on physics, mathematics, metallurgy, anatomy, astronomy, chemistry, etc. You will be fascinated by Martin Gardner's analysis of the sincere pseudo-scientist, Moritz's account of Newton's absentmindedness, Bernard's examples of human vivisection, etc. Illustrations from the Diderot Pictorial Encyclopedia and De Re Metallica. 64 pages.   **FREE**

THE STORY OF ATOMIC THEORY AND ATOMIC ENERGY, J. G. Feinberg. A broader approach to subject of nuclear energy and its cultural implications than any other similar source. Very readable, informal, completely non-technical text. Begins with first atomic theory, 600 B.C. and carries you through the work of Mendelejeff, Röntgen, Madame Curie, to Einstein's equation and the A-bomb. New chapter goes through thermonuclear fission, binding energy, other events up to 1959. Radioactive decay and radiation hazards, future benefits, work of Bohr, moderns, hundreds more topics. "Deserves special mention . . . not only authoritative but thoroughly popular in the best sense of the word," Saturday Review. Formerly, "The Atom Story." Expanded with new chapter. Three appendixes. Index. 34 illustrations. vii + 243pp. 5⅜ x 8.   T625 Paperbound **$1.60**

THE STRANGE STORY OF THE QUANTUM, AN ACCOUNT FOR THE GENERAL READER OF THE GROWTH OF IDEAS UNDERLYING OUR PRESENT ATOMIC KNOWLEDGE, B. Hoffmann. Presents lucidly and expertly, with barest amount of mathematics, the problems and theories which led to modern quantum physics. Dr. Hoffmann begins with the closing years of the 19th century, when certain trifling discrepancies were noticed, and with illuminating analogies and examples takes you through the brilliant concepts of Planck, Einstein, Pauli, Broglie, Bohr, Schroedinger, Heisenberg, Dirac, Sommerfeld, Feynman, etc. This edition includes a new, long postscript carrying the story through 1958. "Of the books attempting an account of the history and contents of our modern atomic physics which have come to my attention, this is the best," H. Margenau, Yale University, in "American Journal of Physics." 32 tables and line illustrations. Index. 275pp. 5⅜ x 8.   T518 Paperbound **$1.50**

SPACE AND TIME, E. Borel. Written by a versatile mathematician of world renown with his customary lucidity and precision, this introduction to relativity for the layman presents scores of examples, analogies, and illustrations that open up new ways of thinking about space and time. It covers abstract geometry and geographical maps, continuity and topology, the propagation of light, the special theory of relativity, the general theory of relativity, theoretical researches, and much more. Mathematical notes. 2 Indexes. 4 Appendices. 15 figures. xvi + 243pp. 5⅜ x 8.   T592 Paperbound **$1.45**

FROM EUCLID TO EDDINGTON: A STUDY OF THE CONCEPTIONS OF THE EXTERNAL WORLD, Sir Edmund Whittaker. A foremost British scientist traces the development of theories of natural philosophy from the western rediscovery of Euclid to Eddington, Einstein, Dirac, etc. The inadequacy of classical physics is contrasted with present day attempts to understand the physical world through relativity, non-Euclidean geometry, space curvature, wave mechanics, etc. 5 major divisions of examination: Space; Time and Movement; the Concepts of Classical Physics; the Concepts of Quantum Mechanics; the Eddington Universe. 212pp. 5⅜ x 8.   T491 Paperbound **$1.35**

CATALOGUE OF DOVER BOOKS

*THE EVOLUTION OF SCIENTIFIC THOUGHT FROM NEWTON TO EINSTEIN, A. d'Abro. A detailed account of the evolution of classical physics into modern relativistic theory and the concommitant changes in scientific methodology. The breakdown of classical physics in the face of non-Euclidean geometry and the electromagnetic equations is carefully discussed and then an exhaustive analysis of Einstein's special and general theories of relativity and their implications is given. Newton, Riemann, Weyl, Lorentz, Planck, Maxwell, and many others are considered. A non-technical explanation of space, time, electromagnetic waves, etc. as understood today. "Model of semi-popular exposition," NEW REPUBLIC. 21 diagrams. 482pp. 5⅜ x 8.
T2 Paperbound **$2.25**

EINSTEIN'S THEORY OF RELATIVITY, Max Born. Nobel Laureate explains Einstein's special and general theories of relativity, beginning with a thorough review of classical physics in simple, non-technical language. Exposition of Einstein's work discusses concept of simultaneity, kinematics, relativity of arbitrary motions, the space-time continuum, geometry of curved surfaces, etc., steering middle course between vague popularizations and complex scientific presentations. 1962 edition revised by author takes into account latest findings, predictions of theory and implications for cosmology, indicates what is being sought in unified field theory. Mathematics very elementary, illustrative diagrams and experiments informative but simple. Revised 1962 edition. Revised by Max Born, assisted by Gunther Leibfried and Walter Biem. Index. 143 illustrations. vii + 376pp. 5⅜ x 8.
S769 Paperbound **$2.00**

PHILOSOPHY AND THE PHYSICISTS, L. Susan Stebbing. A philosopher examines the philosophical aspects of modern science, in terms of a lively critical attack on the ideas of Jeans and Eddington. Such basic questions are treated as the task of science, causality, determinism, probability, consciousness, the relation of the world of physics to the world of everyday experience. The author probes the concepts of man's smallness before an inscrutable universe, the tendency to idealize mathematical construction, unpredictability theorems and human freedom, the supposed opposition between 19th century determinism and modern science, and many others. Introduces many thought-stimulating ideas about the implications of modern physical concepts. xvi + 295pp. 5⅜ x 8.
T480 Paperbound **$1.65**

THE RESTLESS UNIVERSE, Max Born. A remarkably lucid account by a Nobel Laureate of recent theories of wave mechanics, behavior of gases, electrons and ions, waves and particles, electronic structure of the atom, nuclear physics, and similar topics. "Much more thorough and deeper than most attempts . . . easy and delightful," CHEMICAL AND ENGINEERING NEWS. Special feature: 7 animated sequences of 60 figures each showing such phenomena as gas molecules in motion, the scattering of alpha particles, etc. 11 full-page plates of photographs. Total of nearly 600 illustrations. 351pp. 6⅛ x 9¼.
T412 Paperbound **$2.00**

THE COMMON SENSE OF THE EXACT SCIENCES, W. K. Clifford. For 70 years a guide to the basic concepts of scientific and mathematical thought. Acclaimed by scientists and laymen alike, it offers a wonderful insight into concepts such as the extension of meaning of symbols, characteristics of surface boundaries, properties of plane figures, measurement of quantities, vectors, the nature of position, bending of space, motion, mass and force, and many others. Prefaces by Bertrand Russell and Karl Pearson. Critical introduction by James Newman. 130 figures. 249pp. 5⅜ x 8.
T61 Paperbound **$1.60**

MATTER AND LIGHT, THE NEW PHYSICS, Louis de Broglie. Non-technical explanations by a Nobel Laureate of electro-magnetic theory, relativity, matter, light and radiation, wave mechanics, quantum physics, philosophy of science, and similar topics. This is one of the simplest yet most accurate introductions to the work of men like Planck, Einstein, Bohr, and others. Only 2 of the 21 chapters require a knowledge of mathematics. 300pp. 5⅜ x 8.
T35 Paperbound **$1.85**

SCIENCE, THEORY AND MAN, Erwin Schrödinger. This is a complete and unabridged reissue of SCIENCE AND THE HUMAN TEMPERAMENT plus an additional essay: "What Is an Elementary Particle?" Nobel Laureate Schrödinger discusses such topics as nature of scientific method, the nature of science, chance and determinism, science and society, conceptual models for physical entities, elementary particles and wave mechanics. Presentation is popular and may be followed by most people with little or no scientific training. "Fine practical preparation for a time when laws of nature, human institutions . . . are undergoing a critical examination without parallel," Waldemar Kaempffert, N. Y. TIMES. 192pp. 5⅜ x 8.
T428 Paperbound **$1.35**

CONCERNING THE NATURE OF THINGS, Sir William Bragg. The Nobel Laureate physicist in his Royal Institute Christmas Lectures explains such diverse phenomena as the formation of crystals, how uranium is transmuted to lead, the way X-rays work, why a spinning ball travels in a curved path, the reason why bubbles bounce from each other, and many other scientific topics that are seldom explained in simple terms. No scientific background needed—book is easy enough that any intelligent adult or youngster can understand it. Unabridged. 32pp. of photos; 57 figures. xii + 232pp. 5⅜ x 8.
T31 Paperbound **$1.35**

*THE RISE OF THE NEW PHYSICS (formerly THE DECLINE OF MECHANISM), A. d'Abro. This authoritative and comprehensive 2 volume exposition is unique in scientific publishing. Written for intelligent readers not familiar with higher mathematics, it is the only thorough explanation in non-technical language of modern mathematical-physical theory. Combining both history and exposition, it ranges from classical Newtonian concepts up through the electronic theories of Dirac and Heisenberg, the statistical mechanics of Fermi, and Einstein's relativity theories. "A must for anyone doing serious study in the physical sciences," J. OF FRANKLIN INST. 97 illustrations. 991pp. 2 volumes.
T3 Vol. 1, Paperbound **$2.25**
T4 Vol. 2, Paperbound **$2.25**

SCIENCE AND HYPOTHESIS, Henri Poincaré. Creative psychology in science. How such concepts as number, magnitude, space, force, classical mechanics were developed and how the modern scientist uses them in his thought. Hypothesis in physics, theories of modern physics. Introduction by Sir James Larmor. "Few mathematicians have had the breadth of vision of Poincaré, and none is his superior in the gift of clear exposition," E. T. Bell. Index. 272pp. 5⅜ x 8.
S221 Paperbound **$1.35**

THE VALUE OF SCIENCE, Henri Poincaré. Many of the most mature ideas of the "last scientific universalist" conveyed with charm and vigor for both the beginning student and the advanced worker. Discusses the nature of scientific truth, whether order is innate in the universe or imposed upon it by man, logical thought versus intuition (relating to mathematics through the works of Weierstrass, Lie, Klein, Riemann), time and space (relativity, psychological time, simultaneity), Hertz's concept of force, interrelationship of mathematical physics to pure math, values within disciplines of Maxwell, Carnot, Mayer, Newton, Lorentz, etc. Index. iii + 147pp. 5⅜ x 8.
S469 Paperbound **$1.35**

THE SKY AND ITS MYSTERIES, E. A. Beet. One of the most lucid books on the mysteries of the universe; covers history of astronomy from earliest observations to modern theories of expanding universe, source of stellar energy, birth of planets, origin of moon craters, possibilities of life on other planets. Discusses effects of sunspots on weather; distance, age of stars; methods and tools of astronomers; much more. Expert and fascinating. "Eminently readable book," London Times. Bibliography. Over 50 diagrams, 12 full-page plates. Fold-out star map. Introduction. Index. 238pp. 5¼ x 7½.
T627 Clothbound **$3.50**

OUT OF THE SKY: AN INTRODUCTION TO METEORITICS, H. H. Nininger. A non-technical yet comprehensive introduction to the young science of meteoritics: all aspects of the arrival of cosmic matter on our planet from outer space and the reaction and alteration of this matter in the terrestrial environment. Essential facts and major theories presented by one of the world's leading experts. Covers ancient reports of meteors; modern systematic investigations; fireball clusters; meteorite showers; tektites; planetoidal encounters; etc. 52 full-page plates with over 175 photographs. 22 figures. Bibliography and references. Index. viii + 336pp. 5⅜ x 8.
T519 Paperbound **$1.85**

THE REALM OF THE NEBULAE, E. Hubble. One of great astronomers of our day records his formulation of concept of "island universes." Covers velocity-distance relationship; classification, nature, distances, general types of nebulae; cosmological theories. A fine introduction to modern theories for layman. No math needed. New introduction by A. Sandage. 55 illustrations, photos. Index. iv + 201pp. 5⅜ x 8.
S455 Paperbound **$1.50**

AN ELEMENTARY SURVEY OF CELESTIAL MECHANICS, Y. Ryabov. Elementary exposition of gravitational theory and celestial mechanics. Historical introduction and coverage of basic principles, including: the ecliptic, the orbital plane, the 2- and 3-body problems, the discovery of Neptune, planetary rotation, the length of the day, the shapes of galaxies, satellites (detailed treatment of Sputnik I), etc. First American reprinting of successful Russian popular exposition. Follow actual methods of astrophysicists with only high school math! Appendix. 58 figures. 165pp. 5⅜ x 8.
T756 Paperbound **$1.25**

GREAT IDEAS AND THEORIES OF MODERN COSMOLOGY, Jagjit Singh. Companion volume to author's popular "Great Ideas of Modern Mathematics" (Dover, $1.55). The best non-technical survey of post-Einstein attempts to answer perhaps unanswerable questions of origin, age of Universe, possibility of life on other worlds, etc. Fundamental theories of cosmology and cosmogony recounted, explained, evaluated in light of most recent data: Einstein's concepts of relativity, space-time; Milne's a priori world-system; astrophysical theories of Jeans, Eddington; Hoyle's "continuous creation;" contributions of dozens more scientists. A faithful, comprehensive critical summary of complex material presented in an extremely well-written text intended for laymen. Original publication. Index. xii + 276pp. 5⅜ x 8½.
T925 Paperbound **$1.85**

BASIC ELECTRICITY, Bureau of Naval Personnel. Very thorough, easily followed course in basic electricity for beginner, layman, or intermediate student. Begins with simplest definitions, presents coordinated, systematic coverage of basic theory and application: conductors, insulators, static electricity, magnetism, production of voltage, Ohm's law, direct current series and parallel circuits, wiring techniques, electromagnetism, alternating current, capacitance and inductance, measuring instruments, etc.; application to electrical machines such as alternating and direct current generators, motors, transformers, magnetic magnifiers, etc. Each chapter contains problems to test progress; answers at rear. No math needed beyond algebra. Appendices on signs, formulas, etc. 345 illustrations. 448pp. 7½ x 10.
S973 Paperbound **$3.00**

ELEMENTARY METALLURGY AND METALLOGRAPHY, A. M. Shrager. An introduction to common metals and alloys; stress is upon steel and iron, but other metals and alloys also covered. All aspects of production, processing, working of metals. Designed for student who wishes to enter metallurgy, for bright high school or college beginner, layman who wants background on extremely important industry. Questions, at ends of chapters, many microphotographs, glossary. Greatly revised 1961 edition. 195 illustrations, tables. ix + 389pp. 5⅜ x 8.
S138 Paperbound **$2.25**

BRIDGES AND THEIR BUILDERS, D. B. Steinman & S. R. Watson. Engineers, historians, and every person who has ever been fascinated by great spans will find this book an endless source of information and interest. Greek and Roman structures, Medieval bridges, modern classics such as the Brooklyn Bridge, and the latest developments in the science are retold by one of the world's leading authorities on bridge design and construction. BRIDGES AND THEIR BUILDERS is the only comprehensive and accurate semi-popular history of these important measures of progress in print. New, greatly revised, enlarged edition. 23 photos; 26 line-drawings. Index. xvii + 401pp. 5⅜ x 8. T431 Paperbound **$2.00**

FAMOUS BRIDGES OF THE WORLD, D. B. Steinman. An up-to-the-minute new edition of a book that explains the fascinating drama of how the world's great bridges came to be built. The author, designer of the famed Mackinac bridge, discusses bridges from all periods and all parts of the world, explaining their various types of construction, and describing the problems their builders faced. Although primarily for youngsters, this cannot fail to interest readers of all ages. 48 illustrations in the text. 23 photographs. 99pp. 6⅛ x 9¼. T161 Paperbound **$1.00**

HOW DO YOU USE A SLIDE RULE? by A. A. Merrill. A step-by-step explanation of the slide rule that presents the fundamental rules clearly enough for the non-mathematician to understand. Unlike most instruction manuals, this work concentrates on the two most important operations: multiplication and division. 10 easy lessons, each with a clear drawing, for the reader who has difficulty following other expositions. 1st publication. Index. 2 Appendices. 10 illustrations. 78 problems, all with answers. vi + 36 pp. 6⅛ x 9¼. T62 Paperbound **60¢**

HOW TO CALCULATE QUICKLY, H. Sticker. A tried and true method for increasing your "number sense" — the ability to see relationships between numbers and groups of numbers. Addition, subtraction, multiplication, division, fractions, and other topics are treated through techniques not generally taught in schools: left to right multiplication, division by inspection, etc. This is not a collection of tricks which work only on special numbers, but a detailed well-planned course, consisting of over 9,000 problems that you can work in spare moments. It is excellent for anyone who is inconvenienced by slow computational skills. 5 or 10 minutes of this book daily will double or triple your calculation speed. 9,000 problems, answers. 256pp. 5⅜ x 8. T295 Paperbound **$1.00**

MATHEMATICAL FUN, GAMES AND PUZZLES, Jack Frohlichstein. A valuable service for parents of children who have trouble with math, for teachers in need of a supplement to regular upper elementary and junior high math texts (each section is graded—easy, average, difficult —for ready adaptation to different levels of ability), and for just anyone who would like to develop basic skills in an informal and entertaining manner. The author combines ten years of experience as a junior high school math teacher with a method that uses puzzles and games to introduce the basic ideas and operations of arithmetic. Stress on everyday uses of math: banking, stock market, personal budgets, insurance, taxes. Intellectually stimulating and practical, too. 418 problems and diversions with answers. Bibliography. 120 illustrations. xix + 306pp. 5⅝ x 8½. T789 Paperbound **$1.75**

GREAT IDEAS OF MODERN MATHEMATICS: THEIR NATURE AND USE, Jagjit Singh. Reader with only high school math will understand main mathematical ideas of modern physics, astronomy, genetics, psychology, evolution, etc. better than many who use them as tools, but comprehend little of their basic structure. Author uses his wide knowledge of non-mathematical fields in brilliant exposition of differential equations, matrices, group theory, logic, statistics, problems of mathematical foundations, imaginary numbers, vectors, etc. Original publication. 2 appendixes. 2 indexes. 65 illustr. 322pp. 5⅜ x 8. S587 Paperbound **$1.75**

THE UNIVERSE OF LIGHT, W. Bragg. Sir William Bragg, Nobel Laureate and great modern physicist, is also well known for his powers of clear exposition. Here he analyzes all aspects of light for the layman: lenses, reflection, refraction, the optics of vision, x-rays, the photoelectric effect, etc. He tells you what causes the color of spectra, rainbows, and soap bubbles, how magic mirrors work, and much more. Dozens of simple experiments are described. Preface. Index. 199 line drawings and photographs, including 2 full-page color plates. x + 283pp. 5⅜ x 8. T538 Paperbound **$1.85**

*****INTRODUCTION TO SYMBOLIC LOGIC AND ITS APPLICATIONS, Rudolph Carnap.** One of the clearest, most comprehensive, and rigorous introductions to modern symbolic logic, by perhaps its greatest living master. Not merely elementary theory, but demonstrated applications in mathematics, physics, and biology. Symbolic languages of various degrees of complexity are analyzed, and one constructed. "A creation of the rank of a masterpiece," Zentralblatt für Mathematik und Ihre Grenzgebiete. Over 300 exercises. 5 figures. Bibliography. Index. xvi + 241pp. 5⅜ x 8. S453 Paperbound **$1.85**

*****HIGHER MATHEMATICS FOR STUDENTS OF CHEMISTRY AND PHYSICS, J. W. Mellor.** Not abstract, but practical, drawing its problems from familiar laboratory material, this book covers theory and application of differential calculus, analytic geometry, functions with singularities, integral calculus, infinite series, solution of numerical equations, differential equations, Fourier's theorem and extensions, probability and the theory of errors, calculus of variations, determinants, etc. "If the reader is not familiar with this book, it will repay him to examine it," CHEM. & ENGINEERING NEWS. 800 problems. 189 figures. 2 appendices; 30 tables of integrals, probability functions, etc. Bibliography. xxi + 641pp. 5⅜ x 8. S193 Paperbound **$2.50**

CATALOGUE OF DOVER BOOKS

THE FOURTH DIMENSION SIMPLY EXPLAINED, edited by Henry P. Manning. Originally written as entries in contest sponsored by "Scientific American," then published in book form, these 22 essays present easily understood explanations of how the fourth dimension may be studied, the relationship of non-Euclidean geometry to the fourth dimension, analogies to three-dimensional space, some fourth-dimensional absurdities and curiosities, possible measurements and forms in the fourth dimension. In general, a thorough coverage of many of the simpler properties of fourth-dimensional space. Multi-points of view on many of the most important aspects are valuable aid to comprehension. Introduction by Dr. Henry P. Manning gives proper emphasis to points in essays, more advanced account of fourth-dimensional geometry. 82 figures. 251pp. 5⅜ x 8.   **T711 Paperbound $1.35**

TRIGONOMETRY REFRESHER FOR TECHNICAL MEN, A. A. Klaf. A modern question and answer text on plane and spherical trigonometry. Part I covers plane trigonometry: angles, quadrants, trigonometrical functions, graphical representation, interpolation, equations, logarithms, solution of triangles, slide rules, etc. Part II discusses applications to navigation, surveying, elasticity, architecture, and engineering. Small angles, periodic functions, vectors, polar coordinates, De Moivre's theorem, fully covered. Part III is devoted to spherical trigonometry and the solution of spherical triangles, with applications to terrestrial and astronomical problems. Special time-savers for numerical calculation. 913 questions answered for you! 1738 problems; answers to odd numbers. 494 figures. 14 pages of functions, formulae. Index. x + 629pp. 5⅜ x 8.   **T371 Paperbound $2.00**

CALCULUS REFRESHER FOR TECHNICAL MEN. A. A. Klaf. Not an ordinary textbook but a unique refresher for engineers, technicians, and students. An examination of the most important aspects of differential and integral calculus by means of 756 key questions. Part I covers simple differential calculus: constants, variables, functions, increments, derivatives, logarithms, curvature, etc. Part II treats fundamental concepts of integration: inspection, substitution, transformation, reduction, areas and volumes, mean value, successive and partial integration, double and triple integration. Stresses practical aspects! A 50 page section gives applications to civil and nautical engineering, electricity, stress and strain, elasticity, industrial engineering, and similar fields. 756 questions answered. 556 problems; solutions to odd numbers. 36 pages of constants, formulae. Index. v + 431pp. 5⅜ x 8.
T370 Paperbound $2.00

PROBABILITIES AND LIFE, Emile Borel. One of the leading French mathematicians of the last 100 years makes use of certain results of mathematics of probabilities and explains a number of problems that for the most part, are related to everyday living or to illness and death: computation of life expectancy tables, chances of recovery from various diseases, probabilities of job accidents, weather predictions, games of chance, and so on. Emphasis on results not processes, though some indication is made of mathematical proofs. Simple in style, free of technical terminology, limited in scope to everyday situations, it is comprehensible to laymen, fine reading for beginning students of probability. New English translation. Index. Appendix. vi + 87pp. 5⅜ x 8½.   **T121 Paperbound $1.00**

POPULAR SCIENTIFIC LECTURES, Hermann von Helmholtz. 7 lucid expositions by a preeminent scientific mind: "The Physiological Causes of Harmony in Music," "On the Relation of Optics to Painting," "On the Conservation of Force," "On the Interaction of Natural Forces," "On Goethe's Scientific Researches" into theory of color, "On the Origin and Significance of Geometric Axioms," "On Recent Progress in the Theory of Vision." Written with simplicity of expression, stripped of technicalities, these are easy to understand and delightful reading for anyone interested in science or looking for an introduction to serious study of acoustics or optics. Introduction by Professor Morris Kline, Director, Division of Electromagnetic Research, New York University, contains astute, impartial evaluations. Selected from "Popular Lectures on Scientific Subjects," 1st and 2nd series. xii + 286pp. 5⅜ x 8½.   **T799 Paperbound $1.45**

SCIENCE AND METHOD, Henri Poincaré. Procedure of scientific discovery, methodology, experiment, idea-germination—the intellectual processes by which discoveries come into being. Most significant and most interesting aspects of development, application of ideas. Chapters cover selection of facts, chance, mathematical reasoning, mathematics, and logic; Whitehead, Russell, Cantor; the new mechanics, etc. 288pp. 5⅜ x 8.   **S222 Paperbound $1.50**

HEAT AND ITS WORKINGS, Morton Mott-Smith, Ph.D. An unusual book; to our knowledge the only middle-level survey of this important area of science. Explains clearly such important concepts as physiological sensation of heat and Weber's law, measurement of heat, evolution of thermometer, nature of heat, expansion and contraction of solids, Boyle's law, specific heat. BTU's and calories, evaporation, Andrews's isothermals, radiation, the relation of heat to light, many more topics inseparable from other aspects of physics. A wide, non-mathematical yet thorough explanation of basic ideas, theories, phenomena for laymen and beginning scientists illustrated by experiences of daily life. Bibliography. 50 illustrations. x + 165pp. 5⅜ x 8½.   **T978 Paperbound $1.00**

History of Science and Mathematics

THE STUDY OF THE HISTORY OF MATHEMATICS, THE STUDY OF THE HISTORY OF SCIENCE, G. Sarton. Two books bound as one. Each volume contains a long introduction to the methods and philosophy of each of these historical fields, covering the skills and sympathies of the historian, concepts of history of science, psychology of idea-creation, and the purpose of history of science. Prof. Sarton also provides more than 80 pages of classified bibliography. Complete and unabridged. Indexed. 10 illustrations. 188pp. 5⅜ x 8.   T240 Paperbound **$1.25**

A HISTORY OF PHYSICS, Florian Cajori, Ph.D. First written in 1899, thoroughly revised in 1929, this is still best entry into antecedents of modern theories. Precise non-mathematical discussion of ideas, theories, techniques, apparatus of each period from Greeks to 1920's, analyzing within each period basic topics of matter, mechanics, light, electricity and magnetism, sound, atomic theory, etc. Stress on modern developments, from early 19th century to present. Written with critical eye on historical development, significance. Provides most of needed historical background for student of physics. Reprint of second (1929) edition. Index. Bibliography in footnotes. 16 figures. xv + 424pp. 5⅜ x 8.   T970 Paperbound **$2.00**

A HISTORY OF ASTRONOMY FROM THALES TO KEPLER, J. L. E. Dreyer. Formerly titled A HISTORY OF PLANETARY SYSTEMS FROM THALES TO KEPLER. This is the only work in English which provides a detailed history of man's cosmological views from prehistoric times up through the Renaissance. It covers Egypt, Babylonia, early Greece, Alexandria, the Middle Ages, Copernicus, Tycho Brahe, Kepler, and many others. Epicycles and other complex theories of positional astronomy are explained in terms nearly everyone will find clear and easy to understand. "Standard reference on Greek astronomy and the Copernican revolution," SKY AND TELESCOPE. Bibliography. 21 diagrams. Index. xvii + 430pp. 5⅜ x 8.   S79 Paperbound **$2.25**

A SHORT HISTORY OF ASTRONOMY, A. Berry. A popular standard work for over 50 years, this thorough and accurate volume covers the science from primitive times to the end of the 19th century. After the Greeks and Middle Ages, individual chapters analyze Copernicus, Brahe, Galileo, Kepler, and Newton, and the mixed reception of their startling discoveries. Post-Newtonian achievements are then discussed in unusual detail: Halley, Bradley, Lagrange, Laplace, Herschel, Bessel, etc. 2 indexes. 104 illustrations, 9 portraits. xxxi + 440pp. 5⅜ x 8.   T210 Paperbound **$2.00**

PIONEERS OF SCIENCE, Sir Oliver Lodge. An authoritative, yet elementary history of science by a leading scientist and expositor. Concentrating on individuals—Copernicus, Brahe, Kepler, Galileo, Descartes, Newton, Laplace, Herschel, Lord Kelvin, and other scientists—the author presents their discoveries in historical order, adding biographical material on each man and full, specific explanations of their achievements. The full, clear discussions of the accomplishments of post-Newtonian astronomers are features seldom found in other books on the subject. Index. 120 illustrations. xv + 404pp. 5⅜ x 8.   T716 Paperbound **$1.65**

THE BIRTH AND DEVELOPMENT OF THE GEOLOGICAL SCIENCES, F. D. Adams. The most complete and thorough history of the earth sciences in print. Geological thought from earliest recorded times to the end of the 19th century—covers over 300 early thinkers and systems: fossils and hypothetical explanations of them, vulcanists vs. neptunists, figured stones and paleontology, generation of stones, and similar topics. 91 illustrations, including medieval, renaissance woodcuts, etc. 632 footnotes and bibliographic notes. Index. 511pp. 5⅜ x 8.
T5 Paperbound **$2.25**

THE STORY OF ALCHEMY AND EARLY CHEMISTRY, J. M. Stillman. "Add the blood of a red-haired man"—a recipe typical of the many quoted in this authoritative and readable history of the strange beliefs and practices of the alchemists. Concise studies of every leading figure in alchemy and early chemistry through Lavoisier, in this curious epic of superstition and true science, constructed from scores of rare and difficult Greek, Latin, German, and French texts. Foreword by S. W. Young. 246-item bibliography. Index. xiii + 566pp. 5⅜ x 8.
S628 Paperbound **$2.45**

HISTORY OF MATHEMATICS, D. E. Smith. Most comprehensive non-technical history of math in English. Discusses the lives and works of over a thousand major and minor figures, from Euclid to Descartes, Gauss, and Riemann. Vol. I: A chronological examination, from primitive concepts through Egypt, Babylonia, Greece, the Orient, Rome, the Middle Ages, the Renaissance, and up to 1900. Vol. 2: The development of ideas in specific fields and problems, up through elementary calculus. Two volumes, total of 510 illustrations, 1355pp. 5⅜ x 8. Set boxed in attractive container.   T429,430 Paperbound the set **$5.00**

Psychology

YOGA: A SCIENTIFIC EVALUATION, Kovoor T. Behanan. A complete reprinting of the book that for the first time gave Western readers a sane, scientific explanation and analysis of yoga. The author draws on controlled laboratory experiments and personal records of a year as a disciple of a yoga, to investigate yoga psychology, concepts of knowledge, physiology, "supernatural" phenomena, and the ability to tap the deepest human powers. In this study under the auspices of Yale University Institute of Human Relations, the strictest principles of physiological and psychological inquiry are followed throughout. Foreword by W. A. Miles, Yale University. 17 photographs. Glossary. Index. xx + 270pp. 5⅜ x 8. T505 Paperbound **$2.00**

CONDITIONED REFLEXES: AN INVESTIGATION OF THE PHYSIOLOGICAL ACTIVITIES OF THE CEREBRAL CORTEX, I. P. Pavlov. Full, authorized translation of Pavlov's own survey of his work in experimental psychology reviews entire course of experiments, summarizes conclusions, outlines psychological system based on famous "conditioned reflex" concept. Details of technical means used in experiments, observations on formation of conditioned reflexes, function of cerebral hemispheres, results of damage, nature of sleep, typology of nervous system, significance of experiments for human psychology. Trans. by Dr. G. V. Anrep, Cambridge Univ. 235-item bibliography. 18 figures. 445pp. 5⅜ x 8.   S614 Paperbound **$2.35**

EXPLANATION OF HUMAN BEHAVIOUR, F. V. Smith. A major intermediate-level introduction to and criticism of 8 complete systems of the psychology of human behavior, with unusual emphasis on theory of investigation and methodology. Part I is an illuminating analysis of the problems involved in the explanation of observed phenomena, and the differing viewpoints on the nature of causality. Parts II and III are a closely detailed survey of the systems of McDougall, Gordon Allport, Lewin, the Gestalt group, Freud, Watson, Hull, and Tolman. Biographical notes. Bibliography of over 800 items. 2 Indexes. 38 figures. xii + 460pp. 5½ x 8¾.
                                                                T253 Clothbound **$6.00**

SEX IN PSYCHO-ANALYSIS (formerly CONTRIBUTIONS TO PSYCHO-ANALYSIS), S. Ferenczi. Written by an associate of Freud, this volume presents countless insights on such topics as impotence, transference, analysis and children, dreams, symbols, obscene words, masturbation and male homosexuality, paranoia and psycho-analysis, the sense of reality, hypnotism and therapy, and many others. Also includes full text of THE DEVELOPMENT OF PSYCHO-ANALYSIS by Ferenczi and Otto Rank. Two books bound as one. Total of 406pp. 5⅜ x 8.
                                                                T324 Paperbound **$1.85**

BEYOND PSYCHOLOGY, Otto Rank. One of Rank's most mature contributions, focussing on the irrational basis of human behavior as a basic fact of our lives. The psychoanalytic techniques of myth analysis trace to their source the ultimates of human existence: fear of death, personality, the social organization, the need for love and creativity, etc. Dr. Rank finds them stemming from a common irrational source, man's fear of final destruction. A seminal work in modern psychology, this work sheds light on areas ranging from the concept of immortal soul to the sources of state power. 291pp. 5⅜ x 8.   T485 Paperbound **$2.00**

ILLUSIONS AND DELUSIONS OF THE SUPERNATURAL AND THE OCCULT, D. H. Rawcliffe. Holds up to rational examination hundreds of persistent delusions including crystal gazing, automatic writing, table turning, mediumistic trances, mental healing, stigmata, lycanthropy, live burial, the Indian Rope Trick, spiritualism, dowsing, telepathy, clairvoyance, ghosts, ESP, etc. The author explains and exposes the mental and physical deceptions involved, making this not only an exposé of supernatural phenomena, but a valuable exposition of characteristic types of abnormal psychology. Originally titled "The Psychology of the Occult." 14 illustrations. Index. 551pp. 5⅜ x 8.   T503 Paperbound **$2.00**

THE PRINCIPLES OF PSYCHOLOGY, William James. The full long-course, unabridged, of one of the great classics of Western literature and science. Wonderfully lucid descriptions of human mental activity, the stream of thought, consciousness, time perception, memory, imagination, emotions, reason, abnormal phenomena, and similar topics. Original contributions are integrated with the work of such men as Berkeley, Binet, Mills, Darwin, Hume, Kant, Royce, Schopenhauer, Spinoza, Locke, Descartes, Galton, Wundt, Lotze, Herbart, Fechner, and scores of others. All contrasting interpretations of mental phenomena are examined in detail — introspective analysis, philosophical interpretation, and experimental research. "A classic," JOURNAL OF CONSULTING PSYCHOLOGY. "The main lines are as valid as ever," PSYCHO-ANALYTICAL QUARTERLY. "Standard reading . . . a classic of interpretation," PSYCHIATRIC QUARTERLY. 94 illustrations. 1408pp. 2 volumes. 5⅜ x 8.   Vol. 1, T381 Paperbound **$2.50**
                                                             Vol. 2, T382 Paperbound **$2.50**

THE DYNAMICS OF THERAPY IN A CONTROLLED RELATIONSHIP, Jessie Taft. One of the most important works in literature of child psychology, out of print for 25 years. Outstanding disciple of Rank describes all aspects of relationship or Rankian therapy through concise, simple elucidation of theory underlying her actual contacts with two seven-year olds. Therapists, social caseworkers, psychologists, counselors, and laymen who work with children will all find this important work an invaluable summation of method, theory of child psychology. xix + 296pp. 5⅜ x 8.   T325 Paperbound **$1.75**